LIBIDO SEXUALIS

STUDIES IN THE PSYCHOSEXUAL LAWS
OF LOVE VERIFIED BY CLINICAL
SEXUAL CASE HISTORIES

By

ALBERT MOLL, M.D.

AMERICAN ETHNOLOGICAL PRESS
New York   ::   ::   1933

MANUFACTURED IN THE UNITED STATES OF AMERICA

I dedicate this book to the new generation who no longer whisper furtively about sex as a thing unclean.

—ALBERT MOLL

· CONTENTS ·

CONTENTS

13

ANALYSIS OF THE SEX INSTINCT

PART ONE

Like many psychological concepts, the word "sex instinct" has the following objection: Everybody employs it, yet everybody employs it in a different sense. One writer means by it simply some subjective sensation in the genital; another authority believes it to be a feeling connected with the opposite sex; a third relates it with reproduction. For this reason alone, it seems to me advisable to analyze this psychological concept, the sex instinct. I need only mention the fact that to define the dividing line between normal and abnormal in the sex instinct, it is necessary first to know definitely what we mean by it. All erotic relationship between two persons of the same or the opposite sex brought about by the influence of this instinct cannot be understood but by the analysis of this concept.

The expression *sex instinct* consists of two words, "sex" and "instinct." We meet with the same difficulty in defining instinct as we do in defining any of the other psychological concepts which are being so diversely applied by various authorities. In order to avoid any misunderstandings we must mention here two of the numerous applications of the concept "instinct." One corresponds closely to the definition used by Wundt, who defines an instinct as an emotion which strives to express itself in an external bodily movement of such a nature that the completion of the movement may bring about the enhancement of a pleasure, already present, or the removal of a feeling of displeasure. "Striving and resistance form the basis of all volitional acts. The intelligence of men is of little account in this connection: it neither destroys the instinct nor does it suppress it. It merely awakens new and higher forms of the instinct, gradually gaining mastery over it. Thus the advances of civilization are to be looked for neither in our freedom from instinct nor in their suppression, but in their versatility; the animal in whom physical cravings govern all activity has not the slightest inkling of this."

In this sense of the word we everywhere meet with the expressions "instinctive movements" and "instinctive acts." Everything that pleases man sets in action the instinct to have and to possess. When we employ "instinct" in this sense there is no necessity for an activity to follow the instinct as inferred from the definition of Wundt. It is quite a different matter, though, when we employ the second definition of "instinct." In this second sense, as it is used, a more general idea is suggested, for it signifies a psychical disposition driving one to acts of the same kind in which logical considerations play no part, and a voluntary suppression of the act is impossible because of the strength of the impulse. We shall not go into any discussion here as to how many such instincts there are. Krafft-Ebing recognizes two of them only: self-preservation and the sex-instinct. Former psychiatrists assumed that there was also an instinct of stealing, an instinct for murder, etc. It was assumed that in such cases there was present a psychical disposition which led to insuppressible acts. It is quite apparent that instinct in this sense differs widely from the first definition. The point as to whether there was or there wasn't any such thing as an instinct of stealing would be useless if not for the fact that the term was applied in the second sense which stresses the insuppressible element in it. It is true that many an honest man has an occasional impulse to steal—in the first sense of the word—but other motives suppress that inclination. If then we were to employ the term "instinct of stealing" in the first sense, that is in the Wundtian sense, we would be dealing merely with a fugitive tendency to steal, at one time or another; we would be justified in recognizing the existence of an instinct of stealing and all discussion of the point would be unnecessary. But whether we have such an instinct in the second sense of the word, *e.g.*, instinct which drives normal healthy-minded people to the insuppressible act of stealing is quite another question. This question will be discussed later. What differentiates "instinct" in this second sense from that discussed in the beginning is the irrepressible element in it as well as the disposition to repeat it.

To avoid all possible misunderstandings in our future discussions I shall not employ the term in the second sense at all. On all such occasions I shall substitute other words, such as impulse, craving, wish, inclination or drive; the word "instinct" will be used in the first sense.

From this brief discussion of instincts let us pass to a discussion of the sex instinct proper. According to Hegar, and also of Eulenburg, the sex instinct is composed of two parts, the impulse to copulate and the impulse to reproduce. Hegar admits that the instinct of reproduction occurs only in very few people, that at best it is to be observed only in woman, and that in civilized societies there is too much thought attached to it, so that we cannot any longer talk of an "instinct of reproduction." Accepting "instinct" in our own sense, I believe we might even go a step further than Hegar, and deny the existence of an "instinct of reproduction," altogether. It is true, of course, that many people wish to have children; but it is quite unnecessary to imply an "instinct of reproduction."

Among primitive peoples, it is maintained, such an instinct is still to be found. Marshall, as cited by Westermarck, relates that among the Todas he met with numerous cases where this desire for chidren was so strong that he got the impression that there was present an instinct of reproduction and that it possessed the character of an impulse more than that of an intelligent human emotion. However true this may be, it must still be emphasized that in most of these common reports there is a wrong use of the term. For example, we cannot speak of an "instinct of reproduction" when someone performs the sex act to produce children who will be a support to him in old age or who will be useful to him in the struggle for existence. Nor may we speak of such an instinct, when, as among the Jews in the past, procreation took place to obey a commandment of God. My opinion is that the general assumption that woman performs the sex act as a result of an instinct of reproduction is quite unjustified; for a woman who performs coitus in order to beget children has considered the pros and cons and when she yields herself to beget a child the act is voluntary and not instinctive. This is even less so when the woman performs the act from other motives, for example, to experience excitement or pleasure, or, like the prostitute, to earn money; in all these cases the act has been performed voluntarily. We can refer to an instinct of reproduction only under the following conditions. Motive for the act should not be the impulse to copulate with a man nor the desire for pleasure; there should be present the overwhelming thought that without a child one is, as it were, incomplete. Furthermore, there should be present the idea that without them there is no joy in life. Hegar and Eulenburg have justly stated that since thought plays too prominent a role in human life such an instinct is hardly, if ever, to be found. However, it seems, that in some exceptional cases this instinct is still to be met with. Loura Marholm says of German maids that when a strange man woos they see nothing in him but a possible father of their future children; that the hearts of all German virgins yearn for the joys of motherhood—to become a mother, a mother at any price. After years of vain hope for this happiness, she even becomes indifferent as to who gives her this happiness, so long as her desire is satisfied. When a German girl sees a child or perhaps touches one she already dreams of her own future baby. Lombroso and Ferrero, also write that the love of woman is an expression of her maternal instinct and of her need for protection; the sexual element is a thing of minor importance. The utterance of Rachel to Jacob "Give me children or else I die" is to be taken in this physiological sense. Even this interpretation is not as extreme as Laura Marholm, who assumes the existence in woman of an absolute need for reproduction. She sees in woman's love for man nothing but love for the father of her future child. If it were true that there are still such women, then, in my opinion, we would be justified in referring to an instinct of reproduction; and according to the information gathered by Laura Marholm we occasionally do meet with such. In my own practice, several women have corroborated this assertion; such women, however, are only rare exceptions. Of course, we must not so interpret this desire and impulse of begetting children in any such way that the mother considers the child to be a mere plaything, easily to be displaced by some other object. There must be present a veritable inner drive to bring forth a new being from one's own self.

That generally the sex instinct is also called the instinct of reproduction is due to the fact that the conscious aim of the instinct is confused with its unconscious purpose. The sex instinct serves the purpose of reproduction which is, as it were, its objective side, while its subjective side is what Hegar has called the instinct of copulation: in other words, the instinct of copulation is subservient to that of reproduction.

In order to avoid the confusion of the terms, "instinct of reproduction," "instinct of copulation" and "sex instinct" it is first of all necessary to come to an agreement of the meaning of "instinct." Eduard von Hartmann calls instinctive acts purposive without the consciousness of such purpose. We shall adopt this definition with certain limitations. Wundt terms instincts hereditary drives. The hereditary element, is indeed stressed by almost all. Thus Wilser in his discussion on the hereditary criminal maintained the hereditary impulses to be the chief characteristics of an instinct. Darwin designates instinctive actions those functions which we can only perform with the aid of thought and habit; but which are

exercised by animals and especially by young and inexperienced ones—and in the case of a great number of
animals—without their seeming to know the end-purpose
of such actions. This definition, essentially is the same
as that of Hartmann. At any rate, those authors who at
all recognize the existence of instincts must agree that
acts which satisfy the definition of Hartmann should be
called instinctive. Such is the migratory instinct of
birds, who, without knowing why and whither they are
bound, will leave their habitat at a definite time of the
year; such are also the gregarious life of many animals,
the caterpillar's spinning of its coccoon at the time when
it changes into a pupa. In essence I am upholding the
definition of Hartmann but with a limitation, in order to
avoid misconceptions. I believe that the ignorance of the
purpose is not a necessary condition for its presence.
For example, I would speak of instincts also in those
birds, who, having found out the purpose of their wandering will still continue year after year to migrate.
For the knowledge of purposes may also occur with instinctive actions. Otherwise, we could not continue calling the desire for food when hungry an instinct, when
aware that its purpose is to keep us alive. The knowledge
of the purpose does not modify an instinctive action;
what we do have is the motive for the act through such
knowledge. When birds fly to a definite place driven by
the migratory instinct, knowing at the same time that
there they will find food I will continue calling such
migration an instinctive act. Only after the search for
food has become the conscious motive for its flight would
we be justified in not calling it an instinctive act. Eduard
von Hartmann, in fact, says the same thing, but on account of the special significance of the word "purpose,"

which is to be found in his definition, one may easily be led to misunderstandings. Therefore, I did not omit my qualification. The purpose then does not necessarily have to be unconscious. This could no longer be called an instinctive act if a man with homosexual predilections, wishing to appear a Don Juan to other people, were to approach a woman and cohabit with her, having induced an erection by imagining the presence of a man, such intercourse could no longer be counted among the instinctive acts; it is, rather, the consequence of the man's reflection and experience.

Turning from these general discussions and applying it to the sex instinct we come to the conclusion that it serves the instinct of reproduction. It is therefore permissible to call the sex instinct the instinct of reproduction; the two expressions overlap each other; as already mentioned, the sex instinct is then the subjective side and the instinct of procreation the objective side of the same process. But it is wise in order to avoid confusion not to use the term "instinct of reproduction" at all unless we restrict its usage to the rare cases mentioned above.

According to Hegar's division we are left with the instinct of copulation. As we shall see, however, this instinct may be divided into two distinct processes, which, merely because as a rule they occur together, have been designated as one, the sex instinct. One of the processes takes place in the genitals; it brings about a transformation in them and in the male its culmination is ejaculation. The latter might also be called the impulse of ejaculation. I shall not, however, use this expression because it has not been observed in all cases. Matters are quite different in the case of women in whom ejaculation sometimes occurs at the height of coital orgasm or after masturbation, the secretion originating in the glands of Bartholin and perhaps also in the mucous glands of the uterus. But it is questionable whether ejaculation in woman plays a very important role. Since ejaculation in woman is not for the purpose of expelling sex cells as in man, it must be assumed from the very outset that ejaculation for her in intercourse is not as important as in man. This also may be seen in the fact that in woman the development of the secretions of the glands of Bartholin is not tied up with puberty. It cannot easily be determined whether some women ejaculate at all during coitus for the presence of the man's fluid prevents a clear examination. The question might best be answered in the case of homosexual women who are gratified through cunnilingus, masturbation or voluptuous erotic dreams. I have been assured, however, that some women may reach the highest pitch of orgasm with a feeling of complete satisfaction without ejaculation. In man the feeling of gratification is brought about through ejaculation only; it is not necessarily so in woman. The man is satisfied when his semen is expelled; this may best be seen in the fact that in *coitus interruptus,* when ejaculation is protracted as long as possible, the real feeling of satisfaction occurs only after the semen has been expelled. It is difficult to say on what process the feeling of gratification in woman depends. Sometimes gratification takes place when the *corpora cavernasa* of the clitoris, after having become tumescent, again subside, and when the rhythmic contractions of her genitals during coitus, have come to a stop, without the occurrence of ejaculation. However, in woman the quantity of the fluid ejaculated may perhaps be too small to be perceived, just as the ejected

fluid is decreased in men who have performed coitus
several times at short intervals. Therefore, since it has
been established that ejaculation in woman does not
play the same important role as in man; and, moreover,
since the impulse to bring about a certain discharge limited to the genitals, is not always achieved through ejaculation, I shall not employ the term "instinct of ejaculation." On the contrary I shall call the impulse bringing about a transformation in the genitals *detumescence,*
applicable both to men and women.

I may further stress the circumstances that in the
evolutionary process ejaculation took place also in the
female and it was of very great importance. This may
be observed even today in fish which extrude their eggs
through ejaculation.

There are also male individuals who may be said to
lack the impulse for ejaculation, but who nevertheless
have the urge to bring about a change in their genitals.
Such is the case in masturbation practiced at an early
age, in which there is both an erection and also a kind
of voluptuous sensation, without ejaculation taking place.
Such facts, I shall designate "detumescence."

We have now become familiar with one of the essential processes of the sex instinct, the impulse to bring
about transformation in the genitals. The other process
is the urge to approach another person—a person of the
opposite sex, in normal conditions—to touch, to fondle,
to kiss that person. To be as general as possible we shall
call this impulse, *contrectation.* This term is to indi-
cate an impulse to touch another person, be it of a mental
or sensual nature. In normal persons contrectation
manifests itself as an heterosexual drive, towards a
member of the opposite sex. Matters are quite different

in the history of evolution, as we shall later see. We find that though each individual in hermaphroditic animals, as the leech, possess both male and female sex glands, yet it is necessary for two individuals to couple for the purpose of fertilization. The question now comes up whether contrectation is as primitive as detumescence. This question from the very outset is to be answered in the negative. Detumescence is the primitive, and later in our discussion we shall take this up in more detail. At this point I only wish to comment upon the two components into which the sex instinct of mature normal human beings may be separated.

The two components of the sex instinct are contrectation and detumescence.

Though it may be possible in some cases for contrectation and detumescence to occur separately, yet, actually they appear together in most cases. This being so, the impulse is to perform the sex act through contact with an individual of the opposite sex. There are, of course, certain modifications. In many species of fish, for example, the instinct does not manifest itself as detumescence through bodily contact with a member of the opposite sex. It is true that the male has the impulse to ejaculate only in the presence of the female, but the semen is not injected into the body of the female; it is deposited on the eggs previously expelled by the female. But the final expression in the sex impulse of man is not only detumescence through contact with a person of the opposite sex, but coitus. And in the last analysis the sex urge consists in ejaculating semen into the vagina of the female, and on the part of the woman receiving the male's member and absorbing the semen in her vagina followed by detumescence.

The fact that contrectation and detumescence almost always occur together, should not prevent us from theoretically dividing the two, for, as we shall see later, they sometimes do occur separately. A priori, it cannot be understood what detumescence has to do with contrectation, the impulse to touch another being. The instinct of detumescence often impels us to empty a fluid. But we also evacuate materials in other ways, *e. g.* the secretion of saliva, the emptying of the bladder, defecation and vomiting. In these cases none but sexual perverts feel that the material to be emptied should come in contact with another individual, or that the material should be emptied through contact with another individual. Since we have always observed the same phenomena to occur, we have become accustomed to consider ejaculation in contact with a woman as something self-evident. In reality, matters are not so simple. To come to an understanding of the reasons for the simultaneous occurrence of contrectation and detumescence we only have to consider both the purpose that the latter serves as well as its evolutionary development. Eduard von Hartmann some years ago very justly pointed out that it was strange how the gratification of what is commonly called the sex instinct may be brought about through an act with a woman; and though Duhring was filled with indignation at this opinion of von Hartmann, its correctness cannot be denied.

That detumescence does not always occur in connection with an idea of another individual may be seen in the practice of masturbation which in numerous cases represents almost a purely physiological act. In all such cases the person masturbating does not think of a person of the opposite sex or of anything else, whereas in

the majority of cases the masturbator pictures to himself a sex act with a member of the other sex. Gustav
Jager, relying on the guaranty of M., has described these
former cases, *i. e.*, without any image representation as
monosexual idiosyncrasy. It remains an open question
whether the warrantor of Jager has not exaggerated the
number of these autoerotic persons. In my own experience, at any rate, I have also come across a number of
grown-up persons who have gratified themselves only
through masturbation without the thought of another
individual in their minds. Let me here mention the
following cases.

Case I. Mrs. A. D., married, living in happy union
with her husband; she is the mother of several children,
all said to be in good health. Mrs. A. D. loves her husband and is loved by him in return. Her chief pleasure,
however, is not to bring her genitals in contact with those
of her husband in any manner whatever, or to perform
coitus with him; on the contrary, the chief excitement
for her is to practice masturbation on herself to the
highest pitch of orgasm. Mrs. A. D., who is otherwise
a very respectable woman, thus masturbates several
times daily.

Case II. A forty-five year old woman, who has never
had a love-affair, told me that she also gratifies herself in
the same manner without the activity of the imagination.

Case III. A woman-artist, who was in love with a
man, had the opportunity to have sexual intercourse with
him; occasionally she also practiced coitus with other
men, but only for material reasons. But she found satisfaction neither in intercourse with the latter persons
nor in coitus with the man she loved. On the other hand,
she very frequently gratifies her passion through mas-

turbation. It is well known that she gratifies herself once or twice daily and sometimes even more frequently. The person in question is a nervous and excitable woman of twenty-eight; but she states that without
masturbation she would be even more nervous.

The following case will illustrate that for a long time
detumescence and contrectation may occur separately.
It will further establish that even in very early childhood subjective sensations in the genitals may appear
without the thought of another person; such conditions
may lead to innumerable acts of masturbation. The
patient was still a child when he began to practice masturbation excessively; of course, no ejaculation had then
taken place.

Case IV. Mr. S. L., merchant, twenty-eight years old.
Already in his early childhood ,when he was only four,
there cropped up "forebodings and feelings of a sexual
nature, strange as it may seem," to which was very soon
added the strong urge for gratification. The goal of this
gratification S. L. achieved through friction of his genitals; first of all when at exercise and especially in climbing; later he indulged in masturbation wherever and
whenever possible. He felt—perhaps instinctively—
that it was wrong and so he made an effort to hide his
activities from his parents and his neighbors in which
respect he succeeded quite well. As he grew older and as
his feeling of guilt was transformed into knowledge he
found himself confronted by his moral self; the impulse
which had given rise to his activity contending with his
will to suppress it but without much success. Usually
his impulse to masturbate was so strong that it appeared
again as soon as it was removed; and not seldom self-
abuse took place four to five times in quick succession

and this mainly between the ages of sixteen to twenty-three. The more it became clear to S. L. that he was a plaything in the grip of an evil predisposition the deeper it sank into his soul and the more dejected he became; in such moods of despair he often contemplated suicide. But there were also other times when he had an inner conviction that he would be able to become master over his passion. This conflict made such heavy claim on S. L.'s mind that he had no interest for other things and his education was greatly neglected thereby. From his twenty-third year on S. L. succeeded in abating his impulse; from an interval of three and four days between practices he brought it to six and seven days, though it sometimes would break forth afterwards with even greater severity. Since the last half year S. L. believes that he has at last achieved full mastery over his passion. At the same time he cannot escape the fear that at some future time masturbation will again win the upper hand.

S. L., an unusually nervous person, of a very melancholy and anxious appearance, is strongly convinced that up to the age of twelve he had already had from 800 to 1000 sexual excitations, without any thought of another person. The masturbatory practices began at the age of four. Now his sex instinct is also directed to that of normal intercourse with women. He is not sure when he first conceived the thought of another person in connection with masturbation; but at any rate, it had not occurred before he was fourteen; so that in his case the purely local impulse of detumescence had existed a long time before that age. And many times later S. L. had practiced masturbation without any thought of another person, merely for the local voluptuous sensations.

The two cases that follow also belong to this discussion. They refer to homosexual men. The first case will show this impulse towards another person to appear only at a relatively late time and at the same time directed to a person of the male sex.

Case V. D. T. is thirty-two years old, a merchant. His parents are dead. He has two married sisters, both of them living a happy married life. He has no brothers. Most members of the family are somewhat nervous and easily excitable. No other hereditary taints can be traced. As a child he had been suffering from scrofula.

As far as his sex instinct is concerned we may clearly distinguish between its physical and psychical aspects. The latter appeared considerably late. He started the practice of masturbation when he was still in school; a fellow student having induced him to do so when he was thirteen years of age. One day he was masturbated by another boy and so occurred the first emission of semen which he can remember. He denies ever having felt any sexual inclinations towards either men or women until the age of twenty-five or having masturbated with the thought of men or women. Though he had permitted himself to be masturbated by other boys, he had no inclination to those boys.

D. T.'s propensity for men appeared at the age of twenty-five without his having had any inclination towards women before that. It is true that at the same time he began to have intercourse with women; though he never had the impulse to perform coitus. He had the belief, however, that since other men had relations with women he had to force himself to perform the same acts. When he did so he always pictured to himself a man. Without such an image before him he would not have been capable of performing coitus. Though at the present time he can remember such thoughts of men having sprung up in his mind, he was not at the time aware of any perverse inclinations. This insight into himself came only at the age of twenty-eight when another male homosexual explained the entire matter to him; since then and as a result of this enlightenment D. T. has occasionally practiced mutual masturbation with other men. When he lacks such opportunities he practices it for himself. On these occasions there is always the image before him of another man. At least this has been so for the last three years. He never pictures a woman. Sexual thoughts and the impulse for their gratification come to him in long intervals, so that at times he is rather free from them. After such intervals, however, they crop up again with greater force, so that he is driven to masturbation, which in consequence is practiced regularly for some time, until he is again freed.

In the last few years D. T. has had no pollutions whatsoever. Previously he had had such pollution quite frequently. But on those occasions he always saw a man in his dreams. He does not remember, however, whether he had pollutions at the time when there were no psychosexual stimuli present, e. g. before he was twenty-six years old.

D. T. never liked to kiss girls. As far as men are concerned, there is only one category which is sympathetic to him; the urning especially repels him very much. He prefers to have intercourse with men who possess a normal sex instinct.

D. T. recalls that as a school-boy he liked very much to dress in women's clothes; he also liked to play with dolls. Otherwise he had been a wild boy.

It may further be added that D. T. makes the impression of a very nervous person, and that he had been suffering from attacks of melancholy. His heart beat is exceedingly weak. From time to time thoughts of suicide cropped up in his mind; for some time this tendency was so pronounced that his nearest relatives had to watch over him very closely. Later on, though, these suicidal ideas disappeared.

In some respects the following case seems to me to be just as worthy of notice. This patient, too, is homosexual, though he occasionally also has heterosexual inclinations. While it will be seen that he had feelings for the opposite sex, his passionate love was for the male sex; it will be observed at the same time that the thought of playing with the genitals of a young boy whom he loves is frequently repugnant to him. One might speak here of an ardent platonic love.

Case VI. B. S. is twenty-six years of age, theologian. His mother comes from a healthy family; his father was the son of an epileptic. Though there had been no cases of mental diseases in the family, there were abnormalities. Brothers and sisters of B. S. are in good health. He himself is of normal build. His features and posture, however, make an effeminate impression. As a child he busied himself much with needle-work, and even up to the age of twenty he liked to do such things. B. S. has a certain interest in music; he also has a fine understanding for questions of literature. His memory is not very strong, nor has he a strong reasoning power; he is, however, endowed with a very rich imagination. He lives a very retired life. When he was a child he preferred to associate with grown-ups whom he pleased with his precocious and sprightly nature. Aside from a few favorites, most of his fellow-students at the gymnasium were indifferent to him. He was not much given to play. And only later did he begin to understand how wrong his retired mode of life had been. The activities of the students' clubs appeared to him entirely stale, and he himself was somewhat shy. He was not seldom reproached for his effeminate behavior. He himself felt that he deserved rebuke. At the age of seventeen he recognized the feminine in himself. On the occasion of a small theater performance in school he was cast for the role of a lady. And he claims to have played his part wonderfully well. In company, B. S. was either taken for a dreamer or for an "effeminate," never for a "man." When he himself used the appelation "man" in reference to himself, it sounded strange to his ears. This fact is the more unpleasant to him, as he himself hates everything feminine in other men. He is not very successful in the company of girls, as he cannot find the right tone in his social intercourse with them, without appearing affected. Older people usually like him very much. He also makes a good impression upon old ladies, winning their confidence easily. His landladies at the various university cities were especially very enthusiastic about his quiet mode of life. He likes dancing very much and, as he himself states, dances gracefully.

As a child B. S. had a very early interest in his own sex organs, their smell especially exciting him. In his fifth year he was one day surprised by his father, while he was engaged in playing with his genitals and was reprimanded by him. He masturbated in his eighth and ninth year, but gave up the practice for several years and did not resume until he was twelve or thirteen, then repeating it often. Later, however, he practiced it less

frequently and only after great intervals, for on account
of the bodily weakness it brought with it he always felt
remorse after the act. He continued the practice until
the completion of his sixteenth year. Even after that
the impulse cropped up again, especially after drinking
of beer or wine, but he always managed to master it.
He believes that since he had sexual intercourse with
women the impulse to masturbate might not reappear.
When in the act of masturbation he never had imagined
any other person, girl or boy; he had simply gratified
himself through "the boundless voluptuous feeling and
the nervous excitation." B. S. is convinced that had
he been enlightened by a physician about the harm of
masturbation, he would have been spared the ill effects
of his excessive mode of life from his twelfth to his
fourteenth year.

B. S. further adds that punishments and perturba-
tion of the spirit, also have a decidedly exciting effect
upon his sexual make-up. In his feelings of remorse for
being kept in after school there was something inexplicable as after an act of masturbation.

His first pollution appeared at the age of fourteen
and a half, and in connection with a dream of a nude
Venus lying in front of him. Since then pollutions have
taken place in intervals of about ten days; but even at
the period of his most intimate friendships they were
never accompanied by images of male persons; rather,
always by images of females and also by those of animals, and especially dogs. Pollution without dreams
occurred only very rarely. In his nineteenth year pollutions took place very frequently, for a long period
three times weekly. They exhausted him, so that finally
he had to see a physician who prescribed cold washings.

As a boy he was sometimes psychically very strongly attracted to other boys of his age, but they were only fleeting attachments. On the other hand, when he was seven to nine years old, he felt a very strong and longing passion for a girl of his own age. At that time he wished to be a girl himself in order to be able to be with that girl all the time. Again, at the age of twelve he had felt a strong ardor for another girl, but his love for her remained unanswered, because, as he himself believes, "in spite of all his inner ardor he did not proceed aggressively enough." They went as far as pressing of the hands, but they never kissed; this grieved him very much, especially as he once had a very good opportunity of doing it. B. S. recalls that whenever he thought of the girl a voluptuous tremor would pass through his frame.

When B. S. was thirteen years of age, an artist lived in the house of his relatives. This artist liked to have young B. S. with him continually and often would not leave him alone. The boy was not attracted towards the artist physically, the latter drew him to himself reciting purported letters to his sweetheart, stroking his arms, giving him presents and spoiling him in many ways. When the artist became more passionate B. S. instinctively feared and detested him. One night when he was asleep in his bed the man kissed him passionately all over his body. B. S. awoke directly and could see the man leaving the room. He ran out to tell his parents, but they told him that it must have been a dream. Another time he was lured by the man into his room and made to sit down near him, on the edge of the bed. The artist threw him on the cushions, bent down over him, and again began to kiss him passionately. He was spared any further manipulations by the entrance of the maid. B. S. did not dare tell anybody of these occurrences, but an antipathy for the man was developed. B. S. avoided him in every way and played so many tricks on him, that the artist had to leave the house.

When he was fifteen years old B. S. lost all interest in the girl above-mentioned. He led a very peculiar emotional life; he was in love homosexually, in the widest sense of the term. One of his fellow-students he liked so much for "his woody and mossy smell" that he put more efforts into his studies, in order to be near the other, more advanced student. For two years, day after day, he also watched the movements of another dark-haired boy, from ten to twelve years of age, spying upon him with beating heart without ever saying a word. But B. S. was quite happy when he could meet him, and very dejected when the boy did not appear on some occasions. He always refused to be accompanied by any other friends in order not to miss the pleasure of seeing him. There was only one other who knew of B. S.'s inclination for his own sex; Y who was of the same age. Y knew his secret because they both loved the same lad a year and a half their junior. Both of them, in the face of the jeering and surprise of their fellow-students, on one and the same day, fell violently in love with the younger boy. This occurred while they were on an outing. Jealous of each other, they had to be content with only a divided love, but, nevertheless, each in nightly wanderings with their "love" lived through many a happy hour. B. S. does not know whether the younger boy had responded to either of them; but that he had permitted himself to be kissed and when B. S. had to leave town one day, the other had thrown himself upon him with passionate sighs and had kissed him all over with a feverishly beating heart. A feeling of passing indifference, which surprised him very much, came over him, when he kissed the other boy and found stubbles of beard growing on his chin. Y, to whom B. S. confided his love for the other boy, regarded the impulse as sinful; this B. S. would not admit, saying that he loved like the Greeks and that such love had nothing at all to do with sexual intercourse.

B. S. maintains that according to his own observation, it was in first-borns that homosexual leanings were to be found. On the contrary I have ascertained that it is mostly the youngest child that becomes homosexual—both in men and in women. I do not believe, however, that great importance should be laid to this fact, as it is mostly a matter of accident.

During his school days B. S. had only insignificant and chaste affairs with girls. Some four years ago, *i. e.,* when he was twenty-two years of age, he made the acquaintance of a lad "to whom he was devoted with an ardor" the like of which he had had no conception before. He loved his "beau" with all the pleasure and pain that goes with a genuine attachment. He fell in love with him at first sight. He did everything in his power to come closer; got in touch with his family, rented a room near the house. The other at least according to the patient's statement, came to know only good things from him. B. S. at the time avoiding all other social intercourse and devoting himself exclusively to him. He was of great service to him in his studies. Of course, he concealed his inclination from him. "In spite of my ardent desire to kiss him I have only done so about ten times. I did not want to kiss him oftener because I knew that he

could not respond with the same ardor, and that my love
might become annoying to him. I also feared that the
bloom of the spirit of this beautiful young man might
become faded with the incense of my adoring love if I
should love him to excess. My greatest pleasure was to
hold his soft, fleshy hand, sit near him, take walks with
him and tell him stories. At times it was impossible for
me to sit near him at dinner because my stomach was
affected.'' At such times B. S. talked very excitedly and
with a stammer. He also developed a very peculiar
fetishism. Whereas most people cannot stand the smell
of iodine, B. S. came to like it very much, because he
first observed it on the boy's skin when the latter cut himself. B. S. also kept one of his handkerchiefs, fondling
and kissing it. His image was always in B. S.'s mind
unbidden. Filled with such strong erotic thoughts B. S.
has spent many a dreamy hour. It was disgusting to him
to imagine the boy naked. He loved him without wanting to know to what sex he belonged; in his presence he
never felt any reflex in his sex organs; in fact in order
not to think of his love as a spiritual stain, he coined
a new expression for it, paedagapese from the Greek.
His love for the boy was a great puzzle to B. S. He
would study the boy attentively to try to discover what
there really was in him, but the only answer he got was
that he must continue loving him. He could not bear
to part from him. When circumstances forced him to
change his residence, he became so unhappy that he had
to return after a very short time. He tried to justify
his feelings to himself, adhering to one of Schopenhauer's remark that an inclination must serve the purpose of Nature; that is, though he himself did not bring
forth a new offspring yet the younger generation in many

beautiful legend that he had read in the writings of
Goethe and Horace, of the joy and love of youths and
maidens; until very recently he believed that such dreams
of love could never be realized.

After the extinction of his homosexual propensities
there came upon him the desire for women. He gave
himself up to thoughts of coitus, and strong erections
followed; however, as far as women in actual life were
concerned, he was as weak and shy as previously. His
timidity prevented him from approaching girls he did not
know. This was humorously regarded by his comrades,
who did what they could to set him at ease. He remained unhappy and depressed. Love for his own sex
had disappeared without his finding an adequate substitute in a strong love for women. Life became very irk-
some to him. Thoughts of suicide often cropped up, and
oppressed him. He was also grieved at the fact that he
still retained his feminine appearance. The thought of
being alone, without a woman, seems terrible to him.
He has no aversion for women; the thought of nude
bodies calls forth erections in him; he finds a beautiful
bust charming. At present he has no pronounced predilection for any certain type, like that he showed at the
time of puberty for brunettes.

When he was twenty-four friends of his own age encouraged him to perform coitus. Very soon afterwards
he gave in, but his desire did not materialize because the
naked woman did not excite him in the least. At the
second attempt he had only a feeble erection, but it was
brought about artificially only through manipulation on
the part of the woman. Though B. S. stayed with her
for fully a quarter of an hour the erection remained
weak. Finally both ejaculation and orgasm took place.

After he had undergone electro-therapeutic treatment for a few weeks he performed coitus for the third time, this time with erection and ejaculation *in vaginam,* but without any voluptuous sensation.

Since that affair, which had occurred before puberty, B. S. for a long time was unable to experience any love for other women. At present a woman has only a sexual, sensual charm for him. It seems to him that he can find complete gratification only in a girl of about sixteen or seventeen; for he feels like a "dwarf" when confronted by a fully developed woman. The only exception to this feeling was the following incident. When he was twenty-five he made the acquaintance of a very beautiful, youthful woman of nineteen, and he observed with great joy that he developed a liking for her, which was reciprocated. But this love for her died completely after about fourteen days, through no fault of the girl. In the short period of its duration, B. S. had not observed in himself any real ardor or feeling of self-sacrifice. For, as he adds, this feeling is quite well-known to him, as he had experienced it towards his young friend, of former days. Later, another girl declared her love for him in unmistakable language. Unhappy and not knowing what to do, he spent many a sleepless night because he could not respond to her love. It seems to him an unbelievably difficult task to write a love-letter to a girl, whereas before without any trouble he could write page after page to his "beloved boy."

More recently B. S.'s sex life as a whole began to take on a different aspect. He is interested in women, and earnestly hopes, that in time, this feeling will become more strengthened, so that he may later marry.

After thus bringing before you a number of cases in which the two components of the sex instinct do not occur together, I will add a few remarks. It can be proven that without the thought of the other sex or of any other person masturbation is practiced especially by many young people. But the normal impulse, too, may express itself without any reference to the genitals. This is quite frequently to be observed at the time of puberty; at least such persons in question are not conscious of any erotic sensations. A young man with such a sexual make-up feels himself drawn towards a female person without any thought of performing coitus. The same phenomenon may also be observed in the female sex; it appears, that in the case of grown-up women, the contrectation without reference to the genitals, is more common than in men. In a separate chapter of the next volume, I shall return in more detail, to the subject of the so-called sexual anesthesia in woman. But let me remark here that what is referred to as sexual anasthesia in woman, is frequently connected only with coitus. These women, at times, love their husbands very passionately, are devoted to them with great love, thought of another man being repellant; what does lack in such case is the absolute orgasm in the sex act and of the impulse to perform the coitus.

Numerous cases of masturbation, especially in women, point to a division between contrectation and detumescence. Various authors have written about masturbation in woman, such as Torggler, Laker, and Loiman. In many cases it cannot be clearly ascertained what brought about masturbation. Krafft-Ebing has justly pointed out that in cases of non-gratification in coitus one must distinguish between those cases in which orgasm is

brought on by a morbid and severe excitability of the
reflex center, situated in the lumbar region of the spinal
cord; and between cases in which the fault is to be ascertained to excessive masturbation, which has a deleterious influence on the psycho-sexual centre. Let me
also mention a third possibility—applicable, of course,
only to a few cases—the sundering of contrectation and
detumescence. This last case may easily be separated
from all others, simply by asking the woman who masturbates whether she uses her imagination during the
practice. Of course, when she thinks of a man or of a
woman, in the case of a lesbian, before her, we may not
speak of the sundering of the two impulses, but merely of
another form of gratification; such forms of gratification are sought after either because circumstances prevent the occurrence of orgasm in coitus, or because the
sex act cannot be performed, and masturbation with
the aid of the phantasy being substituted. However,
when masturbation takes place without any aid of the
phantasy, when only a local titillation is desired, we may
assume that contrectation and detumescence are not
closely tied up with each other.

Reference has frequently been made to Platonic love.
The expression has often been misunderstood. When
one goes back to the original meaning of the word, one
understands by it the love of men to each other; but in
a wider sense one understands by it non-sexual love,
Plato having described such love as praiseworthy. This
is not quite true. Plato merely describes the relationship
of a man to a youth, in such a manner, that physical and
spiritual beauty are conceived as identical; and consequently such relationships (undoubtedly of a sexual
nature) between a mature man and a youth are ennobled,

as it were. However, when we speak of Platonic love, we usually mean a love that has a non-sensual basis. But in such a non-sensual love one has to take into consideration whether the reference to the genitals only is to be excluded, or whether the sense organs play in it no role whatsoever. If the first is the case we should meet with many cases of Platonic love. Such cases are very frequently to be met with in lovers, to whom the goal of the instinct does not lie in the performance of coitus, but merely in satisfaction by mutual contact, embracing and quite frequently kissing. Such forms of love are observed at the beginning of puberty, in so-called student "crushes." "That Wolfgang could withstand the prickling charm of sin, was due to an innocent girl ... The sensual receded entirely. To see her was the only thing he desired. For the first time in his life Wolfgang felt the influence of innocent womanhood . . . A new world was opened to the boy. Her greeting, a nod of her head satisfied him." Goethe was fifteen years old then. However, when we refer to Platonic love in the second sense, *i. e.* in which the sense organs do not play any role at all, we find many such cases, as well. Let me bring to your mind, the example of the erotomaniacs, who show this form of Platonic love with such pathological exaggeration. It seems to me that when a woman's mind is continually preoccupied with the thought of a man when she shows the liveliest interest for him, but has not the least desire to come in bodily contact with him, though she show all the signs of spiritual love—I believe that such a case we are justified in calling a sex instinct corresponding to that Platonic love. The entire direction of the thoughts is determined by the man. The objection will be raised that until now we have referred to instincts only where movements and actions are the result, that we have designated the sex instinct as an impulse to perform certain acts. It might be in place to mention here that some writers, *e.g.,* Wundt, divided the instincts into higher and lower, while others, among them Kulpe, were opposed to such a distinction. To the lower instincts might then be counted those, in which there is a desire for sensual pleasure and a dislike for feelings of displeasure. On the other hand, the higher insincts, according to Wundt, have their roots in the manifold configurations of the aesthetic and individual emotions. In the sex instinct, though we define this concept some-what differently from Wundt, these higher impulses, in my opinion, would correspond to the spiritual complexion taken on by a person in love with another. In that form, devoid of every sensual thought, not only of performing coitus, but also of bodily contact, the spiritual feelings which tying up the two persons in love, would belong to the higher impulse. But when the lower impulses are also present, it is upon this higher impulse of love that the spiritual bond uniting man and woman rests.

Though the sex instinct, in the last analysis, is directed towards the performance of coitus, yet, as a matter of fact, there are many other processes that revolve around this impulse; these, as it were, only prepare for the sex act. The female bird delighting in the song of the male; the female of the cuckoo continuously flying about the male in order to bring it into the wildest ardors of love; the peacock displaying the splendor of his plumage for the admiration of the hen; the otter performing wildest motions around the female; these are all activities belonging particularly to the sex instinct. However, they

seem to point only indirectly to an act of the genitals
and often only unconsciously. The very same is true of
man. A man approaching a woman whom he desires to
win with a most irreproachable moustache; another
burning in ardor at the pure song of a lady, seeking to
enjoy this singing as frequently as possible; when the
young woman in question, in order to fascinate the man
practices her art of singing; when other women, try as
best they can to enhance their physical charms through
the use of rouges and powders; when another man finds
his satisfaction in close conversation with a lady; when
an officer, in order to increase the excitement of a woman
comes to meet her in his uniform; these particular actions, in all cases, are performed—often unconsciously,
it is true—in order to prepare for the one final act, coitus.
This may best be seen in romantic love, in which the relations of the sexes are not directed by the conscious urge
to perform coitus.

Finck, in opposition to Ernst Eckstein, believes that
romantic love, as we know it today, is a modern phenomenon. He believes that premarital love did not exist in antiquity; and that it was born with Dante's love
for Beatrice in 1274. We may agree with Finck that
the main aspects of romantic love are to be seen in those
activities that precede the "animal act" proper. But
otherwise the assumptions of Finck are not correct. It
is true that in those countries where woman has occupied a very low position in the social scale, it has hardly
existed. And, as a matter of fact, it does not exist today
in the Mohammedan countries. Still, there have been
several periods in history where such pre-marital love
has been observed. I do not believe that it is a product
of modern times, as Finck assumes. I should like to

point out the fact that in the animal world, *e. g.* among birds, romantic love plays quite a conspicuous role. For is not such romantic love the coquetry of animals, the shy retreat of the female? Neither do I believe that the cases from antiquity with Finck cites as exceptions, such as Jacob's length of service for the winning of Rachel, or the love described in the story of "Daphnis and Chloe," are not to be observed more generally. On the contrary, many other cases may be pointed out from antiquity, such as the love of the ancient Germans, whose ideal love for woman so astonished Tacitus.

As we have seen, contrectation and detumescence are the two components of the sex instinct in human beings. All phenomena of the sex instinct may with facility be assigned to either of these; at the same time it must be considered that contrectation extends not only to bodily contacts, but also to the psyche, to thoughts, of the person loved.

We may now introduce the further question what the relationship is, both physiological and psychological, between these two instincts, contrectation and detumescence; whether or not the one induces the other; and which of the two is the primary. Let me state here, that in mature man, both detumescence and contrectation may be brought about by peripheral processes, by the charging of the seminal vesicles and of the seminal tubules, and by the activity of the testicles or of the ovaries. On the other hand central processes, ideas of a voluptuous nature may also call forth both contrectation and detumescence. But this is the case only with mature persons, in whom both impulses apparently are equivalent, the one inciting the other. In the development of the individual matters are different. We shall observe the relationship of the two impulses most clearly in *evolutionary history*. From a study of this, it may be demonstrated that peripheral processes are primary while the central processes are secondary, *i. e.* that detumescence precedes contrectation. When we follow through the genealogical tree of man from the protozoa to his present day development, we may see *that the coupling of two animals for the purpose of propagation, i. e. contrectation, occurs at a much later period than propagation through mere detumescence, in which one individual suffices, parts of the individual separating off and changing into a new organism.* However, egg cells and sperm cells of higher animals, are nothing else but such part of the parent-organism.

It is a well known fact that the higher animals have gradually developed from the lower. Phylogenetics rests on the theory of evolution, which though it has received much support from Darwin, is only a small part of Darwinism, *i. e.* that part, which before the time of Darwin had been accepted by Lamarck, Goethe, Oken and Geoffroy Saint-Hilaire.

One may distinguish between *asexual* and *sexual* reproduction. The latter takes place when two sexually differentiated germ cells, one female, the egg cell, and the other male, the sperm cell, come together, the new individual being developed from the fusion of the two germ cells. The two germ cells, as shown by the microscope, have a different structure; the egg cell is round, while the sperm cell is distinguished by a head and a characteristic tail. In sexual reproduction the two fusing germ cells may either be produced in the same individual (this is the case in hermaphrodites); or the male and female cells may be produced in different individuals. Furthermore, though the male and female cells might be produced in the same individual, one individual does not suffice for the purpose of reproduction, but two; one of whom supplies the male cells and the other the female cells; this may be observed in the leeches. For example, in the amœba, the mother-animal grows uniformly and then divides into several daughter-animals.

But there is also another form of reproduction in unicellular animals. There is first a union of the two germ cells, identical with the parent-animals in this case. Such union is called conjugation. But after conjugation and the interchange of certain parts the two parent animals again separate and only then reproduction through fission takes place. It is this process which distinguishes conjugation from sexual reproduction. Another difference is that in conjugation the cells coming together are not sexually differentiated. In spite of this, Haeckel classified conjugation as a form of sexual reproduction. Besides, there are, of course, also certain histological differences between conjugation of unicellular animals and impregnation of egg-cell by sperm cell, as may be presupposed from the protracted separation of these two. The more recent researches of Maupas, R. Hertwig, and Weismann and others, on the other hand, have shown that conjugation is very similar to the sexual reproduction of higher animals, preceded by impregnation. Weismann assumes that both sexual reproduction of higher animals and conjugation serve the same purpose, namely the fusion of hereditary tendencies, through which the offspring are enabled to stand their ground in the struggle for existence. It must be considered that more recent researches have given us numerous examples of unicellular animals who reproduce after conjugating. However, let me again stress here that the main difference between sexual reproduction and conjugation lies in the fact that in the former the offspring is not brought forth directly out of the conjugated cells.

In the lowest animals separate *organs of generation* have not as yet been developed. However, though investigations so far have not as yet ascertained the existence of such separate organs of generation, but rather reproduction through a regular growth of the entire individual. Still in other comparatively low-standing multicellular animals special cells serving reproduction have been observed. We may assume that the first step toward the differentiation into the organs of generation has been taken in those animals which multiply through budding. Together with v. Wagner, Weismann distinguishes fission from budding in this, that in the former multiplication is through regular growth of the mother-animals, while in the latter the process is initiated by an uneven growth. It is doubtful whether budding has evolved from fission. At any rate, reproduction through budding, *e. g.* in the coelenterata, takes place through certain cells. In multi-cellular animals, differentiation into male and female organs of generation takes place, sexually differentiated germ cells being developed. Male and female germ cells are thus already generated in hydra. Male and female organs of generation in separate individuals already presupposes a higher development, while hermaphroditism represents a lower stage of development. Thus many of the ascidia, from which have developed according to Kowalewsky, Haeckel and others, the amphioxus, the lowest living vertebral animal, are hermaphrodites. And even though in animals of a higher stage of development, *e.g.*, in some fish, the hag-fish, male and female organs of generation occur in

the same individual, this is not of much import from
the point of view of evolution, inasmuch as lasting and
continuous progress is not a necessary consequence of
that theory. For the history of development may show
occasional regressions and the possibility of less developed lateral branches is not excluded. The insects
are considered side-branches which have already reached
a high stage of development. The intelligence of several
very considerable groups of insects *e. g.* some species of
ants, and their bodily organization, too, is often more advanced than that of many vertebrates. Insects also are
more advanced than lower vertebræ in the development
of organs of reproduction and copulation, which latter
will be our next topic of discussion. In the bees, I only
have to point to the formation of vagina and penis as
well as the corresponding germ glands.

In addition to interal organs of generation, the higher
organisms also show external genitals, serving the purpose of *copulation*. In most species of fish the eggs are
deposited by the mother-animal in any ᴠenient place.
It is there that the eggs, the so-called spawn, is impregnated by the semen. In all viviparous animals, however, and also in many animals whose offspring develop
from the impregnated egg outside of the mother-organ-
ism fertilization takes place in the organism of the mother. This is to be observed not only in several species of
fish, for example in the shark, but also in all amniota
(reptilia, birds, and mammals). For this purpose male
and female must come together and copulate. The higher
we go up in the classification of the vertebræ the more we
see the gradual development of organs facilitating copulation. In the birds, who most likely represent a lateral
branch, and in some of the mammals, ornithorhychus and

monotrema, the germ-glands open into the cloaca, which
is the common outlet of the rectum, the uninary and
the genital apparatus. In the other mammals, however,
the cloaca are very soon displaced and the external sex
organs are developed more distinctly. In the male is
developed the penis, in the female the vagina where the
sperm cells are deposited. In all higher mammals, as in
some species of fish, the maternal organism is not only
the locus where the egg-cell is impregnated, but also a
resting place for the embryo until it is born. This is the
case in all viviparous animals.

Let us sum up what we have stated so far. Unisexual
reproduction is the primordial fact. Yet even at a rather
low stage of development two individuals, as yet un-
differentiated sexually, may come together for the purpose of interchanging substances before reproduction.
In a higher stage of development reproduction ori-
ginates from specific cells. The separation into male
and female of the cells serving the purpose of reproduction is an even higher stage. As far as I know, this has
been observed only in multi-cellular animals. The differentiated cells are produced in separate organs, the ovary
and testicle. At first these two organs are present in
each individual; however, at a certain phase of development it is necessary for two of these hermaphroditic animals to come together for the purpose of reproduction.
In the course of further development either the ovaries
or the testicles remain undeveloped and only the germ
cell of one sex is preserved in each individual. On a still
higher level is the development of organs which serve to
carry the impregnated eggs to full time. This last stage
is reached by all viviparous animals.

Up to the present time I have intentionally not mentioned *anything about the psychical factor in reproduction, the development of the sex instinct.* We have seen how the means for reproduction have gradually changed in the higher species of animals, how sexual reproduction changed in the higher species of animals, how sexual reproduction has originated, how separate organs of reproduction have been formed, and how these were transmitted to sexually differentiated animals; but we have not as yet raised the question when the psychical activity in reproduction first made its appearance. We know that in man the meeting of the sexes is brought on by the sex instinct, and that instinct is consciously perceived. The question we now propose is whether in animals, too, this instinct is present. On the basis of innumerable observations, it is not to be doubted in the least that this instinct with its two components, of detumescence and of contrectation are present in the higher mammals, *e. g.* in dogs, stags, and monkeys. Driven by this instinct dogs will search long to find a bitch. The instinct leads to ferocious battles between the males seeking after the favor of the female; it is well illustrated in the restlessness which these animals show before the act of copulation, or when they are prevented from performing it. We must suppose it to be present also in fish. When we take into consideration that male fish will pursue the female in order to fertilize her; that the male fish will do everything possible to chase off rivals; that, driven by restlessness he will sometimes travel long distances, which serve only the purpose of reproduction; then the existence of a sex instinct in these animals will not be denied. It is a well-established fact that the sex instinct occurs already in animals which in their development are far below man.

We have not as yet been able to determine how far down in the animal world this may be followed through. We would first of all have to discover in which animal sensations first made their appearance. Oskar Schmidt stated that an investigation into the question of the first appearance of perceptions, would lead one into the famous sophism of Eubulides about the "heap." Similarly, the question of the first appearance of perceptions cannot be answered. In spite of this, I do believe that du Bois-Reymond was quite correct in stating that the appearance of perception covered an unbridgeable chasm. Neither Schmidt's comparison with the heap, nor Nageli's attack on Bois-Reymond, can change the fact that there is a certain point when awareness first made its appearance; what Nageli tried to prove was that perception was the consequence of mechanical processes. Volkman held that in brainless animals the sex instinct seems to be absent altogether; that it only came into being with the appearance of the cerebral ganglion in the cephalophora and the annulata. At any rate, the sex instinct may be traced back through a long series of vertebrates, perhaps to the very lowest of these still existing today. Of course, I am here referring to both components of the instinct, detumescence and contrectation, and which, except for a few species of hermaphrodites among the vertebrates, is always directed towards the other sex.

Let us now observe those unicellular beings which multiply through conjugation, and let us not take the question whether or not a simple form of consciousness already exists among them. That such animals exchange substances in a regular manner, as may be ascertained histologically, proves that there is a mutual attraction

of the cell substances. Very similar to this is the observation of human cells, which have a special affinity for
certain materials brought to them, attracting these from
the blood through an increased cell activity. In this kind
of reaction the cells do not maintain a passive attitude;
not only physical factors, such as endosmosis and exe-
mosis take part in this process. The cells lively activity
attracts suitable materials from the blood, drawing them
into the cell and assimilating them. "It is only when
one conceives the absorption of nutrient material to be
the consequence of the activity (attraction) of the tissue
elements themselves, that one may understand why the
separate divisions are not every time open to the danger
of blood congestion." When we consider the lively activity of the cells in those lower organism during conjugation, we must conclude that here, too, we are dealing
with an attraction which the cell exerts upon other materials. On first sight, this process is apparently similar to nutrition in multicellular animals. Nay, it is so
similar, that the conjugation of the infusoria has even
been conceived as a devouring of the cells, a process of
nutrition. Kierman, for example, saw in it an analogy
with sadism in human beings. It is the same, whether
one follows this opinion, which assumes conjugation to
be an act of nutrition, or assimilation, an opinion much
opposed nowadays, or whether, following in the footsteps
of the latest research, one places this act in a category
with the impregnation of the egg cell by the sperm cell,
as in higher animals; or again, whether we accept the
standpoint of Haeckel, who draws no sharp distinctions
between nutrition ad reproduction, declaring the latter
to be a nutritive process and a growth of the organism
beyond the individual mass. The very fact of conjuga-

tion proves that there is an attraction between unicellular animals. For, were this not so, the two animals, as soon as they came close together, could not exchange materials. Of course, for some time, they might be in close proximity, but they would part again unchanged. Whoever is of the opinion that, only chemical and physical forces are active in these unicellular animals, may conceive the process to be like the affinity of chemical substances for each other, or even like the attraction of iron by the magnet; while others, who consider also the unicellular animals to be animated ascribing to them perceptions, will also conceive a psychical activity to be present in the process of conjugation. We do not know whether perceptions like that of higher animals are present in the lower beings, the infusoria. The fact that a nervous system, as in the higher animals, is not to be observed is not enough to solve this difficulty. For we do not know whether certain cell particles, which still escape the scrutiny of the microscope may not here take the place of a nervous system. When we take into consideration that in some infusoria different parts of the cell show a very marked division of labor, the idea of sensations can not be dismissed too easily. I do not maintain that this is so. But what I wish to point out is the fact that perception and feeling may be already present in the absence of a perfected consciousness and especially of self-consciousness.

The evolutionary examination of the sex instinct has been both positive and negative; firstly, in showing that the sex instinct, in human beings, may be traced back a long way; and, secondly, in convincing us, that, unless we want to lose ourselves in uncritical speculations, we cannot determine where to draw the line of demarcation. It is possible that a psychical activity is present already in conjugation of unicellular animals. Considering the great similarity which conjugation shows to impregnation, such a possibility is very important, even though we may not assume that the vertebrates are derived from the infusoria.

After thus having considered the evolutionary development of the sex instinct we may now take up the question of the primacy of detumescence or of contrectation. We have seen that even unicellular organisms unite for the purpose of reproduction, at the same time absorbing certain materials from one another. We have seen that infusoria after uniting exchange materials which should be regarded as the carriers of hereditary tendencies. The intermixture of hereditary tendencies which follows corresponds entirely to fecundation in higher animals. However, since such juxtaposition perhaps takes place only physiologically, *i. e.* without psychical mediation, we may not here as yet talk of contrectation. At least, we cannot prove it. And just as little may detumescence in lower animals be shown to exist. Aside from the fact that we do not know anything about the psychical life of these infusoria, we must consider also that the materials they ejaculate do not correspond either to the sperm cells or the eggs of mammals; they are rather to be identified with certain ingredients in the egg and sperm cell. Of great importance, though, is the conclusion that the exchanged parts are to be regarded as the same as the essential parts of the egg and sperm cell, *i. e.* as the bearer of the hereditary tendencies. In view of the great difficulties in fathoming the psychical life of lower animals, it cannot be ascertained, as pointed out, in which animals, in the evolutionary tree, we have the first appearance of the two psychological components of the sex instinct.

For the above reason we shall be unable to answer the question of the primacy of detumescent or contrectation. I will, therefore, consider it preferable to exclude the psychical factor, *e. g.* the instinct, from our discussion altogether and only investigate which of the two physiological processes is the primary one. In my opinion, the answer to this would be that detumescence is the original process. Animals of higher species may still be observed in whom pairing off is unnecessary for reproduction; in whom, on the contrary, the female produces the eggs, from which the offspring is developed directly without impregnation. This form of reproduction is called parthenogenesis, and is among others to be seen in bees, in phylloxera vastatrix, in aphis, some spiders, etc. And though, parthenogenetical reproduction takes place in some of the eggs only, this furnishes us with proof that even in higher animals reproduction through a single individual is possible, *i. e.* contrectation is superfluous. It may be objected here that the depositing of eggs is not identical with detumescence. In the human male detumescence causes the expulsion of cells, which in themselves are not capable of reproduction; and in the animal world, those cells which correspond to the human spermatozoa are in no case sufficient for reproduction. Detumescence in woman at the time of coitus, on the other hand, is not identical with expulsion of eggs. This latter process, on the contrary, occurs at greater intervals, as in the case of menstruation. On the other hand, detumescence in woman brings about, at most, only the separation of an indifferent secretion, the contents of certain glands and separated during the performance of coitus, through the activity of

the muscles; *i. e.,* the secretion of the gland of Bartholin
and perhaps also the secretion of the mucous glands of
the uterus. The egg, however, is not expelled during
detumescence, but must remain in the uterus in order
to develop. Still, we may also assume that in woman
the separation of detumescence and expulsion of the egg,
is only a secondary phenomenon that originally detumescence coincided with the expulsion of the egg. This
simultaneously may best be observed in fish. Here the
expulsion of the egg takes place at the same time as
detumescence. This may be observed in many other of
those organisms, in which the egg expelled develops
into the new being. Accordingly, I consider secondary
the disconnection between detumescece and expulsion
of the egg. And since detumescence originally was identical with expulsion of the ovum, and since, furthermore,
the egg alone without the previous impregnation by another individual was originally sufficient for the development of the new individual, we may very well assume
that *detumescence is the primary process, from the
point of view of evolution, and that the approaching of
another individual for the purpose of reproduction is
only secondary.* At present there are still numerous
lower organisms which reproduce without the aid of
another member of the species. Let me mention here
those animals which multiply through fission. Though
we find conjugation to be the mode of reproduction prevalent in the very lowest of animals, we must nevertheless
regard reproduction through fission or budding as the
earlier process. However, fission and budding, may also
take place without the activity of a second individual.

It should not be objected here that the differentiation into sexes may already be observed in unicellular

organisms. Such differentiation, nevertheless, must be
regarded as a secondary phenomenon, an assumption
much adhered to at the present time. Of course, it is
true, that there are unicellular animals, in which the
sexes are separated, as for example, *volvox,* the latter a
colony of algae. Already at this low stage of development it is apparent that some of the cells having long
flagellæ are analogous to the spermatozoa while others
resemble the female egg-cell. So that we may already
differentiate between male and female sex cells in these
unicellular plants. Here reproduction may take place
either through the development of the new individual
from the female cell itself, or through the meeting of
male and female cells with the consequent formation of
the new offspring.

An erroneous conclusion might easily be adduced
therefrom. For since the meeting of two members of
the species for the purpose of reproduction has been
observed to take place already in the lowest of animals,
one might consider such a pairing off as the primordial
fact. However, such a conclusion would be premature,
as may also be seen in the fact that in the colony of algæ
mentioned above, the female cell is sufficient for reproduction. I do not stress the fact that it is algæ, *i. e.*
plants, which we have here selected to study this differentiation into sexes in unicellular organisms. Of course,
it is not impossible that unicellular animals, too, may be
found, which will show such differentiation, or that such
animals might have existed in the past. Of greater importance is the fact that reproduction takes place in the
plant through *one* individual. The separation, in these
unicellular organisms, into sexually differentiated cells
would thus only prove that even at this low stage of de-

velopment such conditions already exist which necessitates a differentiation. Such a separation, however, would not prove that the need for the presence of two individuals is primary. Almost all facts in the history of evolution speak against such an assumption.

It must be mentioned again that in most unicellular individuals there is no sexual differentiation at all. Even in conjugation, as we have seen, certain parts are separated from the cell; and even though these parts are identical with the egg and sperm cell of higher animals, though on the contrary, they correspond at most to certain parts of these, it follows that in the evolutionary process ejaculation is not subsequent to the meeting of two members of the species. It is further to be remembered that in many lower organisms fission without conjugation takes place, and though this process is not directly identical with detumescence in higher animals, this is nevertheless even further removed from the process of the union of two individuals. And finally let me stress also that animals which reproduce through conjugation, such reproduction may often take place also without conjugation.

We have seen that in the history of development the peripheral processes in the genitals are primary and that contrectation, therefore, must be considered only secondary. In the individual development of man this may not be ascertained with the same certainty, because the stimuli which originate from the peripheral sex glands often do not reach the threshold of consciousness. We often find that stimuli coming from internal bodily organs are often and for a long time not perceived, yet they cause certain reactions. In like manner may we assume that the stimuli originating from the sex glands may cause certain reactions which are perceived without the stimuli themselves being felt. It is due to this that contrectation sometimes will be present without the consciousness of detumescence. For example, we are familiar in literary history with numerous cases of prominent poets who in their early childhood fell in love with women, that is at a time, when we could not as yet speak of physical puberty. Let me mention Dante who fell in love with Beatrice at the age of nine; Canova, at the age of five; Alfieri, at the age of ten; and Byron, who at the age of eight, is said to have fallen in love with Mary Duff. Sollier makes mention of the fact that in idiots we may sometimes observe the impulse towards the other sex long before physical puberty. He rightfully adds that this is also the case with normal individuals. At any rate, I may state, on the basis of many questions which I have addressed to numerous persons, that the inclination towards the other sex, with all its signs of sexual passion, may be observed long before the onset of puberty. I have known cases in which at the age of five or six there were indubitable inclinations originating from the sex instinct.

In higher animals, too, as in human beings, flirtations and love-playings are sometimes observed, long before they reach physical puberty. It may appear thus that in these animals contrectation, to a certain degree, is already present before the appearance of detumescence. These observations in animals, in my opinion, are very important in order to destroy the common belief that physical puberty is a necessary preliminary condition for the sexual inclination of male and female. On the contrary, as has already been mentioned several times, the psychical element, in a number of cases, may develop much earlier than physical puberty. In our own times, Groos has collected numerous examples of the play of young animals and is of the opinion that their play as well as that of children is not an imitation of the activity of mature grown-ups, but rather a preactivity. The activities which the animals later exercise in the struggle for existence are practiced by them in play in childhood, but only, as it were, as preparatory exercises for their later activities. The female child plays with a doll and in such play already exercises her later activity as a mother. Such play may even reach the point where the child will give her breast to the doll. Of course, it is not always possible to state what in such play of young animals, is to be regarded as sheer play and what is really sincere activity. Chr. L. Brehm reports that in many cases among birds, the love for the other sex, is awakened at a time when we may not speak of physical puberty, when the testicles of the male bird are not developed, thus precluding the possibility of copulation. In all such cases, it cannot always be determined whether we are dealing with play, or with a premature psychical puberty. Some observations, though, do convince us that these playings are not preactivities but rather activities, arising from an awakened sex instinct, and perceived as play. To these activities would belong courtship by means of the movements, sounds and noises, excellently described in the works of Groos, also the flirtations of the young females. It is true that in a number of cases, such activities represent only play. But then Brehm following Groos also refers to the love in young birds living at large, which is apparent long before copulation.

We have seen that contrectation may make itself felt

even before the genitals become mature. The same is also true of detumescence. I have previously mentioned only in passing that the latter may likewise express itself prematurely. It is commonly assumed that it appears only at the time of somatic puberty, that is to say, when the testicles begin to produce the semen. But there are also cases where long before the onset of puberty, a decided tendency to bring about a change in the genitals has been observed; and even though in such cases there is no secretion of semen, we have only to remind ourselves that in the female, too, there is no necessity for such a secretion when referring to detumescence. It expresses itself in some feeling of voluptuousness, a titillation which one experiences or desires to experience in the genitals; erections also may occur a long time before puberty. It is due to this that very young children begin to masturbate sometimes even at the age of one or two. Another very remarkable fact is that both components of the sex instinct, contrectation and detumescence, may sometimes be developed before puberty.

In the following case I shall bring an example illustrating how both components of the sex instinct may apparently come into being long before the onset of somatic puberty. The case refers to a girl and is especially remarkable because her sexual inclination was directed towards her own brother. I do not maintain at all that we have here already a case of sharp differentiation of the sex instinct. Her brother was still very young and a more well-defined differentiation commonly takes place only at the time of physical puberty. This case, however, will at least tend to show that various aspects of the sex instinct may appear long before puberty, a very important fact in psychology of sex.

Case VII. J. B., a girl of seven. Her mother was a hysterical woman. The girl makes a sprightly and lively impression. She has a smaller brother of three and a half. One day, the boy by chance asked his mother, whether it was a nice thing for his sister to touch him below, that is, in his genitals. This was the first reason for the discovery. Closer questionings elicited the fact that a boy of the neighborhood had asked her to touch his genitals; *after this she developed an impulsive tendency towards her own brother, to touch his genitals. She also induced him to touch her own sex parts.* Occasionally the girl had also practiced this on herself. It was also found out that in the presence of her brother she would blush and show a peculiar embarrassment. Apparently she had a certain sexual inclination towards her brother. As a result of these occurrences the brother was sent away from the house. Since then the inclination of the child has been much allayed. The girl, however, is very intelligent and fears that her impulse may be awakened again; and so she often asks her mother not to allow her to mingle with other children, because of the evil consequences which might result. At first sexual play with her brother took place in the presence of the parents, without them noticing it. It was sufficient for the children to touch each other beneath the table for them to get excited.

The following case is of more interest. The young boy in the case had been described as morally insane by those who accept such a concept in psychiatry. He shows very serious hereditary taints. Though in his early childhood he had already performed sexual acts with other children, it is to be doubted whether these

were due to contrectation, or whether he merely used
the other boys to masturbate him. Detumescence seems
to be developed more distinctly in the following case.

Case VIII. N. S., eleven years of age, has eight other
brothers and sisters, of whom a twelve year old girl
is highly nervous. Another girl of three and a half
shows the same character traits as the patient. N. S.
had never been a good student in school, being lazy and
far behind the others. His handwriting is good but his
copy-books are very sloppy. Already in his early childhood he was a very peevish child. Neither correction nor
punishment could make him obey people. Chicanery and
cruelty are his most pronounced character traits. Physically he gives the impression of retarded growth. Several people who did not know him took him to be seven
years of age, though he was already eleven. The low
forehead is very conspicuous. His features have a decidedly sullen expression, and his forehead usually shows
a few furrows, like that of ill-humored persons. In contrast to several of his brothers and sisters whom I know
personally, the boy has a very shut-in nature. These
others have sympathetic, frank and honest expressions
and behave accordingly. N. S. seldom shows the desire to play with other children; and has actually never
played with any unless it was to torture them.

The abnormalities are prevalent mainly in the sphere
of sex. By resorting to choking and other means of torture he had compelled his brothers and sisters to give
in to him in this respect. When he was only four
years old he had by resorting to choking compelled one
of his sisters, his senior by a year, to titillate his genitals with her tongue. For several years he had constantly been caught with erections. His parents were able

to corroborate this. At present he likes to lie down on top of his brother with whom he sometimes sleeps. It cannot be ascertained, however, whether any positive sexual acts are then performed. On the other hand, it is a fact that already at the age of eight he performed unchaste acts with girls of his own age, placing his hand beneath their skirts, and performing mutual masturbation with them. It is remarkable that the girls permitted these things only when he gave them money; he gave them twenty cents every time, from monies which he stole from the people with whom he stayed. Another circumstance that has been proven is the fact that N. S. still continues to play with his genitals. His mother states that on these occasions she had noticed that a liquid issued from the genitals; and as a matter of fact his shirts do show distinct spots. Dr. Robert Kutner, however, who examined the spots upon my request, has assured me that it was not semen. It is not known whether it comes from the secretions of the prostatic gland. Dr. Kutner believes it to be a discharge from the urethra which must have been inflamed by the numerous manual irritations. His parents have frequently caught him while masturbating. On those occasions he had his two hands on the genitals. While masturbating he sometimes feels a peculiar twitching and always during these twitchings he neighs like a horse. These statements were made by his parents. When questioned the boy says that he feels a ticklish sensation when he plays with his hands ''down there.'' N. S. is given to much stealing, both tidbits and other things, but especially money. Recently he threatened to beat another boy if he did not give him money. As a whole he did his stealing cunningly. Neither his parents nor anyone else have ever caught him at it. Only the disappearance of the things is noted. When a coin is placed on the table he has the knack of pilfering it at the moment when nobody is looking. His parents declare that they have never as yet been able to catch him in the act. Even afterwards when they look through his clothes they fail to find it. Like the pickpockets, who will immediately hand over a stolen article to another person so as not to throw suspicion upon themselves when examined, so N. S. usually places the coin in a particular spot where he can always get at it. When searched, therefore, nothing is ever found on him.

N. S. treats his brothers and sisters with a baseness which sometimes gives one a very strange impression. For example, when they have all gone to bed after the older children have done their home work, N. S. would get up, take out their slates from their bags, wipe off their exercises, and then replace them into the bags. Then when the children came to school, thinking that they could show their work to the teacher, they were greatly surprised to find their slates bare.

Recently, in order to choke him, he placed a pebble into the nose of one of his brothers while the latter was asleep. When his father once lectured him, he threatened to stab him; when asked why, N. S. spoke of the beatings he sometimes received from him. He also wanted to stab his mother because she often reported his misbehaviour to her husband. The latter had often been surprised to see his son carrying a knife.

Asked whether he considered it wrong to steal money, N. S. said no. He did not see why he should not take money that is lying on the table.

N. S. talks quietly and appears very shy. When

closely questioned he claims that he does not like his brothers and sisters and that he cannot bear to look at them. He admits that they do not maltreat him. Thus he cannot say why he feels such a dislike towards them. Especially hateful to him is one of his sisters, three and a half years old. Nor can he bear the sight of his parents. A short time ago N. S. attempted to poison his brothers and sisters but failed in the attempt because he did not proceed with caution. His parents had bought some wash-bluing and the mother, in order to hide it from the children, had placed it high in the cupboard. N. S. pushed the table from the center of the room to the cupboard, placed a chair on top of the table and was able to get the desired article. He put it on the table where the children played. When he was asked why he had done it he declared that he wanted them to taste it. The blue was noticed, fortunately, and was removed. When he was further questioned as to why he had wanted to poison the children he stated that he wished them to die. He did not know why.

Another thing to point out is the boy's lying disposition, also a veritable mania for destroying things. Several times in order to burn them he threw his own things into the oven. One day his mother told him to put away a pair of shoes and he deliberately pulled off the buttons. He destroys his mother's thimbles by crushing them flat. He plays tricks on his brothers and sisters such as hiding their school materials in order that they may be punished. One day, threatening to choke her, he compelled his sister to stand on a hot oven; she still shows the scars from the burns. Recently he was brought to police headquarters where Inspector von Meerscheidt-Hullessem lectured him severely threatened him, etc.

The hope that this would have an effect for a few days at least was vain. The very same afternoon he took an axe and willfully damaged the staircase railing. He also tried to induce another boy to step on the frozen lake because he thought that the ice would give in. Some time later he forced a girl to climb up a heap of coal which was then tumbling down. The severest punishments could not bring about any changes. It was of no avail either to send him to a reformatory institution. He does not show the slightest trace of pity. He tortures animals every day. He ran away from home on several occasions, even at night, and goes around begging against the wishes of his very decent folks. He cries out a good deal in the night, which may be ascribed to sexual excitement, though any proof for this assumption is lacking. A few days ago he dragged his infant sister from bed and put her on the floor without any reason. The child crawled over to the bed of her parents and the cruel act was thus discovered. It is to be remarked that this child of a year and a half already plays with her genitals.

As far as the general impression of the boy's mental development is concerned, it must be stated that in spite of all slyness, he stands far below the average.

These last two cases should show that local sensations in the genitals, together with detumescence may occur at a period when puberty has not as yet made its appearance. It is to be pointed out in regards to the last case that the spots examined by Dr. Kutner were not attributable to semen. In both cases, and especially the latter, there are hereditary taints.

One might conclude from the preceding reports that neither contrectation nor detumescence result from the function of the sex glands; at least, the maturity of the sex glands, in these cases, cannot be proven. I do consider it necessary to stress here that the sex glands may grow to maturity though the age of an individual may seem to contradict this. In other cases the sex glands may be mature while the other organs still lack the signs of physical puberty. While in some cases of precocious maturity of the sex glands one may, as a matter of fact, show that the rest of the organism is mature.

As early as 1812, Barez published the case of a boy of three named Jacques Aime Savin, which was later discussed by Brachet in Paris. It could not be ascertained whether semen had been produced in him. What seemed to point to this was a smell like that of semen, and spots which were often observed in the bed and on his shirts. His voice was deep like that of a person of about seventeen. A thick down was noticeable on his upper lip as well as on the sides of his face. The pubic region was provided with a strong growth of hair like that of a youth of seventeen. The penis was about 4 in. long. The child very often had erections, especially in the presence of young girls or women which caused him great excitement; so that he wished to bring his hands close to the sex parts of the female person. Similar cases have also been described in the older literature and sometimes in the more recent writings (Mead, Yelloly, Dupuytren). In the case above cited we thus have contrectation, as well as distinct signs of physical puberty without our being able, however, to say with positive assurance that the secretion of semen—the most important and most decisive symptom of such puberty—could be proven; though, in all probability, it seemed to be present.

In regard to the female sex we are familiar with many cases in which the external impression of the body does not warrant our assuming that puberty has been reached while the full maturity of the genitals may be established. Girdwood, following Steinhaus, observed a mature follicle in the ovary of an eight year old girl, who was normal otherwise. Beigel and others have known cases where ova capable of impregnation were present in the ovaries of children. Prochownick describes the case of a girl of three in whom the process of ovulation has already set in. There are also cases where pregnancies took place at the age of nine or even earlier. Especially remarkable is the case of Anna Mummenthaler (1751-1826) who became pregnant at the age of eight and in due time bore a still-born child.

Menstruation in a great number of such cases of premature ovulation had not as yet been observed; one has no proof as to when true puberty had set in. And it is likewise difficult to demonstrate whether or not the testicles had already begun to produce semen, in boys with precocious symptoms of puberty.

When we thus observe the symptoms of psychosexual puberty in young children we must use every precaution in concluding that it is not the consequence of the activity of the sex glands. We have just seen that these sex glands may function without the appearance of puberty or of the other functions of the body, especially of menstruation. In the female sex, particularly this may be asserted with great assurance. Moreover, when the external symptoms of physical puberty are not as yet perceptible, while psychosexual puberty is to be met with at the same time, we can not under any circumstances draw

the conclusion that such psychosexual puberty has no
connection with the sex glands. It is true that in some
cases psychosexual puberty is probably not tied up with
the maturity of the sex glands, but rather with other
stimuli whose origin lies in the sex glands. On the basis
of these considerations I believe that we may draw the
conclusion that the sex glands both from an evolutionary and ontogenetical point of view are the primary
phenomenon in the sexual life of man. The proof for
this may be seen in the consequences of castration.
The sex glands bring about detumescence and contrectation. When a number of persons are asked which they
have experienced first, the impulse to bring about a
change in their genitals, *i. e.*, detumescence, or a sexual
inclination towards another person, many will say the
latter. But as matters stand, both contrectation and
detumescence are the result of the sex glands. This
difference, however, is to be observed: Detumescence is,
so to speak, the immediate effect of the sex glands. These
glands press on for release of their function and from
this tension follow all those physiological processes
which are present in detumescence; this at least is the
case in male individuals. In them detumescence is nothing more than the urge to empty a glandular secretion,
just as one has the desire to evacuate a full stomach or a
full bladder. Contrectation is essentially different.
Though it too is a consequence of the presence of the
sex glands, it is not to be considered the immediate function of these glands. On the contrary, *it is to be considered to some extent as an indirect consequence, con-
ceivable only from the history of evolution and from
the purpose which the sex organs serve.* We have seen
that in the history of evolution there is a certain stage

where sexual reproduction takes the place of asexual reproduction. It becomes necessary for two germs to unite with each other, and in the end, those beings which had developed asexually remained behind in the struggle against those which had developed sexually. In sexual reproduction, according to Weissman, two hereditary tendencies come together and of necessity this resulted in better offspring than from asexual reproduction, *i. e., natural selection, in the end, permitted only those beings to survive which had come forth as a result of sexual reproduction* and so had inherited the instinct to reproduce sexually, and together with it also contrectation.

It is only thus that we may understand the simultaneous occurrence of detumescence which in man is the immediate effect of the testicles, and contrectation which represents something psychical. It is only when we take into consideration the primary importance of the peripheral sex glands that we may understand how as soon as ejaculation has taken place, both detumescence and contrectation are set to rest. *Omne animal post coitum triste,* or as we might put it, *omne animal post ejaculationem triste.* This simply follows from the fact that contrectation is only secondary, having its source in the function of the peripheral genitals. As soon as this function is brought to a close contrectation, too, is extinguished. We have an indifference or at least a lessening of the impulse for bodily contact, while satisfaction in contrectation is not reached again even in the most intimate embraces until detumescence has taken place. This assumption is at least justified in those cases in which the union of the two impulses is brought about through normal puberty when sex-instinct is brought to full completion.

We have seen that in the individual development either
contrectation or detumescence may sometimes be felt
first. In spite of numerous inquiries I am not able to
say which is the more frequent. I have, therefore, applied to many persons for information. Some asserted
that they did not as yet experience any sensation in their
genitals; even long after they had felt a strong inclination for either men or women, while others declared that
they never had any thoughts altogether about male or
female persons, but had merely felt an impulse in their
genitals which finally led them to masturbate. According to the statement of most authors, however, we would
have to assume as true the statements of Venturi,
who considers even masturbation practiced for a long
time to be merely physiological. At any rate, we shall
have to regard contrectation as dependent on physical
puberty in every individual.

I must reject the assumption that the inclination towards female or male persons, before the onset of puberty has been demonstrated, is to be ascribed to purely social emotions and not to a sexual basis. At any rate, we
find here all those phenomena otherwise observed in
connection with sexual sensations. We may meet with
the wildest scenes of jealousy; the feeling of shame already makes its appearance; the person is thoroughly
dominated by the thought of another one as observed in
sexual sensations. There is also the urge for physical
contact with the beloved person, though not to an act
connected with the sex organs. It is true, that contrectation through excitements originating in the testicles or
in the ovaries may take place before somatic puberty.
But these excitements probably need not always be dependent on the secretion of semen or ova. They need

not be tied up with somatic puberty. And conscious sensations originating in the peripheral sex organs need not obtain.

Before puberty, of course, it is often difficult to draw the line between sexual and social feelings. But such distinctions should be possible in extreme cases. For social relationships of a very intimate nature may be observed before and after puberty especially in childhood. They exceed by far those of a sexual nature. I shall merely refer to the love of the child for his mother. Here we find that the child experiences a certain pleasure in kissing and caressing his mother. And in such social relationships we may also meet with scenes of jealousy. A child may be jealous because his mother pays more attention to another child or when it is otherwise neglected by her. I, nevertheless, believe that even in extreme cases the love of the child for its mother may always be distinguished from the sexual love of a child for another. The complexion of his thoughts and his behavior, his behavior as a whole, point to distinct differences, though I admit that sometimes the line is very difficult to draw.

Indeed, it has been maintained—Littre, Arreat, and Arrufat refer to it—that even altruism is dependent on sexuality. But this cannot without further qualification be referred to individual development, for we find that altruistic feelings exist before the awakening of sexuality. At most, this assertion might apply to the evolutionary development. Whatever one may think about this, the fact remains that even before puberty the sexual inclinations are bent towards totally different persons than is the case in the other social feelings, a fact which proves the separation of the sexual and the social feelings.

The question of the difference between the sexual and the social emotions is further made difficult by the fact that the sexual element is of moment in different kinds of social feelings. This may be observed even in the love of children for their parents. At least, my inquiries about the point have mostly brought the reply that a son prefers rather to kiss his mother, a daughter her father, and *vice versa.* And it must be added, on the other hand, that many of the so-called social instincts, like the sex instinct itself, serve the purpose of reproduction. For example, the gregarious life of animals, the love of the mother for her child, etc. Still these social interests serving the purpose of reproduction only indirectly may very well be distinguished from the sex instinct which serves it directly. Such distinct differences may at any rate, be observed in the extreme cases.

I shall cite here a case of homosexuality which will clearly show us the distinction of sexual feelings, which are independent of social feelings. The case refers to an educated homosexual man, who, as a child, had already shown strong inclination towards male individuals, an inclination which has continued up to the present. It will be observed that he especially preferred soldiers though there was no reason why he should turn his *social* feelings toward them. If the point is the existence of social feelings before puberty, then the inclination should have been towards those persons who stood nearest to him in social relationship and towards whom the social drives urged him (parents, brothers and sisters). Though only the initial stages of our question are being considered in the case, I shall quote it at full length, because it shows the gradual development of a sexual perversion which had its inception in early childhood.

The insistence of the perversion indicates that even at the outset the child's inclination to the soldiers was not only social. In spite of all transformations and signs of refined voluptuousness the contrectation remained unchanged in its direction. The case will further prove that contrectation and detumescence may often be separated. It will also be observed that C. D. masturbated long before the beginning of seminal secretion, merely for the sake of the local titillation. Let me further remark here that Mr. C. D. is a man without will-power. His communications were mostly in autobiographical form, completed and corrected by means of questionings on my part.

Case IX. C. D., twenty-five years of age, gives the impression of being extremely nervous and absent-minded. He does not know of any nervous diseases in the family.

Even in his early childhood he had observed in himself an inclination towards handsome men. When he was a child his brothers and sisters were taken for walks by the maid. There he saw many men and among them the soldiers; and the latter especially made a great impression upon him. *He recalls that when he was seven he permitted a soldier to take him on his lap and found pleasure in stroking his cheeks.* What caused him great pleasure was the roughness of the skin, so he sought other occasions for repeating the act. Cavalrymen excited him more than others. His great pleasure in their smart tightly-clad buttocks, dates back to his eleventh year. As he expresses it himself, they have become a veritable fetish for him. An interest arose also for footmen, servants, bricklayers, and journeymen-locksmiths. Still he did not as yet have any erections, nor did he

consciously feel any sexual sensations. Gradually, however, when he observed cavalrymen or grooms with smart
upper thighs, these sensations began to appear. He sees
the reason for the specially exciting effect of such a
picture in the fact that he had a partly false idea of normal coitus. For he believed that coitus was performed in
a riding position, the man embracing with his thighs the
thighs and body of the woman and then admitting his
penis into the vagina. At any rate, even today a man
who performs coitus in this manner seems to him to be
more virile, and it is this position which gives him the
greatest sexual excitement. "With this peculiar idea in
my mind it was only natural," says C. D., "that at the
sight of a man riding I should also think of one performing coitus. In my imagination, therefore, I often saw a
cavalryman, who while riding, performed coitus very
passionately, his smart buttocks and his thighs being
thrown back and forth. In spite of this I did not have
the desire to overpower the woman. To be able to watch
such a stormy intercourse seemed to me the highest
pleasure. Of course I would much rather imagine myself in the position of the person performing coitus riding, as I envied him his virile, joyful and fiery nature
and his physical potency. For I never had much confidence in my own virility. The same imaginary picture in
time cropped up also at the sight of cavalrymen who
were not on horseback, and also of infantrymen, servants,
etc., especially when I saw them standing with legs
spread apart. Gradually other thoughts came up. Let
me mention again that the greatest pleasure for me was
to imagine myself watching such sexual acts, though
at the same time I begrudged the actor his role." Sometimes, when he followed a cavalryman and became ex-

cited on account of the latter's buttocks, he had the vague impulse to touch his own thighs convulsively and to spread them apart. His state of mind became clearer to him when, as a high school senior of nineteen, he read Horace and other classic authors. The hints of the teachers and especially of his schoolmates introduced him into many of the mysteries of pederasty. He had the desire to pass his member through the thighs of a riding soldier. However, neither this act nor the intermission of his member into the other's anus seemed to him to be entirely satisfactory. For in such a position he would not in the first place be able to see the other person's face clearly enough to excite him; and on the other hand, the naked buttocks did not seem to him to cause as much excitement as when they were in tightly-fitting trousers. However, when intromission of the member actually took place it was absolutely necessary for the buttocks to be naked. And lastly it was even impossible for him to see the buttocks during the act of pederasty.

It was only when he was twenty-one and a half years of age that the performance of homosexual intercourse took place, though he himself had not intended it. It took place with a gardener who frequently came to the patient's house, a handsome man of 26. C. D. liked him "because of his powerful upper thighs and snappy moustache." "It is true that I did not find any special interest in his buttocks and this might have been due to the fact that he did not wear tightly fitting trousers. However, I found great pleasure when I sat down near him, to listen to his piquant stories, and to get excited at the voluptuous smacking of his lips and the flashing of his beautiful eyes. But in the beginning I had no idea of having sexual intercourse with him. On one occasion I asked the gardener what he thought of the little pimples on my penis; and as he asked me to, I showed him my penis which was strongly erect. He touched it and his touch gave me a voluptuous sensation; a sensation, not entirely physical, but brought on by the idea that it was this beloved man who touched me. Then we became more and more intimate. Very soon he showed me his member, and gave in to my desire to let himself be masturbated by me. This was for me the first real voluptuous sensation. As he felt an intensive and enduring excitement he revealed his pleasure in the to and fro movement of his upper thights, also in embraces and in passionate kisses pressed on my lips. What he himself felt I felt in perhaps an even greater degree. Let me mention here that the man was married, and seemed to lead a happily-married life; that according to the opinion of everybody he was in love with his wife. As he himself told me he performed coitus with her daily. To be sure, he thought that the excitements that I caused him were just as intensive as those he experienced in coitus and were even more lasting. My liking for him grew more and more tender after this first attempt and on the days following I permitted him to masturbate me time and again. What caused me an intense voluptuous sensation was when he opened my trousers, took out my member, drew back the foreskin and touched it with his hands. To be masturbated by him was really only a means to an end for I wanted to induce him to let me masturbate him. The latter was, in truth, the most important thing for me. One day we went to bed together. For a few minutes we lay in each other's arms, in an intimate embrace, lip pressed against lip. I found my main pleasure in fondling and

touching his powerful upper thighs and when I noticed
that friction did not give me any satisfaction, I changed
positions with him.   The sensation that I experienced
in it was very pleasurable.   Finally the scene ended with
an act of masturbation, since he, too, was not satisfied
with friction between the thighs.   Let me remark again
that at the time I did not as yet find any interest in
his naked buttocks.   I had no opportunity to give his
hind parts my closer admiration.   Otherwise, my lack
of interest would be inexplicable to myself.   For a
long time this was the last pleasure that I enjoyed from
a man for these experiments ended upon his departure,
which occurred soon afterward.   His departure was
very hard on me, as I loved him dearly.

"My inclination towards handsome young men became
stronger, especially since it began to express itself in
a more concrete form.   For I knew now what it was that
I found attractive in men.   It gave me a great feeling
of pleasure to think of masturbating a strong, handsome man.   At the same time my imagination was
vivid with lively pictures of his body stretching back
and forth and his thighs thrown hither and thither in
sheer voluptuousness.   It also gave me great pleasure to
think of touching and pulling his long and thick penis.
But I thought it even more pleasurable to be able to
feel his buttocks and penis with tongue and lips.   My
impulse to do this became even stronger.   Through a
coincidence, in the end, I found a somewhat satisfactory
substitute in my own person.   One day, while changing
my shirt, I looked behind me in the mirror and became aware of my glistening white hind parts.   An
indescribable feeling of joy!   The sight of my beautiful and naked buttocks called forth an even greater de-

light than the smartly dressed buttocks of a calvaryman.
Thenceforth, I would go into raptures, placing myself in
all kinds of positions before the mirror, and looking at
my body with the aid of hand and illuminating mirrors.
I liked best to look at myself from behind by standing
up with thighs drawn in and moving my body violently
as in coitus. On such occasions the forward and back-
ward movement of the buttocks brought me into raptures of delight. Of course, I imagined it even more delightful to have before me a robust young man instead
of the mirror, who should move his entire naked body
in an outpouring of voluptuous sensation.

"I acquired a more and more general interest in handsome and robust young men. I would imagine even in
clothes that were not well fitted, the naked limbs enclosed. It is true that my imagination was more easily
aroused at the sight of well-fitting clothes, and this ac-
counts for my predilection for cavalrymen, grooms, etc.,
which still persists. It was thus often somewhat exciting sexually for me merely to pass by a cavalry barracks
or even to hear the clicking of a cavalryman's spurs.
Cowardice was the only reason which kept me from
hiring a soldier for the satisfaction of this sex craving,
for often I had the intention of doing it. Gradually the
mirror experiments did not suffice either. I then thought
of the following unique experiment: With feet somewhat
spread apart I placed myself full length on top of several chairs, one close to the other, placed myself in such
a manner that my penis could reach down between two of
the chairs, to enable me to produce friction; my belly
in the direction of the floor. Propped against one of
the chairs, I placed a large mirror, which, when my head
was turned, reflected my body moving as in coitus. I

had oiled my buttocks before that they might appear
more vigorous. This experiment, besides great psychical pleasure it afforded, also gave me physical sensations
because of the friction of the penis. This was only
a secondary consideration. So I delayed its gratification
as long as possible. In order to bring it to a conclusion, I always finished these mirror experiments with
masturbation.

"This experiment has led me to desire to see a male
body in actuality and to touch it; so that another might
insert his penis between my compressed thighs, while
the mirror above reflects the movement of his body,
especially his buttocks. At first I had no desire to have
him insert his penis into my anus, but gradually this
wish, too, came upon me. One day, before the mirror,
at one of my experiments I spread out my thighs the
better to see my anus. I was satisfied on this occasion to know that another could insert his penis into
it. This pleasure was still further enhanced by the
fact that at the time I was suffering from constipa-
tion and the injection of a clyster caused me a very
pleasant sensation. This opened my eyes fully. My lack
of interest in pederasty fell away after that. Since
last year the following ideal of homosexual intercourse
has developed in quick succession, and with increasing
refinement; the object should be a handsome man, strong
and young, a cavalry-man, if possible; he should place
his naked body before me so that I may kiss and fondle
his naked buttocks; while I am reclining on my back
with thighs slightly distended, he should insert into
my anus his penis provided with thick and dark hair
at the root. The act must be performed with the greatest ardor, so that I may be able to guess the delight of

the other from the fire of his burning eyes, from the ardor of his kisses, and also from his hugs. The sighs of pleasure, too, would cause me great excitement. The immission of the penis must be as deep as possible. It would also add to my pleasure if I should experience the sharpest pains as a result of his back and forth movements. For such pain would be a measure of the intensity of his movements, and thus of his voluptuousness. While thus engaged it would be necessary that the mirror show him rolling about with pleasure and I would find it pleasant if his arm-pits exuded the heavy odor of perspiration. In order that the sense of taste should also partake I would consider it a great pleasure to swallow the other person's semen. I would rejoice if at the right moment he should transfer his penis from my anus to my mouth. As for myself I would have to be very passive and at most, would express my intense voluptuous sensation in passionate and biting kisses as well as in a convulsive pressing of the other's buttocks. In order to bring the act to an end, masturbation must finally take place. It would afford me the highest pleasure if several men would satisfy me in the above manner, one after the other, one of them embracing me as the others looked on.

"As regards the introduction of the other's penis into my anus, it is not in the least a condition, *sine qua non*. Should there be any difficulties in performing the act in this way, I would permit the placing of his member between my thighs. But, its immission into my anus and the injection of semen would be much more pleasant.

"As for the qualities of the men that attract me, they must, in general, be such as I possess only in a small degree, or not at all, yet the possession of which I imagine to be very desirable. Youthful manhood, perfect health, youthful boldness, high spirits, roughness, great courage, activity and especially the highest possible sexual vigor are what I prefer. These qualities, however, must be perceived through the senses, and especially through the sense of sight. My ideal of a beloved, accordingly, is a young cavalry-man of about 23, with full red cheeks, well-fitting trousers, fiery-looking, cheerful eyes, small smartly-turned moustache, vigorous upper thighs, and last but not least, a very large penis. His manners, his gait and his whole behavior must be rough and ready. No fine airs. A finely shaped face will not do at all. Of course, all these qualities are not to be found in the same person. So, I must be satisfied with infantry-men, sailors,—especially when their chest is deeply tanned—grooms, liveried young servants, with youthful workers, acrobats, and circus-riders in tricot. As regards clothing, besides uniform and tricot, I find ordinary clothes quite attractive. Nevertheless, they must not be torn or dirty. On the whole, I prefer: uniforms, working-clothes, corduroy trousers, etc. Corduroy trousers I have first and mostly observed on Italian workers, to whom I have been attracted on account of their sensual eyes. As regards age, boys and mature men will not do; the right age is between 20 and 25, and up to the age of 30. Moustaches are almost indispensable, while, in no case must there be side-whiskers. I cannot find any special pleasure in urnings.

"I have the following to say about self-masturbation and normal coitus. I was seduced to the practice of masturbation at the age of nine, by one of my sisters. She herself had been led to it by a playmate of her own age. Let me remark, at the outset, that in the beginning while masturbating, I had no contrary sexual ideas of men. Even at present I perform it only because it affords me a physical titillation. The circumstances of my life and especially of school were of great importance in this respect. I was rather temperate in it up to the age of twelve, performing masturbation only because of the titillation and as a result of habit. I had been a good scholar, and sometimes even an excellent one. But as a result of the masturbatory practices weakness and disinclination to work set in. My performances in school also rapidly got worse through bad company. All this made me dissatisfied with myself and so I sought to stifle self-reproach in further masturbation. My great efforts to produce some excellent work in school failed again and again on account of my mental exhaustion, which frequently caused me renewed dissatisfaction, again ending up in masturbation. This vicious circle has continued to the present. My past is a story of dissatisfaction. I am suffering from ever increasing chronic depressions. Though I sometimes do succeed in mastering my vice, I finally succumb to temptation. This habit of drowning my feelings of dissatisfaction in masturbation, has in time so paralyzed my will that the smallest occasion will give rise to it, a tooth-ache at night or a similar trouble. My troubles remind me of the drunkard and his bottle. In time, however, a new motive, that of the contrary sexual feeling, set in. When the sight of handsome soldiers or of other attractive men caused an erection in me, the impulse to masturbate, which for a moment had perhaps been latent, would be intensely increased. But even in masturbation which followed such occasions, I formed no ideas of men. This is to be traced to the fact that up to a few years ago it was not clear to me what it was that attracted me to men. On the other hand when I experience the titillation I am unable to have contrary sexual sensations, whereas, before masturbation my imagination is filled with such homosexual pictures. It is true that gradually the manner of performing masturbation became so peculiar that it can only be explained after assuming unconscious contrary sexual feelings. For, while at the beginning I found pleasure in the mere titillation as such, without the use of refinements, I recollect that already at the age of 17, I had found great delight in taking off my trousers and admiring my thighs.

"A few words about coitus remain to be said. All in all, I have performed this repulsive act with prostitutes twelve times. I have never done it from inclination toward them. At first I performed it because I believed that the immission into the vagina would afford me an intensive titillation and because I thought it less harmful than masturbation; later I tried it in order to suppress my inclination towards men. But because of the abnormal widening of the vagina of most prostitutes, friction and naturally the titillation, too, were only very slight, especially since my penis had been accustomed to vigorous frictions, *i. e.,* in masturbation. The consequence of all this was that I had to masturbate myself afterwards, which gave me a much more intensified feeling of pleasure. Added to this is the complete insensibility and coarseness of these prostitutes, for whom I feel an abhorrence. I have always consoled myself with the hope that I would find more pleasure with non-prostitutes; but I do not consider myself sufficiently potent to satisfy a voluptuous woman. I have often, therefore, decided to curb my desire to masturbate and become stronger physically; but in a weak moment I again succumb, and then I apply myself with so much vigor that for a long time I am afraid to approach a woman. This state of affairs has continued to the present day. I have again and again delayed my resolution to perform coitus with a girl who would do it out of love for me and never fulfilled it till the present time.''

It is apparent that the development of somatic and psychical puberty has not made clear to us the relationship of the sex glands to the two components of the sex instinct as well as the evolutionary phylogenetic development of man. However, one may possibly be enabled to discover this relationship through a different method, i. e., by investigating it at a period when the physiological function of the sex glands has ceased, an event which usually takes place at a certain age in men and women. But the following objections must be considered here: first, though the physiological function of the organs has ceased, the organs still exist and may possibly continue to cause certain stimuli exerting an influence in a certain direction on the psychical behavior. Secondly, the memory pictures of the past can not be eradicated through the evolution of the peripheral organs; the psychical behavior, e. g., the direction of the sex instinct, at most, might be influenced so that the processes of involution, taking place peripherally, may now arise also in the brain. Thirdly, it must be considered that the duration of the function of the sex glands varies according to the individuals, and its cessation may not always be determined.

It is thus evident that just as psychosexual and somatic puberty do not always coincide, the sex instinct may continue functioning after the sex glands have apparently ceased. That the proofs adduced in support of this conclusion are often hardly plausible is quite true. Kisch, showing statistics of women who have married after the cessation of menstruation and ovulation, deduces from this the continued functioning of the sex instinct. No one who considers the numerous reasons for marriage will regard such proof as sufficient. Borner observed the continuation of the sex instinct in women long after the appearance of the climacteric. He mentions the extreme case of a woman who showed signs of it at the age of 60, six years after her last menstruation. I myself have known several elderly women who had completely passed the climacteric and who did not show any traces of menstruation; women in their fifties, nay, even in the sixties, who told me that their sexual inclinations had only diminished slightly. I know a woman of 58 whose sex instinct and voluptuous sensations are still very keen, and draws her to the other sex. One might conclude from the fact of the menstrual process having stopped for a number of years that the processes of the peripheral organs have also ceased functioning. The most important process, of course, is the cessation of menstruation. Thus, Renaudin describes the case of a woman of 61 giving birth to a living child twelve years after her last period. I do not consider these cases important, (they are at the same time very rare) because I do not consider it necessary that those impulses which had previously been induced secondarily should stop after the sex glands have ceased functioning. The same is true of men. Therefore, we shall not be surprised to find in men the desire to perform coitus when their peripheral genitals have already ceased functioning. At the same time let me add that the testicles, too, may sometimes retain their productive powers until a very advanced age. Hufeland recounts cases of men who have been married at the age of 100, 112 and even in later years, and not only *pro forma*. From reasons given above we shall not go very far in the analysis of the sex instinct, if we dwell exaggeratedly on its occurrence in old age. However, the following section will show the great importance of the sex glands and their strong influence on the two components of the sex instinct.

It is also a fact that in those men and women who are pathological cases sexual inclinations may continue to an advanced age. In this connection let me mention the following cases chosen from numerous observations at my disposal. They deal with women who have continued homosexual intercourse several years after the cessation of menstruation.

Case X. Mrs. L. T., fifty-three years of age. Both of her parents died of apoplexy. She herself has formerly suffered from epileptic fits; the last fit occurring about three years ago. L. T. does not remember having had any such convulsive attacks since then, but up to the present she has been suffering from vertigo, which, in all probability, must be of an epileptic nature. Mrs. L. T. further adds that she had formerly been a syphilitic.

L. T. was brought up in the country. In the village school she had played with the genitals of her playmates. She has never done it with boys. She liked to play with the daughter of a neighbor: "When it became dark, we would tell each other stories, at the same time feeling with our hands between each other's thighs." She cannot remember having any sexual gratification at the time. Such intercourse took place only very seldom. When she was 15, she went into service in a hotel. Here she became acquainted with a woman of 32. This woman frequently induced her to homosexual practices. Since the woman was L. T.'s superior in the hotel service she felt somewhat flattered by this intimacy. She had to undress completely, then the woman would touch her genitals. Often she had to go to bed with her. This usually resulted in mutual masturbation. Later the two also practiced cunnilingus. L. T. practiced it on the other woman, first as an active partner but felt no especial excitement; as a passive partner she did. This relationship lasted for six months, after which they parted. This pleased L. T., for though the sex intercourse had caused her a certain pleasure, their intimacy had been noticed by other persons, who teased her about it very much. She believes that the woman, though married, had similar relationships with other girls. When she completed her eighteenth year, L. T. had intercourse with a man. As a cook in a large restaurant she made the acquaintance of a man-cook who induced her to perform coitus with him. She had complete sexual satisfaction in it, even more than with the woman mentioned. She became pregnant and bore a child though their relationship had lasted only a short time. On account of her pregnancy she had to leave her position. After a few years the child died and the relationship between her and the man was broken. When she had given birth to her child L. T. had been a nurse for a short time. Soon she began to practice sex intercourse with men for money, and consequently she came under police surveilance. During all this time she had almost never found any satisfaction in intercourse with man. However, she frequently had intercourse with women "for the pleasure of it." Even then she was on the lookout for a "lasting relationship," and she has actually had one from then to the present. She did not practice intercourse with men for a long time, as she married, at 23. However, she very soon separated from her husband, to this very day. This occurred because she had relations with a female friend of hers when her husband was away; this was discovered and finally led to differences between them. She has had the same woman for homosexual intercourse these last twelve years. Now and then, without the knowledge of her woman-friend she has relations also with another woman but never with a man. In former times L. T. had practiced homosexual intercourse very frequently. Today, being much older, it takes place very seldom, about once or twice every six weeks. The form of intercourse is mutual cunnilingues. Formerly, with the exception of her first intercourse, L. T. had always been the active partner; later this changed somewhat. She also changed in regards to the age desirable in her partners. Formerly she had been interested only in very young girls of about 16, but with advancing age older girls also attracted her. In cunnilingus she finds her greatest pleasure in homosexual intercourse. She found a certain degree of pleasure also in other physical contacts, as well as in kissing, in regards to heterosexual intercourse, such as in her affair with the man-cook. But as a whole she found less pleasure in it than in homosexual practices which came more and more to the surface. Her sex dreams in sleep are always directed to homosexual intercourse. *Her menstruation has ceased six years ago.*

Dr. Flatau's examination of her larynx shows her thyroid cartilage to be narrow and distinctly protruding. Otherwise, however, the larynx is entirely of a feminine structure. Her voice, too, is feminine.

In this case, then, we have the continuance of a homosexual excitement, several years after the cessation of the periods, though of course, not in its former strength.

Case XI. Mrs. O. M., sixty years of age. Asked to give her first name she said she is called August. In her entire nature she makes a thorough impression of a man. She married at the age of seventeen. But after ten years she and her husband were divorced, though they had previously separated. O. M. is somewhat hard of hearing through some ailment which had been troubling her for years. I have received my information about her, not only from herself, but from many other sources. Her case is extremely interesting from a psychological point of view. It may be mentioned at the very outset that Mrs. O. M. has worked as a common laborer, namely as a breaker of stones. She has worked among men as a man without anybody suspecting her sex. She has gone dressed in men's clothes and thus dressed has met many people who had no idea they were dealing with a woman.

O. M.'s mother has suffered much from headaches and had often complained about a heavy head. She cannot tell anything about hereditary taint in her brothers and sisters, five in all. In her opinion, only one of her brothers, now dead, was a homosexual. It struck her that her brother, even when he was still very young, had been so attentive to many young men that he used to watch them through the window with ecstatic eyes. Consequently she had often asked why he looked at the men so avidly and not seldom he replied; he was then only fourteen years old. "But don't you see what a wonderful pair of strapping calves he has and how handsome he is built!" Later, too, O. M. was informed by a female friend that her brother had intimate relations with other men.

Mrs. O. M. comes from a small town. Here she went to school. As a small girl she never cared much for the boys. When asked how far back her love for women had begun, she answers that even as a small girl she had a certain disinclination towards men. It was some time ... before she discovered her inclination towards women. It is true ... ... members having secretly loved a girl at the age of from ten to twelve, ... at the time she had not placed much importance to it. The girl she loved was her most intimate schoolmate, the daughter of a manufacturer. She was a year older than her. O. M. loved her silently and sought for opportunity to be with her, yet never thought of performing a sexual act. It is true that they sometimes kissed. But even if she had thought of going any farther she would never have dared to. Also, her friend had never made any such advances to her. "We went for a walk together, sat down on a bench in the park, embraced and kissed each other, that's all."

At the age of 15, O. M. removed to a large town and after two years met a girl who became very intimate with her. They went out together and soon fell in love. The relationship of the two girls lasted half a year and expressed itself in mutual masturbation. O. M. had not as yet practiced cunnilingus. This was demonstrated to her by another girl. She had met this girl soon after her marriage, to which I will immediately refer. As soon as their friendship had grown warmer the other told her that she did not satisfy her by masturbation and she suggested cunnilingus to her. O. M. gave in immediately and an intimate relationship arose between them. O. M. acquired masculine habits. At home she always wore men's clothes, sometimes also in the street. It is true that very often she could not leave the house at all as her friend, who supported her, did not permit it. The girls lived together for about four to five years. O. M. then made another acquaintance, which was the cause of her separation from her previous friend. She was informed that the other one had deceived her with a friend; O. M. had spied upon her and in truth discovered her friend's deceit. Her letter of parting filled with gushing sentimentality and unusual ardor, closed with these words: "When I have a friend I must have her all to myself!" But O. M. was not lonely for long for soon she had a new affair. When asked what part she had taken in the sexual relationships with her friend, she answered that she had always licked the other one with her tongue. She had never played a passive role. "I don't care for it, because I cannot bear the masculine in the other person, one way or another." Frequently they had also practiced mutual masturbation.

As already mentioned, O. M. had never felt any inclination towards the male sex. She had never been in love with a man. She maintains that many men had been in love with her and had offered her everything possible if she would marry them, so that she might become a "good and decent housewife." Often she had sat before her window for hours, thinking whether she should marry a man whose love for her she had recognized. Many a night was spent with such considerations.

But she always had to say to herself: "It can't be done."
She couldn't do without women, "and what she was and
is, she will be." Nevertheless, she let a man persuade her
to become engaged to him, and later also to marry him.
But they separated very soon and at the time she had
"sworn to her husband that she would never again
marry." When I asked her what her opinon of men was,
she told me with great exasperation that "whatever my
relationships be, I am what I am, and I will stay that
way until death closes my eyes. I would rather jump
into a river, into the deepest river, than have anything to
do with men." She lived with her husband only eight
weeks and then ran away from him to live with her
friend. The latter had forbidden her to stay on with her
husband. Legal separation finally took place because of
mutual estrangement. Her husband followed after her
for many years but her friend always showed him the
door. When he asked to speak to his wife, she answered:
"She is my friend, I am her reperesentative; your wife
cannot see you." After some time O. M. separated from
this, her last friend. For a long time afterwards she had
no lasting relationship with any woman, having now this
one, now another. When asked whether she had a friend
now, she said that she had relations with a widow, but
did not live with her. At the present time, too, she prefers active cunnilingus. Though menstruation had ceased
seven years ago, O. M. still has strong homosexual inclinations.

When asked what she had liked most to play with
when a child, she answered: "I didn't bother with dolls
and utensils; on the other hand, I liked the presents that
my brothers received, such as tin-soldiers, hobby-horses,
etc. She took great pleasure in tinkering with the paint-

box.'' As a child O. M. had also wrestled with the other children, ''very often we went up with our sleds to the topmost snow-hill, then went down again, myself always in the thick of the fun.'' She also liked to be dressed as a boy by her brothers. This had very frequently happened when she was eight to nine years old. Even as a very small child she liked to walk around in a boy's suit, and deplores the fact even today that she was born a woman. She would rather be a man, a common laborer. All this would be more pleasing to her than her misfortune at being a woman.

O. M. has been a smoker since her youth,—mostly cigars; she also drinks anything she can get, whiskey, beer, etc.

She stutters somewhat. On examining her larynx, Dr. Flatau observed paralysis of recurrent laryngeal nerve. The larynx itself is of feminine structure throughout.

Case XII. Miss T. E., 53 years of age, unmarried. Her parents lived in a small town where she was born and bred. She has only one sister, who, she says, had been in good health. But as T. E. had left her home at the age of 14, she cannot give detailed information about diseases in the family. It was later found that her mother was a very nervous, capricious and very severe woman. ''If father had not been very indulgent things would have turned out pretty bad, sometimes. For father was a little too indulgent and very hen-pecked.'' T. E.'s sister is dead now, having died during her climacteric. Her sister was married and lived happily with her husband. T. E. had inherited a small fortune from her parents but spent it all a long time ago in the company of other girls.

T. E. declares that even in her school days she had

been with small girls and she also admits that then she with other girls had played with each other's genitals. When asked, she denies time and again that she had been seduced. "It was a feeling that drew me even then to the female sex." During her school days the sex activities consisted of mutual masturbation. Cunnilingus had not as yet been practiced. For the purposes of intercourse, T. E. selected only those girls that she liked. She remembers that it was at the age of 12 or 13 that she first felt these inclinations in herself. She had never played with boys in her school days nor has she had anything to do with young men since she left school. She always had an aversion towards playing and dealing with boys.

She came to Berlin at the age of 15, after having stayed away from home for a year, she went to live with a childless widow. The widow very soon seduced her to homosexual practices. T. E. lived with her for five years, until the death of the woman, *i. e.,* until her twenty-first year. She cannot tell whether the woman had been living a happy married life with her husband. She can remember that the woman had told her that her husband had often practiced cunilingus on her. This was how she had first found out about it. Sex intercourse between T. E. and the widow was through cunnilingus. When she had first come to live with the widow she had the intention of going to live with friends of the family in Berlin; but she gave up the idea and remained.

At first she did not know what these caresses of the woman signified. "She was always very affectionate to me and often embraced me very passionately. I often though to myself: my goodness, gracious, how tender that woman is to you all the time. A man could not be more passionate with his wife. When I cooked the noonday meal she would come over to embrace me. But I had no idea as yet what this meant, though as a young girl, as I mentioned before, I had performed sex acts with other girls. One day she asked me whether I would like to go out with her some evening. She proposed that we go to see a play. I agreed. After the play we went to a restaurant, where we drank something. When we came home I went to bed. When I was already in bed, she came to me. I was quite surprised, but I had no suspicion. And then she embraced me so nicely, and what delicate hands she had! And then she kissed me and all of a sudden she came into my bed, after throwing off her sleeping gown. I was very much frightened. But the woman told me to quiet down. Finally, after having sufficiently excited my genitals through manipulations, she practiced cunnilingus on me. This caused me such titillation that I was gratified quickly. The woman then was thirty-five years of age. She was a beautiful woman. I found so much pleasure in the intercourse that I continued it with great delight. Later the woman induced me to take the active part in cunnilingus. At first I didn't want to do it but I gave in after all.'' After the death of the woman, with whom T. E. lived until she was twenty-one, she rented an apartment of her own and procured a new friend for whom she does the housekeeping. This friend is a professional prostitute and in this manner can support herself and T. E. She likes to call herself the ''mother,'' while her friend is the ''father.'' Occasionally, however, their roles in sex intercourse are exchanged. T. E. lived with her present friend for seven years, while she lived with her last friend for six years. She broke off her friendship for the latter because she not only had sex intercourse with men—T. E. had nothing against this—but because she actually *loved* one of them.

T. E. never had any dealings with men. She says she hates them and never touched one. When asked how she could possibly hate a man with whom she only talked, she answered that she didn't mean it that way. "If it's only a question of talking to one, then it is all right. What I mean is, that I can't bear being touched by them. They are repulsive to me, and I have a great loathing for them. I often had occasion to meet with men socially; but even the smartest man was as distasteful to me as all the others."

T. E. often had erotic dreams. She speaks out with a certain enthsuiasm: "Oh, dear me! only lately I had such a lovely dream, and how I talked in my sleep! It was so beautiful! In my dream I embraced my friend, we kissed each other, it gave me gratification, at which my friend woke me up." When asked for more details, she says that she does not usually sleep in the same room as her friend, that the latter had heard her shouting, had been worried about it and come in to wake her. She dreams sexual dreams of women, while she never has any sexual dreams of men.

Formerly T. E. masturbated very frequently and often still practices it nowadays. "Sometimes my friend does not want to gratify me, so I have to satisfy myself. I have indulged in masturbation from time to time since my nineteenth year. During the act I have never thought about a man, only about women."

T. E. gives the impression of being good-natured. It was also told me by someone who knows her that she takes great pleasure in helping other people. Only lately, at the death of a poor, homosexual girl, an acquaintance of hers, she went out collecting money in order to give the girl a decent burial.

When asked why she had relationships with prostitutes, she says that she knows quite well that homosexual intercourse also took place between decent women, but that she herself felt drawn more to girls of this genre (she, of course, meant prostitutes).

T. E. was a bad student at school. As a whole, however, she does not in any way impress one as being stupid. In her school days she liked to play with dolls very much. She also used to make dolls herself. She never took part in boys' games, and as she herself states even the social intercourse with boys was displeasing to her. She smokes cigars and cigarettes, occasionally drinks a glass of beer, but no other liquors. She cannot stand a lot of beer.

Menstruation had begun at the age of 14½ and had ceased five years ago.

Dr. Flatau examined the larynx of T. E., who has a remarkably deep and rough voice. Externally the larynx is feminine throughout. There is no Adam's apple present. The epiglottis, however, makes a very masculine impression. The larynx is somewhat rough, large and wide; the laryngeal cavity is proportionately large. No details can be given about the vocal chords inasmuch as its examination is made very difficult by a chronic catarrh; for she apparently has a rough, remarkably deep voice, with a distinctly masculine timbre.

As we shall see in the following, it may be proved through experiments that the peripheral sex glands, the testicles and ovaries, are primary; and that not only the development of detumescence but also contrectation is

tied up with them. These experiments may be observed
in the many cases of *castration*. We have to differentiate between two kinds of castration, according to whether it has been performed in earliest childhood or later.
In man as well as in animals these operations are performed at different times. It is also well known that in
the Orient the keepers of the harem are not only castrated, but their copulative organs, too, are removed;
such people usually carry the name of eunuch; eunuchs,
then, are such people, whose testicles, as well as their
copulative organs, have been removed. In Italy, where
this operation was performed for the preservation of
the soprano voice, one may encounter many male castrates. Another group of castrates are the Skoptzi in
Russia; also the members of this or the other sect
who uphold the view expressed in the Bible that "the
practice of castration is pleasing to the Lord." However, there are no better opportunities to study the consequences of castration than in animals. One may
observe castrated cocks, castrated rabbits, especially
frequent also is the performance of castration on stallions, steers and rams; such operations transform the
stallion into a gelding, a steer into an ox, a ram into a
wether. One of the first consequences resulting of this
operation is the cessation of ejaculation. One may observe that many male animals which have not been castrated, indulge in onanism just like the human male.
Onanism has been observed in monkeys, bulls, cats,
stallions and dogs among other animals. Stallions usually kick up their hind-legs and contract a few of their
pelvic muscles until ejaculation takes place. In some
animals onanism takes place through movements which
very much resemble those of man. This is most distinct-

ly the case in male monkeys, who masturbate with their hands, either rubbing their penis or shaking it. In sexually mature animals detumescence, as I have been informed, is destroyed through castration, while premature castration hinders its development. To observe the continuance or development of detumescence in spite of castration is a rare experience. In all such cases gathered from many sources my informants have suggested that this rarely, if ever, happens in animals when castrated very young, unless, one testicle or part of one has been left behind after an unskilled operation. But not even the slightest trace of contrectation is to be observed in animals that have been successfully castrated when young. Neither the gelding, nor the ox, nor the wether will approach the female of his respective species in a sexual way. All interest for the female sex has been extinguished in them. Of course, such a castrated animal may still take part in the sports of other animals of its kind; but it does not at all take part in such sports which have a sexual basis. Castration at the same time also causes the cessation of all such psychical phenomena regarded as typical of male animals, such as, in the stallion, a certain excitability and vivacity. All this is true, at least, in premature castration. And also in castration performed on male animals completely mature sexually, these psychical symptoms are brought to a close.

Very similar are the results of castration on man. Theile draws a distinction in these cases, according to whether the castration has been performed in early childhood or later. It is maintained that in castrations after the onset of puberty, contrectation continues and in many cases detumescence, too, continues at least for a few years more. It is also claimed that instead of spermatozoa, prostatic fluid is ejaculated; in other words, that ejaculation is actually present there. It is not necessary to further discuss whether the capacity for reproducing may continue after castration, as some have maintained. Theile justly points out that we might deal here only with such cases resulting from an incomplete operation, performed, as by the ancients, by crushing the testicles; or such in which the semen was left over in the seminal vescicles, consequently, permitting reproduction for at least some time. Varro already tells of a castrated steer which impregnated a cow a short time after the operation [de quibus (vaccis) admirandum scriptum inveni, exemptis testiculis si statim admiseris taurum, conscipere]. A similar story of a gelding has been told by Hausmann. Theile, on the other hand, observes that castration does not necessarily result in impotentia of coition. I need cite here the well-known story of Juvenal, who relates that in ancient Rome the women liked to perform coitus with castrates.

The many reports of J. P. Frank, according to which our castrated men in a certain town of Italy had become a public nuisance through their sex intercourse with women, also belong here. And it might also be mentioned that the wives of Roumanian bojars who for their sexual graification keep servants of the sect of the Skoptzi. Pelikan, in his very diligent work on the Skoptzi, says that when castration takes place before the onset of puberty, or immediately after, the secondary results of the operation are comparatively unimportant. But if castration takes place in childhood or at the beginning of adolescence, from the seventh to the fourteenth year, the consequences are much more ominous. Pelikan also believes that those who have been castrated at puberty still have erections. This is a rarer occurrence in those who have been castrated in infancy or in childhood. The conditions favoring the inclination of the sexes towards each other are missing in castrates operated upon in their childhood, though not in those castrated at the time of puberty. However, what especially favors the continuance of the capacity for erection in late castrates, is the fact that the nervus pudendus, the nerve running from the spinal cord to the corpora cavernosa of the penis, remained intact during the operation. Under these circumstances one should not wonder that persons who still show contrectation should also have voluptuous imaginations and erections. Nay, such persons may also have ejaculations, caused by certain gland secretions. One often cites the famous case of Cooper of a castrated man who for quite a few months had ejaculations (prostrate secretions?) and even ejaculatory sensations; a man who even performed coitus a long time afterwards, though at ever increasing intervals.

It is true that in most communications pertaining to the subject one usually cannot sufficiently determine whether the operation had occurred in earliest childhood or not; or whether the sex instinct is still alive, is directed towards the other sex or merely a mechanical process which manifests itself only in a reflex induction of erection and eventually in ejaculation of secretions of the prostate or the seminal vesicles.

Thus the reports of Juvenal saying that Roman women enjoyed fornication with castrates seem very dubious in this respect. One may raise the question whether these castrates actually possessed the sex instinct, and whether like the common female prostitutes they gave themselves in lieu of money.

In castrated females we seem to find very similar results. It is a well-known fact that after castration menstruation ceases. We know very little on the other hand about the development of contrectation in castrated women. It is very difficult to give any detailed data about sex instinct. I have had several opportunities for procuring information about it. However, as the operation in most cases occurred after the fifteenth year, one should not be surprised that contrectation existed. It is very likely that in premature castration the instinct would not have been present. This is corroborated by the occasional reports of other authors, as well as by reports told by travelers. Miklucho-Macley on the basis of reports tells the following: The latter knew a castrated native girl, who had poorly developed breasts and sparse adipose tissues. Her buttocks were lean, while a few hairs on her chin gave her the appearance of a boy. The girl avoided women, neither had she any inclination towards young men, for whose sexual gratification she was destined. Castration was the result of an ovariotomy, performed as was the custom for the purpose of diminishing the offspring. In his "Travels from Delhi to Bombay" Roberts also speaks of a female eunuch, whose ovaries had been removed. This woman had no bust, no pubic hair and no fatty layer on the mons veneris. Her buttocks were those of a man, the menstrual flow was absent, also she had no sex impulse. We have witnessed the publication in modern times of a number of studies on the sex instinct of women after castration. Most of the authors, among them Pean, Tissier, Spencer,

Wells, Le Bec, maintain that no change in the sex instinct is evident. Other authors, like Hegar, Bruntzel and Schmalfuss, claim that they have sometimes observed a diminution of the instinct, at other times its continuance. Occasionally its intensification has also been reported (Spencer, Wells). Other authors again report that the sex instinct either diminishes or altogether ceases. (Bailly, Anger, Goodell, Boinet). Glavecke, from whom I took several of the above bibliographies, made a detailed study of the sex instinct of 27 women on whom he had performed the operation, their ages ranged from 21 to 45 years. He found that in most of the cases there was an impairment of the sex instinct as well as of the orgasm. He does not, however, separate the two components of the instinct. In order to reach a clear judgment one would have to determine first of all whether detumescence had been modified and then whether changes had occurred also in regards to the inclination towards the other sex. It seems clear from the writings of Glavecke that allowing for these sources of error, a diminution of the desire for coitus actually took place in a number of cases. In any future statistics of this nature it is desirable that the two components of the sex instinct be sharply differentiated. Let me mention further that in a number of cases changes in the genitals have been observed such as shrinking of the vagina, of the uterus, etc. Yet, one seldom hears of the influence of these processes of involution on the desire for coitus. Glavecke believes that in the cases of the seven women reporting the performance of coitus to be painful, the operation had resulted in an extensive shrinking and their orgasm was considerably decreased or had entirely disappeared.

In all other relevant literature which I had occasion
to study, the authors agree that contrectation is never
developed in male and female persons castrated at a
very young age. It is true that contrectation is treated
only very cursorily. The results have been corroborated by inquiries in regards to eunuchs personally con-
ducted by me in the Orient. However, as already indicated, one must distinguish between castration performed in early childhood or later. In some cases contrectation has been observed also in persons castrated
before genital puberty. However, one must eliminate
one important source of error here, namely, that psychosexual puberty does not always coincide with puberty
of the peripheral genitals. Thus psychosexual puberty,
i. e., at times the inclination of a male individual towards
the female, and vice versa, occurs before genital puberty
may be observed. Therefore, it should not be surprising
that contrectation should not have ceased, for the simple
reason that it had already taken place before the operation. Here, too, perhaps migh⁺ be reckoned the case of
Mardian, depicted by *Shakespeare* in his "Anthony and
Cleopatra:"

Cleo. Thou, eunuch Mardian!
Mar. What's your Highness' pleasure?
Cleo. Not now to hear thee sing, I take no pleasure
    In aught an eunuch has; 'tis well for thee,
    That being unseminar'd thy freer thought
    May not fly north of Egypt. Hast thou affections?
Mar. Yes, gracious madam .
Cleo. Indeed!
Mar. Not in deed, madam; for I can do nothing
    But what indeed is honest to be done:
    Yet have I fierce affections, and think
    What Venus did with Mars!

When we take into consideration the fact that many of
those being castrated are aged seven to ten, we might be

justified in asking whether psychosexual puberty had not already existed in such cases when somatic puberty could not have taken place.   After taking into account this source of error, it is not to be doubted that certain castration performed in early childhood exerts an enormous influence on detumescence and the development of contrectation.   That castration after the onset of psychosexual puberty does not always have an inhibitory effect on contrectation is due to the fact that memory pictures giving one a sensation strikingly resembling erection, and formed as a result of the peripheral processes, are not necessarily always dispelled after castration.   This source of error that psychosexual processes might have taken place already in very early castration cannot be emphasized too much.   As far as the effects of late castration are concerned, various effects in different individuals have been observed.   Perhaps, these depend on the strength of the previous impressions and on other psychological conditions.   This is also proven by Abelard's love for Heloise.   In spite of common opinion to the contrary, his love for her did not diminish, when as a result of an attack which turned him into an eunuch, and which made him seek the seclusion of a monastery. The coldness which he allegedly but only apparently showed towards Heloise after the mutilation we must understand rather to be the result of his mishap and of his feeling of shame than to a real diminuation of his affection.   He again communicated with Heloise after ten years' silence when she was in distress and Hausrath believes that though he had appeared cold for so long it was because he had to fulfill his monastic duties, which compelled him to regard Heloise as one dead, even though such a performance of one's duty might strike our tender minds nowadays as a very heartless deed.

Thus, we have seen that sexual impulses may sometimes make their appearance very early and that one must be careful in drawing conclusions from the effects of castration. Let us now return to our previous considerations. When we bear in mind that the sex instinct—that is to say, its two components—does not make its appearance in cases of castration performed in early childhood, we may see in this a proof that there is an internal connection between these two components. For without such connection, we could not understand how the removal of the testicles may check the growth not only of detumescence, which is directly dependent on them, but also how it could hinder the development of contrectation. On the basis of the preceding we may now easily draw a parallel between certain other phenomena and the sex instinct. We know that male individuals castrated at a very early age retain the infantile structure of their larynx, their voices do not assume the male tone, the growth of beard is checked, etc. After castration animals change their instincts or assume instincts not proper to their sex. The capon begins to sit on eggs and to hatch; the castrated cock ceases to crow. Many, and perhaps even all the so-called secondary sex characteristics do not reach development. This leads us to the question whether we are justified in considering contrectation to be a secondary sex characteristic. This question may be answered in the affirmative. In the following chapter, however, we shall see that not only contrectation but its direction, too, are to be regarded as secondary sex characteristics.

My friend, Havelock Ellis, has succeeded to give a definition of this concept. Man and woman are dis-

tinguished not only by their external genitals, but also
—and is of even greater importance—by their sex
glands.   Woman has ovaries for the production of the
ova, man has testicles for the production of the semen.
These germ glands are the primary sex characteristics.
But there are also other differences between man and
woman, for example, in the larynx, which is larger in
man than in woman; in the hair, which in men is more
plentiful in the face, in woman on the scalp; in the
breasts, which are developed in woman.   But not only
the organs, the functions, too, are different in the two
sexes; for example, the voice of man is deeper than that
of woman, etc.   These differences between man and
woman may be considered as secondary sex characteristics.   But Ellis makes a further division, separating
the tertiary characteristics from these secondary ones.
Among these he counts such differences, as are less conspicuous, and often only relative, and which only become apparent when considering the average.   Such tertiary differences, among others, are the lesser average
amount of red blood corpuscles in woman, and the pro-
portionate flatness of her cranium.   The differences in
the sex glands we also call primary sex characteristics.
What Ellis calls secondary in contradistinction to tertiary characteritics are those, which through their greater differentiation, exert a mutual attraction on the two
sexes and so promote the union of the sperm cell and
the egg cell.   The man with a deep voice, for example, is
more attractive to a woman than a man with a high-
pitched, shrill feminine one.   According to Ellis the tertiary characteristics have very little importance in the
mutual attraction of the sexes.   But he justly declares
that it is difficult to distinguish between the secondary

and the tertiary characteristics. In this sense, at any rate, the direction of contrectation might be considered a secondary sex characteristics. For it makes the sexes appear more attractive to each other and so facilitates copulation and reproduction. In general, at least, the woman-loving man is more sympathetic to the woman than the man-loving man, and vice versa.

Darwin apparently has understood the concept of secondary sex characteristics in a wider sense. For, though he does not offer a sharp definition, he mentions among these secondary sex characteristics such differences which do not result in more attraction between the two sexes. He also describes how one may produce such secondary characteristics through sexual selection. That Darwin did not intend to include among these only such qualities as make for the mutual attraction of the two sexes may be seen from the fact that he reckoned among these secondary characteristic such an incipient secondary feature as baldheadedness in man, which would be a very peculiar means of attraction for woman.

No matter what standpoint we adopt we see that the direction of the sex instinct, according to all signs, corresponds to a secondary sex characteristic; and this is of most importance to us.

Though the above facts show us that there is an intimate connection between contrectation and detumescence, it does not of course answer the question how this connection is brought about in the life of the individual. Let me, therefore, briefly discuss the physiological connecton between sex glands and contrectation, as represented in the individual. It goes without question that we cannot render an explanation of internal relationship of the sex glands and contrectation since we know nothing about

been brought out either. We would have probable proof of the importance of the chemical products if no testicular substance were found in the region.

Howsoever, we understand the psychic processes, we must hold to the fact which experience teaches us that psychical processes have a certain anatomical correlate. It does not, of course, follow from this that the anatomical is the cause of the psychical process. As long as we cannot establish from our knowledge of anatomy and physiology how sensation, and especially the unity of the personality may be explained on their basis, we shall be unable to consider it a certainty that physiological processes in the brain bring about the phenomenon we commonly call soul. At the same time every day experiences have shown us that psychical processes have their accompanying phenomena in the brain. We know from pathology that the loss of certain parts of the brain brings about transformations. The same has also been proved in experiments, and on the basis of these I consider the question of how we should understand the anatomical correlate for the processes of the sex instinct justified.

In order to facilitate the conception of the anatomical basis of the sex instinct I have enclosed diagram, Fig. I. Krafft-Ebing supposes the existence of a special center for the sex instinct. In this case we would have to assume that there are cells in the brain which serve only this purpose. Such an interpretation is not necessary. It is my opinion that we can adequately explain this phenomenon through associative fibres without bringing in the idea of a circumscribed center—a fact that for the time being cannot be changed by Flechsig's latest studies on the associative centers. I shall start

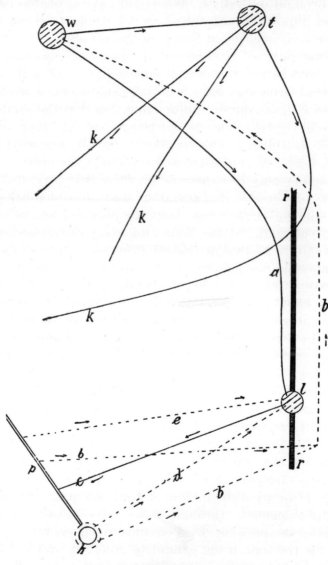

Fig. 1

with the brain. Let us assume that w represents that part of the brain wherein ideas of the female sex are localized. Of course, w does not consist only of several ganglionic cells. It consists of many cells which are united together through association fibres. It must be assumed that these cells w not only take up a certain small section in the brain, but that they are scattered in it, so that the cells containing ideas of man or other ideas of quite a different nature may be found between cells where ideas of women are localized. For this very reason I must repeat that the whole picture is only a diagram. There must further be a section in the brain where the centrifugal stimuli which impel to the appoacn of a woman are set into action, to touch and embrace her, etc. Let us assume that his section be called t. Numerous associative fibres must, therefore, run from w to t.

It will need no further discussion to state that the sexual ideas are to be localized in the cerebrum. We are justified in reaching this conclusion from the hitherto known function of the cerebral cortex. We do not even have to refer to animal experiments in order to prove it. A pigeon whose cerebral hemispheres have been removed does not heed the billing and cooing of its mate. Goltz observed that a dog from whom the largest part of the brain had been removed could no longer be excited by a bitch in a rut. It is well known that Gall sought to localize the sex instinct in the cerebellum and concluded that an enlargement of the cerebellum which corresponded to a larger development of the occiput, represented an especial strength of the instinct. According to Spurzheim only a few portions of the brain are as much explored as those connected with the sex instinct. This author also humorously counseled people whose cerebellum was strongly developed against a profession requiring celibacy. George Combe also placed the instinct of repproduction in the cerebellum.

Having examined the brain and its relation to the sex instinct let us now pass over to the peripheral genitals and the spinal cord. Let h signify the testicles, seminal canals and the seminal vesicles, p the penis and the external sex organs, r the spinal cord, l that part of the lumbar section of the spinal cord, in which are found the reflex centers for erection and ejaculation. (Gotz, Budge). The stimulation of l results in erection and ejaculation, the stimuli being transferred through the centrifugal paths c, which supply the masculature of the peripheral vessels and other muscles which are necessary to bring about erection and ejaculation. Therefore, when the testicles have secreted sufficient semen, a sensation of fullness is felt in the genitals. This is really a sensation of displeasure and impels to its removal, $i. e.$ to ejaculation. Pfluger draws the distinction here according to whether the peripheral stimulation is induced through the motion of the spermatozoa or the complete fullness. According to Hyrtl the impulse arises from the filling of the seminal vesicles. He also believes that the occasional continuance of the sex instinct in castrates is due to the fact that the seminal vesicles produce a certain secretion which like the semen excites the inner walls and impels to ejaculation. This saturation also brings about changes in the external genitals through reflex action, the nerve fibers d transferring the stimulus to l, which excite the fibers c. Thus, erection may finally be induced just as if it had been directly excited. There are, besides, centripetal nerve fibres e which run from p to l. A mechanical stimulation of the external genitals as in masturbation or tripper also leads to an erection, finally to ejaculation.

Thus far we have spoken of the brain, the genital centres in the lower part of the spinal cord and of its connection with the genitals. We have not, as yet, spoken of connection between the brain and the genitals. Ideas of a woman induce erection in man. There must, therefore, be a connection between *w* and *c*. There can be no doubt that this connection lies through the spinal cord and the centers *l*. Let us call this fibre-path *a*. By means of these fibres an erection takes place as a result of the idea of a woman, *i. e.*, in the same manner as through a stimulus that is exerted in *h* or *p*, which is carried over to *l* either through *d* or *e*. Besides these connections there must also be a fibre-path *b* running from the periphery *h* and *p* to *w*, as stimulation of the peripheral genitals, through saturation of semen may awaken ideas of a woman and contrectation. Of course, there must be a connection between *t* and all the body nerves *kkk*. Such a connection must of necessity exist as the stimulus in *t* through the pathway *wt* causes one to approach a woman and to touch her. All motor nerves of the body participate in this. Of course, parts of these fiber paths *kkk* will lead to the cerebral nerves and others to the nerves of the spinal cord. I believe we will be able to trace the more important processes of the sex instinct on an anatomical scheme through the above mentioned fibre paths and bundles of ganglionic cells. The nerve paths *b*, running from *h* and *p* to the brain cause an association here with ideas of woman. The nerve paths *d* and *e* bring about erections through peripheral stimulation independent of psychical activity. While the nerve paths *a*, running from *w* to *l* bring about erection through voluptuous pictures. This, of course, is just schematic.

In reality things are much more complicated. An idea of how complicated may be seen in the fact that it is not only stimulations excited in the genitals which cause erections, but also stimulation in other parts of the body. For example, let me refer here to the erection through fullness of the bladder which occurs in the morning; also erections caused by the stimulation of the rectum which leads many children suffering from worms to masturbation. Many other kinds of body stimulation are capable of bringing about erections, and as it seems, without any primary and direct psychical activity. The so-called erogeneous zones might work in this manner. Stimulation in certain parts of the skin cause voluptuous sensations and are reflected onto the sex organs. They who are sexually excited through flagellation, are probably excited for this reason. We seem to be dealing here with peripheral stimuli, which, like the peripheral stimulations excited in l and carried over to the genital centres$l$ through the nerve paths e, are also carried over to these centres. Such cases would thus have nothing to do with the to be considered phenomena of masochism.

Let us now make a resume of all that preceded:

1—In the mature person the sex instinct may be divided into two components, contrectation and detumescence.

2—Detumescence impels to a local function in the genitals, for example, to the ejaculation in the male. Considered as a peripheral process it is to be conceived as an organic impulse to evacuate a secretion just as a full bladder impels to the emptying of the urine.

3—Contrectation impels the male to a physical and

psychical approach of a female, and the latter to an approach of the male.

4—The union of the two components of the sex instinct in the sex act may best be studied from the point of view of phylogenetic development.

5—Phylogenetically detumescence as a means for reproduction is primary. Reproduction in lower animals through budding or sex cells, where only one parent animal is necessary always presupposes the decrease in volume of the parent animal (detumescence), though it is preceded by the growth of the animal in some part of its body. The reduction in volume in higher animals through the expulsion of sex cell (seminal or unicellular ejaculation) corresponds to the decrease in size in lower animals. The process of detumescence is to be found in higher and lower animals. Contrectation was added only later, when two individuals united for the purpose of reproduction. As a result of which two hereditary tendencies come together. Two hereditary tendencies become one for through it the progeny received more power of resistance. Only through a blending of the hereditary tendencies of two individuals is it possible to retain and increase the good qualities, consdered from the point of view of natural selection.

6—In the history of evolution detumescence in woman has become separated from the function of the sex glands, while originally both processes coincided.

7—Since as a result of evolution two individuals are necessary for the purpose of reproduction we have the union of contrectation with the function of the sex glands.

8—In the individual development of man the sex glands are primary. Contrectation is a secondary sex characteristic. In the man the immediate consequence of the function of the testicles is detumescence. In woman it is somewhat different since the separation of the egg cell from the ovary is not directly connected with the sex instinct. Originally detumescence and the separation of the ova in woman coincided, we may so conclude from the corresponding state of affairs in fish.

9—The dependence of detumescence as well as of contrectation on the sex glands may be seen in the consequences of castration.

10—In castrations performed after the onset of puberty these consequences are less distinct. In old age, too, the cessation of the normal function of the sex glands the two components of the sex instinct may continue.

11—In a discussion of puberty one takes into consideration the fact that psychical puberty sometimes occurs before physical puberty. It seems that the stimuli originating in the sex glands and controlling contrectation, do not always depend on the maturity of the glands.

EVOLUTION OF THE SEX INSTINCT

PART TWO

As a result of the increased attention which pathological aberrations of the sex instinct have received in modern times, and as a result also of the preoccupation of scientists of various countries with the investigation of this subject, the question whether these aberrations are hereditary or acquired have played an essential role. The disputes are especially linked up with the question of the contrary sexual sensations, the so-called homosexuality, or inversion of the sex instinct. The reason adduced by some in proof of its hereditary nature and by others in disputing their contentions, are, in my opinion, not always conclusive. In recent years some authors in opposing the idea of the hereditary in sexual perversions have cited proofs which not only lack all conclusiveness, but which also would lead to the most serious consequences. Havelock Ellis has justly pointed out that the reasons these authors brought forward, if they were worthy of our consideration, would argue for the acquired nature of the normal sex instinct as well as for that of homosexuality. If their arguments, therefore, had any foundation in fact, we would have to conclude that the normal man feels himself drawn to a woman,

131

and the normal woman to a man, not through reasons of an inherent nature, but because mere accidents in life determine the direction to which the sex instinct will point. Most adherents of the environment theory overlook these consequences without expressing themselves distinctly on them. They are either ignorant of them or they choose not to notice them and have a dread of drawing these conclusions. One of them, however, has without any reserve placed himself upon this standpoint. He states in frank and outspoken language that the connection of the sex instinct with the male or the female sex is a matter of chance. He is the well-known brain-anatomist and psychiatrist, Meynert. "In man and woman the difference in sex does not lie in the brain, but in the external organs. Other differences are differences between the two sexes and not sex differences. Imitation and habit develop all the further courses in the mode of the life of the sexes." Thus Meynert expresses himself in the well-known case of the Countess S., in which he was asked to give his expert opinion. The woman in this case was a homosexual, and Meynert believes that her homosexual nature was developed through education, and not acquired, as another expert claimed. Meynert on that occasion made a general statement about the acquired basis of the direction of the sex instinct, as above-mentioned. Even though Meynert mentions that contrary sexual feelings are easily produced in pathological natures, this does not invalidate the above statement that *all* further consequences in the mode of life of the sexes is developed through imitation and education. In another part of his professional opinion he states: "The regulatory, many-sided perceptions of life form an ascendant, plastic sphere of receptivity for the secondary ego which emerges from the primary infantile ego directed merely by the impulses of sense and imitation.'' In itself this sentence is difficult to understand; but from the context, in which Meynert used it, we may see that, in his opinion, heterosexuality is developed because sexual relationships are perceived in all walks of life; that the influence on the growing child is such that it perceves heterosexual relationships around him. Though normal relationships are also perceived by persons pathologically inclined, any light impression, a relatively slight pressure, exerted counter to these heterosexual influences, may bring about an aberration of the sex instinct into homosexual channels. This is Meynert's opinion.

Another author believes that if homosexuality be regarded as acquired one would have to assume that there exist acquired significant instincts. In this chapter I shall discuss the question whether such acquired significant instincts must be assumed. I shall only point out here that this reason adduced to refute the theory of the acquired nature of the contrary sexual feelings, may with equal rigor, be applied to question such an assumption regarding the acquired nature of heterosexuality, so that the above mentioned reproof of Havelock Ellis does indeed obtain.

In order to determine whether pathological aberrations of the sex instinct are acquired or hereditary, we must first of all see whether the normal sex instinct is acquired or hereditary. Then, we must determine what in it is acquired and what is hereditary. I believe that the reason why the discussions to date have been fruitless in part, is due to the fact that the preliminary question of the nature of the normal sex instinct has ever

been disregarded. We must first of all investigate the
normal just as we must know the healthy organ to study
the organ disease. I consider such an investigation all
the more necessary, since on the basis of late studies,
there is that danger, the exaggeration of the theory of
acquired associations may bring new adherents to
Meynert. If we cannot come to an agreement about what
is acquired in the normal sex instinct then the differences
of opinion about what is acquired in sexual perversions
will be a mere battle of words. Let me remind you of the
discussions which raged about whether there are unconscious acquired ideas. Some denied it, others maintained
it, and the battle of words ran on, without any agreement
at the outset as to what the dispute was about, *i.e.*, what
the nature of such an idea was. Similarly in criminal law
the difference of opinion regarding the guilt of any one
when freedom of the will has been excluded, have degenerated into an empty battle of words, because there was
not sufficient agreement about responsibility. In some
respects, it seems to me, the same error has also been
made with regards to the study of the sexual perversions.
On the basis of the discussion in this chapter we must
avoid such an error.

It is a well-known fact that psychiatrists have been
attacked because they did not sufficiently occupy themselves with normal psychology. Lazarus, Spitta and
Paul Ledig, among others, have pointed it out. In his
history of modern psychology, Max Dessoir states that
this ignorance has been observed among physicians even
before. At any rate, the psychology of normal man is
the basis for the study of pathological mental disturbances. I believe that in regards to the sex instinct, too,
the question of what is hereditary has not as yet been

given sufficient consideration; and this alone can be a basis for the hereditary in the pathological impulses.

The question whether heterosexuality is hereditary has formerly almost always been answered in the affirmative, as something that cannot be doubted. While, today, as we have seen, it is occasionally answered negatively. Many will nevertheless regard the question of the inheritance of heterosexuality as superfluous, because almost no one places any doubt upon it. I believe, however, that the consideration of even such an apparently self-evident question is necessary because we must get a clear understanding of how to explain the inheritance of heterosexuality, and whether we must really presuppose the existence of unconscious significant impulses, *i. e.,* the inherent idea of a man in woman. I consider the discussion of how we should conceive this inheritance both phylogenetically and psychologically very important also for another reason. There are numerous cases of perversions in which no heterosexuality is observed or in which they present certain peculiarities. Often there is a reciprocal relationship between normal heterosexuality and sexual perversion. The stronger the latter the slighter is the presence of normal heterosexuality. Should we now desire to discuss what in such a case of perversion is acquired and what hereditary, it becomes clear that we would have to ascertain the nature of heterosexuality. Should this seem superfluous or rather self-evident, think of the many things that seem self-evident, which in reality are not so. For example, the connection of ejaculation with the touching of a female does seem self-evident in itself, but in reality is by no means so.

Before we can answer the question whether the normal and abnormal sex instincts are acquired or congenital, we must have a clear understanding of the concepts "hereditary" and "acquired." A good deal of confusion prevails. Weissmann pointed out the frequent misapplication of the word "acquired," and Hegar has shown how both terms have been used interchangeably without regard for their meaning. We mean by birth that moment when the child leaves the body of the mother, so we must regard as congenital only those qualities and tendencies which the child possesses at that moment. Everything developed later is not congenital even though it may be proven that anatomical traces already existed at birth. As far as those qualities and functions which are to be developed later are concerned, physical and mental qualities, that is, we can only say that at most it is the embryonic rudiment, the germ which is congenital. We may thus say that the embryonic traces for the teeth are congenital, while the tendency to bite is acquired.

It is much more difficult to define to the satisfaction of all the concept "hereditary" inasmuch as it was exposed to many transformations. One usually designated as hereditary all those qualities which are identical in ancestors and offspring and which continue through descent. In this sense, the general structure of the body, the stomach, the intestines and the brain are inherited.

If through identical external influences identical qualities appear in parents as well as in offspring, the latter have not inherited the quality but acquired it. If, for example, the father accidentally breaks his arm and this later befalls the son, this is not inherited. For, though the symptoms are the same in both, it did not appear in the latter as a result of his descent from the father.

In our times, however, the concept of the "hereditary" was further narrowed down especially by Weissman and Hegar. According to their definition two attributes belong to it: firstly, the descent of qualities from ancestor to offspring by virtue of the special structure of germ plasm, and secondly, the identity of the qualities or at least a resultant of the qualities of the father, the mother and the ancestors. Thus at the time of copulation, a germ of disease may be conveyed into the ovum of the mother by the sperm of the father—something not at all impossible—and this germ may become fixed upon the formative embryo causing it later to become diseased. Such disease of the embryo was not inherited from the father; for the germ of the disease did not change the structure of the germ plasm but has become combined with the germ externally, as it were. However ingenious this distinction might be, I still hold to the opinion that it cannot be carried through in many points. It is even less possible when we consider that Weismann's theory of the structure of the germ plasm is only tentative, whose competency is attacked by many. One need not allow its claims even though one share Weissmann's point of view in other questions. It seems to me sufficient to state here that the qualities of the ancestors are transmitted to the offspring through the nature of germ substance. The qualities of the offspring may also be the resultant of the qualities of many ancestors. We have thus excluded all accidental admixtures to the germ substances without recognizing a structure of the germ plasm in Weismann's sense.

As we have seen, there is a great difference between the ideas "hereditary" and "congenital." Qualities may be congenital without of necessity being inherited, and, on the other hand, the teeth later to be developed have come down through heredity without being congenital.

Furthermore, it will not be denied that many qualities are acquired only later in life, and are neither inherited nor congenital. The simplest example would be the influence of an external cause, as in the above case of the fractured arm. That mental qualities, too, in a similar manner, may later undergo transformations said to be acquired, may be seen quite clearly in the cases of mental defects as a result of operations following an injury of the brain. I intentionally omit an example lying nearest at hand here of progressive paralysis following syphilis, or of conditions or weak-mindness as a result of alcoholism, because, according to some authors, congenital individual tendencies play a role in these cases, while the destruction of the brain through external force alters the mental functions in everyone if such destruction goes deep enough.

No one will contest the fact that heredity and external influences have an important effect on man both before and after birth. Most naturalists nowadays hold that in the case of men these are the only influences to be taken into account. One might ask, however, whether such qualities in man, whose formation through external environmental influences we cannot explain, will also be called inherited, when no trace of such qualities can be proven in the ancestors. It may sometimes happen that a "degenerate" child will be born of parents of the most excellent characteristics, it degenerates, in spite of the fact that the education and all other influences seem to be the same as for all the children. These influences are, therefore, not sufficient to explain the differences. There is no doubt, however, that many

apparently unaccountable cases may in their elements
be reduced to those two principles, heredity and condi-
tioning. At any rate scientific investigation so far has
not come upon any other principles and must exclude
such from its consideration.

Let us consider then the congenital in the sex instinct.
Congenital are the brain and genitals, both of them in
an immature condition. After birth there is further
development of those organs important for the sex life,
the genital organs and the nervous system; but only
after a certain period which is reached sooner or later.
In the female sex the onset of this period takes place
on the average in the fourteenth year, in the male at
the age of fifteen. At this period there is an accelerated
growth of the genitals. This process is the chief symptom of incipient puberty. At this period also begin to
appear, sometimes sooner, sometimes later, inclinations
for the other sex, so that the man feels himself drawn to
the woman, and the woman to the man. At this period
also take place many other mental and physical transformations. In women menstruation sets in, in man
there is the growth of beard and larynx; in both sexes
there is a certain amount of ardor, etc. But since man
has lived for many years until he reaches puberty, all
these phenomena of puberty are not congenital. It is a
different question, however, whether they are inherited.
No one will, of course, doubt that the growth of beard
and other physical phenomena of puberty are inherited
and not acquired. Nor is it possible to learn anything
from experimentation. If the child were removed from
all human society immediately after birth and left to itself, we might be able to ascertain the direction of the

sex instinct when it is brought back into the company of both sexes after a period of years. Such ideal cases are unknown to us and will always be unknown to us inasmuch as experiments on human beings have fortunately not as yet reached such an advanced stage.

To all appearances we do have a number of such observations. They refer to the so-called wolf-children or wild man of the woods, about whom Rauber has written an extensive work. But most of such cases have been so meagerly observed that on their basis we cannot draw any far reaching conclusions. They deal with children who have been placed into the wilds at a very early age and who, after many years, have been discovered and brought back into civilized society. In former centuries many such cases were known. Most reports are very meager, however, and in parts there are no details about the nature of the sex instinct as it expressed itself in them. But it is not only the incompleteness and unreliability of the reports that often makes such cases worthless, but also the fact that we are dealing here with congenitally abnormal individuals. Let me cite one case, that of Peter von Hamelin. Peter was discovered in 1724 near Hamelin, and died in 1785. At the time he was found he was said to be, from the structure of his body, 13 years of age, so that he reached an age of 74. As is reported, Peter since the time he was found showed complete indifference towards money and women. Rauber believes that his indifference towards the female sex was due to the fact that he was probably chased away into the woods by his step-mother. This really happened at the time. It was assumed that the boy turned away was identical with the boy subsequently found. If these assumptions were true his case would be of no value to us whatsoever; for the boy had been chased into the wilds in the year 1723 or 1724. If the identity of the two boys were thus established, Peter would at most have lived one year in the wilderness. What seems to me of most importance, however, is the fact that Peter was undoubtedly weak in understanding, nay, even imbecile and dumb. The little that he learned showed that his brain organization was very poor. As Rauber also remarks, the boy's many peculiarities pointed to a high grade of imbecility, and this makes the case unacceptable to us.

All the other reported cases of wolf-children are so untrustworthy that we cannot use them as material for our argument. So much that is sheer imagination is usually added that one does not know what is truth and what fiction. Into this discussion another case of a child ought to be brought—a child said to have been found in the wilderness and who in recent months has been shown in various cities of Europe. In this case, too, the truth has been withheld. In fact it is my belief that the child had not been found in the woods at all. I believe it was a child of monstrous growth and that its origin has been kept a secret in order to make its case more interesting. Under these circumstances, we shall have to abandon the observation of the sex instincts of these wolf-children.

There may be another possibility of obtaining a certain clarity through experimentation, *i. e.,* persons who at birth are reckoned among the wrong sex and who accordingly receive contrary education. Such persons are called pseudo-hermaphrodites. One has to distinguish between true and false hermaphroditism. The former is very rare in man and consists in the presence of both male and female sex glands, *i. e.,* testicle and ovary, in the *same* person. False or psuedo-hermaphroditism has been observed much more frequently. In the latter case the sex glands of only the one sex have developed, *i. e.,* either testicle or ovaries, but other parts of the sex apparatus, for example, the excretory ducts or the copulatory organs are not developed entirely corresponding to the sex gland present. We may thus find the presence of female sex glands with a distinct development of the penis, and male sex glands with the external genitals of a woman. As a result of this, errors are made at birth and children provided with testicles are taken for female, children with ovaries for male and christened and educated as such. Inasmuch as we make sex dependent merely on the nature of the sex glands, we may utilize such cases for our discussions. Thus, when someone with testicles having external female genitals at the same time (psuedo-hermaphrodisia masculina) is brought up as a girl and considers herself one, one might be able to conclude from the direction of the individual's sex instinct, *i. e.,* whether education and external conditions after birth had an influence on the sex instinct. For, if such an individual, in spite of having been educated as a girld should, nevertheless, feels herself sexually drawn to females, we would have to assume that her upbringing has been of no influence. The same would hold true vice versa, in the case of children mistakenly brought up as girls. If facts should substantiate this, we would have a plausible proof for the assumption that tendencies associated with the sex glands determine the direction of the sex instinct and not education or imitation. But even here other consideration enters, too.

After a clear observation of the material at hand there can be no doubt that the facts sometimes speak for the great importance of the influences in life. But it is necessary to weigh the material with the greatest caution. For two sources of error are to be met with in such cases of psuedo-hermaphroditism. First, the possibility that an inherited instinct may be checked by an artificial suppression cannot be contested, especially when the instinct was never highly developed. One has only to be reminded of the many cases where the suppression of instinct has been observed in animals. The training of wild animals also points to this. Wolves and tigers which have been born with a full-blown disposition for ferociousness and cruelty are nevertheless frequently tamed through breeding and training. Of course, to believe that the natural instincts in such animals have been entirely put aside, is naive. The contrary is in all probability true. This may be seen from the fact that the offspring is always born with the instincts artificially suppressed in the parents. The instinct only becomes latent. Several animal trainers whom I consulted have told me that one cannot refer to a destruction of the instinct of the individual animal, but that the instincts, at most, are made ineffectual. One of the best known animal trainers even compared trained animals with the mentally insane, and he believed that they can be trained to obedience through the threat of the whip, as has been ascertained in recent incidents. Carnivorous animals, who by the entire structure of their alimentary canal are destined to a meat-diet, have finally, through breeding and habit, been changed into herbivorous. Man's fear, the movements which he performs when confronted by an enemy, the protective movements, are all taken to be inherited instictive movements. Yet no one will deny that they may be suppressed through purposive education. One has only to be reminded of the student duels and of the "honor code" during such combats which strictly censures as cowardice all such jerking back of the head which rests completely upon an inherited instinct. Through training one may even produce instincts belonging to individuals of the opposite sex. Darwin mentions an observation of Reaumur, who has trained cocks to take good care of young chicks by means of long detention, isolation and darkness.

And finally instincts may be compared with certain physical processes. By artificial means one may check the natural tendencies from unfolding. It is well known that the Chinese cripple the legs of young girls by means of specially constructed covering for the feet. When this growth is checked through artificial wedging-in, the development is not like the development in normal children. In man the germ of the teeth is congenital and the teeth later develop from the germ. However, should an individual not get the necessary nutrition, they would not develop. Similar experiments have in fact been undertaken in the study of rachitis. The food of certain animals have been deprived of calcium salts and though the growth of the bones was observed to take place they did not reach normal development (Wegner, Roloff, Guerin, Chossat, Baginsky). No one will, however, contest the fact that the normal development of the bones rests on an hereditary basis. That the bones utilize calcium brought in the food for the purpose of their growth is due to the affinity which the bones have for these constituents. They are not absorbed because they are carried in the food—for other organs do not absorb those substances but there is present an affinity which enables the bones to seek out these parts. When these substances are lacking the inherited capacity the bones will not be able to procure the necessary ingredients. On the other hand, no matter how much of such substances are carried to organs having no affinity for them they will not be taken up on that account. Let us take the fact that the supply of calcium and phosphorus are not the cause of the hardening of the bones, but only a preliminary condition and that the real cause is the congenital capacity of the bones to produce for themselves these constituents from the food-materials or from the blood. Still the lack of these constituents does not permit the capacity to become effective. Feré assumes on the other hand that exostosis, produced from a morbid disposition of the bones, said to be inheritable, disappears again when the animals predisposed to this disease are placed in favorable hygienic conditions.

When we take everything into consideration it will not be surprising if instincts, though they are inherited, do not make their appearance, should favorable conditions for their developing be lacking. We may thus explain how in some psuedo-hermaphrodites the sex instinct develops in a contrary direction, corresponding to the false sex which had been assumed at birth and which had been encouraged through education. Thus the inclination towards men in masculine psuedo-hermaphrodites develops in spite of testicles, not because the direction of the sex instinct is not inherited with them.

The inherited instinct,—inclination towards woman—is
artificially suppressed and inclination towards man is
strengthened. But I believe that it must be added here
that only when there is a weak predisposition for the
normal sex instinct is its suppression possible.

Another source of error which we have to take into
consideration is the fact that often psuedo-hermaph-
roditic structures go hand in hand with a contrary development of secondary sex characteristics. Many such
persons not only have a contrary development on some
part of their genital apparatus, but in other parts of
the body, too. Thus the beard may be lacking in spite
of well-formed testicles, the larynx may retain the feminine or infantile form. On the other hand, in the presence of well-developed ovaries, the feminine pelvis and
the development of the breasts may be lacking. Let me
present here the example of a pseudo-hermaphrodite
who had distinctly-formed feminine sex glands. Ovaries
were present and the external genitals, in spite of the
anomaly, were so constructed that the person in question was taken for a girl and educated as such. But the
psychical life of the person developed in the direction
of the male in spite of the feminine education. The person in question became a coachman at the age of 26 and
died at the age of 38 as a result of a kick of a horse's
hoof. Inasmuch as he pursued a masculine occupation
he apparently also had an impulse towards women, *i. e.,*
he developed homosexually. As he was taken for a
woman and educated as such we may find the simplest
explanation for his aberration in the fact that in spite
of the feminine education, secondary sex characteristics
together with a pseudo-hermaphroditis formation of the

genitals were developed in a contrary direction. If, after the death of the person testicles instead of ovaries had been found those who contest the inheritance of the direction of the sex instinct would surely regard this case as proving their contention.   But the case before us proves how careful one must be in drawing such conclusions. Very similar is the case cited by Lesser; here, too, it concerned a girl, who, by her rough voice and whole bearing, was suspected by many people of being a man.

We have seen that in pseudo-hermaphrodites the secondary sex characteristics are often developed in a contrary manner.   In view of the fact that the heterosexual impulse is to be reckoned among the secondary sex characteristics it will not strike one as strange to find such contrary predisposition in them.   This will be discussed in further detail later in this work.   For this and the reasons mentioned above (artificial suppression or transformation of an instinct) it may easily be explained why heterosexuality does not make its appearance in some cases of pseudo-hermaphroditism.   In many cases no clear information about the sex instinct is given. The fact that persons with male sex glands play the role of women—a frequent occurrence—does not prove the presence of a truly feminine feeling.   It is also frequently reported that such persons have sex relations with both sexes.   It is true, that some do state to what sex they feel themselves more attracted.   For example, the male pseudo-hermaphrodite Anna Wilde, who had erection only with women and the pseudo-hermaphrodite Maria Dorothea Derrier, who considered herself a man and was in love with a woman, yet whose sex does not seem to me to be clear.   Other pseudo-hermaphrodites state that they do not give precedence to either sex. In numerous other cases it is stated that they did not possess the instinct at all.

In the case of male pseudo-hermaphrodites who marry as women it is to be taken into consideration that they sometimes react only passively and permit their husbands to use them without themselves feeling any real sex urge. One should not draw any hasty conclusions from such marriage relationships regarding the sex impulse of male pseudo-hermaphrodites. This has also been stressed by Magitot, who published the case of a pseudo-hermaphrodite who later turned out to be a man. This individual had married a man but had relations with women. On the basis of this one case both Gley and Chevalier independently drew conclusions regarding the connection between physical hermaphroditism and homosexuality. But the connection is apparently this, that in the presence of differentiated sex glands several secondary sex characteristics are often developed in a contrary manner, which may be both physical (the external organs of copulation, for example) and psychical (the direction of the sex instinct). Personal motives, too, sometimes perhaps play a part in the reports of pseudo-hermaphrodites. In a case published by Tourtual, a pseudo-hermaphrodite with testicles was married as a woman and refused to be divorced, perhaps for no material considerations. It is possible, though, that the claimed impulse towards men was really present. The Church finally caused the marriage to be annulled.

There still remain the numerous cases of pseudo-hermaphrodites whose sex instinct develops contrary to education and is only later seen to have developed in conformity with sex glands. These cases, which I cannot discuss in more detail here, seem to be a clear indication that the direction of the sex instinct is inherited; that it is dependent on the sex glands, and that it develops in spite of all education and all obstacles. For how else are we to explain these cases if not through an inherited heterosexuality? All other attempts at explanation are far-fetched. Formerly investigators even went so far as to determine the sex of a person whose true sex was not apparent by the direction of the sex instinct. And even though this is not correct for the above-named reasons this assumption has at least something in its favor. In some cases of hermaphroditism, the sex of individuals was investigated in order to establish whether unnatural practices (sodomy) were pursued; one did not determine the structure of the sex glands from the direction of the sex instinct, but on the contrary examined the genitals in order to conclude whether the person in question was guilty of sexual relations with a person of the same sex.

When in the discussion of hermaphroditism we take into consideration the above-named sources of error, we shall have to weigh the conclusions with great caution. I would like to lay special stress here on a significant point. I believe that the suppression of heterosexuality through a form of education not in keeping with the true sex plays a comparatively minor role. On the contrary it is my belief that the sexual inversion, *i. e.*, love of man inspite of testicles, and love of woman in spite of ovaries, in such cases, is an inherited quality. When heterosexuality is inherited education may exert only a very limited influence, which, however, becomes more extensive when it is tied up with certain debilities.

The path of exact observaton to the exclusion of all sources of error is thus closed to us in man, or at least made so difficult that we can hardly enter upon it. At any rate, we must see whether we cannot solve the question we have occupied with, in another manner. This will be possibly only when we bring the sex instinct close to other phenomena accessible to observation. In the first chapter we saw that the sex instinct corresponds to the instinct of reproduction. It will be advisable to study it from the viewpoint of the instincts in general. It is true that the existence of instincts has often been contested. Bain attempted to lead back to learned aptitudes everything ascribed to the instincts, while Büchner and Karl Vogt sought them in experience and intelligence; just as Leroy had earlier assumed the effects of experience reinforces the factor in inheritance. We do not have to dwell upon the point in question. Often the dispute about whether instincts exist or not degenerated into a battle of words inasmuch as the disputants often did not understand what their opponents meant by "instinct." There can be no doubt that associations play an important role in the instincts, but as a matter of fact these associations are in part such as develop on a congenital basis. Likewise, it cannot be doubted that many instincts become more perfect in time, and that experience reinforces the factor in inheritance. The nest-building of birds, which is more perfected in old birds than in young ones, is mentioned as an example. Wallace justly believes that imitation, memory and intelligence add much to the development of instinct. I believe that it isn't necessary to believe all stories of the wonderful instincts of animals. For our topic we shall only take into consideration whether instinctive actions exist at all, and especially, what is the inherited element in these instinctive actions. Instead of endless discussions let me then mention facts.

Even the simple acts of sneezing and coughing are the results of instincts when we accept this concept in its widest sense. Without foreseeing the effect the child coughs and thereby removes a foreign body from the throat, in spite of the fact that experience has not yet taught it that this body can be removed by coughing. Coughing, however, is a comparatively simple movement and is, because of this simplicity, distinguished from truly complex instinctive movements, such as the underground dwelling built by the mole or the bird's nest-building.

In my opinion the recognition of inherited reflexes— and these are generally accepted—also warrants the acceptance of inherited instincts. For at most the latter are distinguished from the reflexes by their greater complexity, i.e., quantitatively, and not qualitatively. For this reason many students of the history of evolution hold that the instincts are derived from the reflexes. Whether a stimulus activates certain muscles only for a few seconds, as in coughing, or other muscles for a longer time according to the same laws, as in nest-building, is only a quantitative difference.

The instinctive actions, however complicated they may be, may be released in a two-fold manner; first through central processes. One may conceive that certain periodical central stimulation occur without our being able to fully understand the mechanism. For example, the migration of fish in spawning season occurs periodically through central processes without any external stimulations, just as variations in temperature, pulse-beat, breathing, and perhaps also menstruation, seem not always to depend on peripheral stimuli, but on internal mechanisms in part not as yet explained. I shall not, however, go into further details about these hypothetical periodical processes in the instinctive life. If they occur at all they play only a very subordinate role. Important for the release of an instinct is the second process, peripheral stimulations. This I shall discuss in more detail inasmuch as it is instincts released in this manner which are involved in our question. Those instincts are modes of reaction in which, as in the reflexes movements take place as a result of a stimulus. Among these stimuli not only external stimuli are to be numbered, such as the influences upon the eye, the ear and the other sense organs, but also stimuli originating from the body itself, swelling of the testicles and of the ovaries. The love-song of male birds often induced by internal stimuli should also be included here. In reference to the question of the instincts we must also take into account that they are sometimes set free only when certain stimuli act on the body, i. e., there is a selective process going on which may be unconscious. This phenomenon will be supported by facts. It is very important for our discussion.

When we return to our topic, the sex instinct, and try to investigate whether the direction is inherited, we must of course presuppose that contrectation is altogether activated by definite stimuli which lie in the direction concerned. The facts that no one will deny these are:

The woman is excited sexually only by the man, the man only by the woman. The man desires to touch the woman, embrace her and perform coitus with her. He does not desire to perform these acts with another man or with another animal, only the stimuli orginating from a woman set free the instinct in him. Only these stimuli permit putting into action those processes discussed in the first chapter. Contrectation in the male does not impel him towards another man, an animal or an inanimate object. It must be only sense stimuli emanating from a woman which are capable of releasing it. It would, therefore, be necessary for the opposite sex to exert a definite stimulation upon the man or the woman, as the case might be. Only after we shall have learned later on that the instincts are inherited modes of reaction shall I be able to discuss the nature of these definite stimuli in each sex. Thus when we desire to prove that heterosexuality is inherited we have only to establish the fact that sexual reactivity of the man in the presence of certain specific stimuli emanating from the woman are inherited. In order to answer this question, we shall do well, in conceiving the sex impulse as an instinct, to satisfy the preliminary question whether there are instincts in which the capacity for reaction takes place only in the face of definite stimuli, and on the basis of an inherited disposition. Should we be able to prove this we would have a sure basis from which to set about answering the question of the sex instinct. We shall then be able to disprove the objection that the assumption of an inherited direction of the sex instinct also presupposes the presence of inherited ideas, inasmuch as we only shall have to assume that a certan capacity for reaction is inherited.

Let us turn from the sex instinct to the instinct in general in order to become familiarized with a few examples in which selection among stimuli takes place on the basis of an inherited disposition. Young chicks which Allen Thomson placed on a carpet did not make any scratching movements. Yet, as soon as some sand was strewn on the carpet they did. It is assumed that the scratching of the chick is inherited. It is set into action only in the presence of specific sense stimuli acting especially on the sense of touch and apparently also on the sense of sight. Such sense stimulus, for example, is the perception of sand, gravel or any similar material and not through the sight of a carpet. Inasmuch as the chicks of Thomson scratched only when sand was placed on the carpet, it must be clear that the sensation of touch in the legs and perhaps also the sight of the sand, released a movement, which under the circumstances was very purposeful, a movement which is frequently observed in grown-up hens digging in the ground for worms, etc.

Many fish migrate from the sea up streams in order to deposit their eggs and fecundate them. Here the females deposit their spawn and after fecundation the spawning fry is left to itself. Long before the young have slipped out of the eggs the sea-fish are again in their old habitat. The smelt is an example. He spawns in April; then goes back to the sea. After some time, in August, the young which have hatched in the meantime follow their example and swim down stream. From this one might draw the conclusion that they let themselves be driven mechanically to the sea. I consider it possible, however, that the flowing-down of the water acts as a specific stimulus for the smelt and that this specific stimulus is released in the act of swimming down-stream. What speaks in its favor is the fact that other fish swim up-steam, *i.e.*, they do not let themselves be driven mechanically through the water. The eel is among that group which swims up-stream. Fresh water eels go down to the sea for the sake of spawning and probably die there. The young eels creep out of the eggs in the sea, and at the end of April or the beginning of May they swim up-stream. They climb over waterfalls, wood piles, flood gates and numerous other obstacles. If it were true that eels let themselves be driven mechanically they would be driven back to the sea as soon as they approached the mouth of a river. The fact, however, that they swim up-stream can only be explained if we assume that the stimulus of the opposing waves releases the movement which drives them against these waves. This thesis is further strengthened by recent investigations according to which the old spawning fish are probably dead by the time the young eel have reached their place or destination.

The pike, as is well-known, will attack almost any fish in order to eat it. But the small stickleback who lives in the same water with him will never be attacked. Even young pikes will only seldom eat a young stickleback. It is known, of course, that the stickleback has spines on his back, which make him a risky food for the pike. As this phenomenon has already been generally observed in young, inexperienced pikes, one would have to assume that the sight of these spines of the stickleback itself exerts a simulus which causes them not to attack it. If experience were a necessary factor each and every pike would have to attack a stickleback at least once in his life. This is, however, not the case, and as a result, the stickleback swims about securely in the immediate neighborhood of the pike while other fish flee before him.

A young honey-buzzard who was bred far away from other buzzards was given his first wasp. Before eating it he took out the insect's sting. As the bird lacked all experience it must have been driven to this complex act by the sight of the insect. The buzzard also must have distinguished between the different parts of the wasp's body and especially those parts containing the sting.

Very young hermit-crabs just crawling out of their eggs throw themselves upon mussels placed in the water. Yet, at the same time they distinguish between the empty and the inhabited shells and will creep only into the empty ones. And when they chance upon shells inhabited by snails they wait until it is dead. The hermit-crab then removes it, devours it and creeps into the empty shell. These young animals were never taught. They had been separated from their parents at the outset and thus had no time or occasion to gather experience. They must have inherited the waiting attitude. Furthermore, they must also have inherited the capacity for distinguishing empty from occupied shells. Observations of this nature were made by Agassis.

Young salmon, just out of the eggs, deserted by their parents long before, go down to the sea by themselves a long time afterwards. It was shown that for some time they remain at the mouth of the river before swimming out into the open seas. Experiments have furthermore shown that a too-sudden transfer of fish from fresh water to the sea results in death. For this reason apparently, the transition occurs also gradually in the salmon. It must also be assumed that the stimulus of the salt sea-water releases the waiting attitude and causes the progress to be slowed up for some time.

Caterpillars seek a special type of food fitted for their consumption. The objection, to the effect that caterpillars always eat the food on which the eggs have been laid, is not justified. When shipping eggs of caterpillars one may sometimes observe that when the monophagous variety come out of the eggs they choose one specific type of food from the several offered to them.

Young animals which have grown up in the wilderness are in the habit of avoiding poisonous plants and will almost never eat such plants or animals as might harm them. Young pigeons which have been separated completely from their elders will become restless and take to flight when they perceive a bird of prey. Ferrets and buzzards which from birth have been kept away from their parents and grown up in captivity will fall upon glow-worms and other non-poisonous snakes and get hold of them as best they can. Yet, as soon as they espy a common adder whose poison could harm them, they go to attack it with greatest caution even though they never saw one before. In order not to be bitten they will try to crush its head. The squirrel begins to gather moss for its nest, not in the summer, but in the autumn. In the fall, too it begins to put by a supply of nuts, etc. The moss, which it hardly noticed before, causes him pleasure. It begins to gather and to hide nuts which previously it had only grabbed for immediate consumption. Here, too, then, there is a selection among different external stimuli, the impressions which take place in the fall causing the squirrel to gather nuts, though not so the impressions of the other seasons. It is an indifferent question whether we are dealing here with atmospheric or other impressions of nature.

Young monkeys which have never before seen a scorpion or a snake will shy away at the approach of the one or the other, while in the presence of other animals they will not show any fear. Ducklings which have been hatched by hens will sometimes run into the water though their foster-mother will try to prevent them from so doing. They must therefore be able to distinguish water from other objects, or rather the water produces a specific stimulus on them. Young coots are said to climb over everything which looks like a heap of dead leaves on the ground. It is assumed that this behavior bears some connection to the nature of its nest and its manner of life. Lloyd Morgan took a coot six weeks old without any experience whatsoever, and let it climb up and down the bank of a river; the animal avoided all obstacles. Redstarts will fly out on their first flight without running against any obstacles. Spalding observed the same in young swallows. All these examples may be explained only by assuming that the birds can distinguish between those objects which are hindrances and those which are not.

No sooner has the butterfly slipped out of its puppa than it flies up into the air—a master among the fliers without ever having been instructed in the art—swarms around the flowers that serve him for food, and sits down on flowers it never saw before. It seeks out and sucks the flower's honey, the existence of which was concealed from it. According to Preyer, who in this is joined by G. M. Schneider, newly born mammals are guided to the finding of the mother's teats merely or mainly by the sense of smell. The scenting of an animal of prey causes deer to take to quick flight before they see the enemy and without having previously been made

known of such danger through experience. Young and
inexperienced wild animals flee at the first scent of a
human being approaching. The impulse for flight, according to Schneider, has been associated with the specific smells throughout many generations, which in the
newly born animal also produce the result of such specific
smells. As soon as external conditions become unfavorable many animals begin their period of hibernation.
They begin to make preparation for it without having
been instructed by others. When the water of a river
dries up some fish dig into the mud. Here, too, specific
extrenal stimuli cause the activity without the animals
knowing the purpose of the activity. Barkow, in his
famous work on the hibernation of animals, had already
assumed that the external cause of hibernation was the
lower outside temperature which had an effect on the
organism.

In the newly-born infant the empty stomach produces
movements of suckling, without any previous experience, of course. In the full stomach these movements
of suckling cease.

We have observed here numerous cases in which now
simple movements, now quite complicated activities, are
carried out and in which various stimuli bring about
different effects without having been preceded by experience. We are therefore justified in drawing the
conclusion that selection of stimuli on the basis of inheritance takes place. Moreover, in order that one may
not misconceive this selection of stimuli for the purpose
of the release of the instincts, I shall state here that there

would be no contra to such a conception if there also took place a certain searching and groping (trial and error). For example, selection through the sense of taste may be clearly inherited in some cases. This is most probably the case in many insects. But it is quite obvious that these insects will fly towards different flowers and taste of each one. When it has at last found the sweet and most agreeable part of the flower, the selection in the future will not only be through the sense of taste but through the sense of smell and sight as well. Plants which promise satisfactory stimuli to the sense of taste will in the future be perceived from afar. Trial and error is not identical with selection through experience.

We have learned at least one thing from the preceding consideration, and this is the fact that a highly differentiated psychical life is not at all necessary for mature instinct. When we compare the sex instinct with the instincts just enumerated we may be able to conclude forthwith that a developed psychical life is not requisite in order that we should regard its direction as inherited. It is not necessary that a male shall have inherited a complex conscious idea of woman. It is only necessary that he be able to perceive the difference between man and woman through some sense impressions, be they ever so crude. Or, rather, all that is necessary is the existence of the possibility for man to react differently to sense impressions which emanate from woman than to those originating from man. If such an assumption should tend to destroy many an illusion, this cannot change anything in the facts. Of course, I do not wish to maintain that matters are always as simple as this; and I would like to mention here that more refined differentiations are entirely dependent on the individual development of the psychical life. To maintain, however, that if we recognize an inherited differentiated sex instinct we must also assume the presence at birth of the idea of woman in man and vice versa, must be regarded as erroneous here, on the basis of the preceding discussions. In order to accept the inherited nature of the sex instinct we do not have to allow for more than in the cases of the instinctive activities just described. In some respects, in fact, the instinctive activities seem to me to be much more complex than the sex instinct, especially at its inception. Let me take the first example for the sake of comparison. The male's capacity to distinguish between woman and other men may be sufficient to produce in him the sex impulse towards woman, just as the chick distinguishes the gravel from the carpet; or is induced by the sense impression of the sand and the distinction between it and the rest of the ground, to dig with its legs. The chick was brought into the world with no conscious idea of gravel or grains of corn and yet it reacts in accordance with the sense impressions. In a like manner we do not have to believe in the inheritance of ideas in order to conceive the inheritance of the direction of the sex instinct. The chick's scratching is a congenital instinct which apparently is essentially different from the later to-be-developed sex instinct. Here it must be remarked that as a result of the delayed development of the sex instinct numerous factors are added which prevent a clear observation of its workings. Innumerable impressions have been received between birth and puberty. The originally deficient activity and incapacity of the sense organs has increased. Consciousness has become perfected and self-consciousness, too, has developed. Num-

erous ideas and concepts have become the intellectual
property of individual. The fact that the sex instinct become more active only many years after birth is no
proof that it has been acquired. Other instincts, too,
may be inherited and yet may not develop until later,
when the corresponding sense stimuli or the capacity to
react to these sense impressions in a corresponding
manner have made their appearance. Such instinct appearing long after birth are, for example, the nest-building of birds, the puppation of the caterpillar, the migratory instinct of birds. These instincts, too, are released
through specific stimuli, which is very distinct in the
case of the migratory instinct of birds in whom it is of
a specific climatic nature. All these instincts make their
appearance long after birth. The fact that in the interval the animals have gathered many experiences
does not disprove anything in respect to the inheritance
of the later-to-be-developed instinct. The same is also
true of the sex instinct in man. At the time of puberty
human beings already know that there are two sexes,
that man and woman love one another, that the genitals
of the two sexes are different, etc. But all this does not
cause the impulse towards the other sex. It is true that
this impulse towards the opposite sex cannot develop
without a certain psychical activity. But the latter is
not the cause influencing the already developed sex instinct. At most, it is a preliminary condition in order
that the sex instinct be developed in a certain direction.
Where a simple perception is sufficient to enable one to
distinguish between objects, instincts may be set in activity, as we have seen. This capacity for distinguishing
between objects is preliminary to the setting of those instincts where a selection of stimuli takes place. Simi-

larly, the impulse towards a woman may develop only
when the sense perception of the person in question has
developed so far that he can distinguish between man
and woman. But the sex instinct develops only a long
time after such capacity for discernment has already
taken place, and in most cases many years after. Consciousness and knowledge of the numerous peculiarities
distinguishing man from woman are only so much
unnecessary ballast, as it were. They are not necessary for the differentiation of the sex instinct. The main
consideration is always to distinguish between the sense
stimuli emanating from man and woman, or rather to
react differently to them. Consciousness is only a mirror, to a certain extent, as Forel remarks. Numerous
processes take place in us without such mirroring. We
have already seen that in the animal world a highly
developed psychical life is not necessary to induce the
impulse towards the other sex. Branchiopods and many
spinners copulate directly after having been freed from
the puppa. And what reason have we to assume anything
different in the case of man? It is true that in human
beings there is later differentiation between members of
the opposite sex—something which is seldom to be observed in animals. But in the animal world, too, we may
already find the most perfected individualization, a male
seeking out a specific female. Let me only remind you
of the storks who until death live in a most tender mari-
tal union. Of course, the numerous psychical impressions which human beings experience until they reach
puberty and later, may differentiate his impulse and will
gradually lead him towards certain kinds of individuals.
However, if we do not wish to ignore the teachings of
comparative physiology and zoölogy, we must regard

heterosexuality as something inherited and not as caused
by these experiences. And being inherited, the direction
of the sex instinct is only a certain mode of reaction, not
the consequence of a significant impulse.

It would be erroneous to maintain that the sex instinct differed from the instincts because it represents a
more complicated act; for not only are the movements
of man towards woman to be taken into consideration but
also anatomical transformations in the genitals, such as
erection and ejaculation. Caterpillars which have never
seen their parents and which have slipped out of the
egg in any haphazard direction, usually after some time
perform quite complicated acts, among which are the
secretion of glands and other movements when they
pupate. The very same complication of glandular secretions and movements by means of muscles may be observed in spiders. All of which has been recognized
as inherited a long time ago. All such objections are
the less significant inasmuch as the animal fluid already
secreted may be capable of inducing the sex instinct.
Nor would it have any significance for our question if
the sex instinct itself should in turn lead to an increase of the secretion of the testicles. For as we know,
other glandular secretions, too, are essentially under
the control of psychical processes. I need only mention the secretion of tear as a result of sadness. And
since the sex instinct does not bring about the secretion of the semen but rather its ejaculation, these objections have no significance whatsoever.

The objection that in accepting an inherited heterosexual impulse we must also accept the inheritance of
ideas, is therefore not valid. At least, we do not have to
accept such inherited ideas in the usual sense of the

term. Scientists who assume the existence of ideas absolutely unconscious may without further ado also accept such ideas with respect to the sex instinct. In order to clarify this point, we shall have to refer to another instinct. Let us consider the migratory instinct of birds of passage. It is certain that in these birds such an instinct is inherited, that it is not only the result of experience. Scientifically, one usually explains this instinct by assuming that certain animals, at the dawn of time, had left their habitations for climatic reasons or in order to secure better food, and had found what they had sought in other places. Because of constant migrations towards these places, generation after generation, and in certain set seasons of the year, their offspring had developed this instinct for migrating. Those birds who did not migrate were wiped out on account of the scarcity of food and left no offspring. Thus according to the principle of natural selection, there must have arisen an offspring which inherited this instinct. This migratory instinct appears in birds which have never before seen the place towards which they are flying. If we were to assume inherited unconscious ideas these would have to be conceived of in the following way in regards to the instinct of migration. In birds the thought of finding better food and better climatic condition in some far region and at certain seasons of the year is inherited. This thought is absolutely unconscious in these birds. They are merely conscious of the act they execute, of the migration itself, not its purpose. Everyone admits that the migratory instinct of birds is not purposeless and that it results in the finding of better food and climatic conditions. From a scientific point of view we assume that as a result of natural selection and heredity certain

changes have developed in the nervous system of migratory birds, which will release the instinct of migrating in
the offspring as soon as certain conditions of temperature and of other atmospheric influences have taken
place.

Adolf and Karl Müller in their "The Caged Song-
Birds," say: "That lack of food as well as unfavorable
climatic conditions may not solve the riddle of the migratory instinct may be established in the peculiar unrest
which dominates caged birds of passage at that time of
the night when their luckier brothers and sisters are
undertaking their long journey into far lands or new
home—an unrest that may only be explained by assuming a compulsive natural instinct. The bird would like
to lift its wings and wreck them in a mighty swinging
movement, in order to express its great yearning for
wandering. But instead of the soft air currents the
bird's wings meet with the hard wires of the cage. Its
bill does not cut through the undulating air regions in
its soaring up and propulsion, but rebounds from the
contact with the roof of the cage, again and again
thrusting against it and all because the natural instinct
dominates the bird irrepressibly and does not allow of
any consideration of reflection." Whether we regard
the specific conditions of the nervous system which release the instinct of migration as an anatomical equivalent of an unconscious idea is after all only a matter of
words. It will depend essentially on the subjective
standpoint whether the concept of "idea" may be recon-
ciled with the assumption that it is unconscious. I shall
not go into any further discussion of this question inasmuch as such a discussion is always merely doctrinal—a
matter of words—and do not contribute anything to the

clarification of the problem. When it is once known
what is understood by "unconscious idea" there is no
purpose in going into a further discussion on whether
the expression is justified or not. At any rate, we must
assume certain specific conditions in the central nervous
system which permit of such selection among the inherited instinct. Without such an assumption we would
be leaving the field of natural science. There can be
no doubt that these specific inherited conditions have a
psychical equivalent. But, of course, we do not know
this equivalent, and we could not express it better than
by the concept of unconscious ideas. No one will, however, deny that such psychical equivalents are inherited. Otherwise we would have to contest the the existence of all inherited tendencies and possibly to assume that a newly-born child is just the same as a more
mature child, and one could shape it as easily as a piece
of clay. We might even reach some stage where not
only the individual differences between newly-born children would be contested, but also those between animals and human beings until finally one would argue
that since both the young ape and the human infant are
born a *tabula rasa,* it depended only on education to see
who should become a genius, the child or the ape. It is
of no moment whether we regard the function of the
brain as the cause or as the accompanying phenomenon
of the psychical process. From the standpoint of natural
science it must be assumed without condition that certain paths and ganglionic cells may be traversed with
greater ease while others are harder to cross and that
these anatomical qualities are inherited. In this manner we are given an anatomical basis for congenital and
inherited psychical processes.

We have seen that in order to regard the sex instinct
as inherited we have only to accept an inherited capacity
reaction enabling the male to react to stimuli emanating from woman. Matters, however, are not as simple as
that. The external stimuli must be received through some
sense organ or other. And no matter whether the sex
instinct is inherited or acquired, the reaction to external
objects must permit of a selection in the sense that only
those stimuli which come from the opposite sex will
bring about a reaction. What are these sense stimuli
which operate as means of sexual differentiation in such
matter. I consider this question a very important and
perplexing one.

We must consider that many influences operate on
each sense organ. For example, the sense of smell is
capable of perceiving the odor of the entire body, the
odor of the hair and the smell of genitals. The sense of
sight may distinguish not only between the shape of
the head, but also between those of the breast, the pelvis,
etc. We thus have to consider the two-fold question:
First, which of the sense organs, then, which of the
particular stimuli operating on these organs, may release the sex instinct? To begin with we may only attempt certain conjectures about them—conjectures, however, which will later receive sufficient support. As I
will state at the very outset, several sense organs, in
my opinion, take a part in the sex instinct of human beings, to a larger or smaller extent. We may, in the first
place, draw certain conclusions from self-observation.
But we must warn the reader here that self-perception
leads to self-deception. For we can pursue introspec-

tion only after an impression has become conscious in us. The fact, that certain sense impressions have become conscious making us feel that they excite contrectation, does not, however, prove their correctness, objectively speaking. The facial lineaments, the distribution of the hair, the shape of the body are different in man and woman. These differences in shape probably play an essential role in the sex instinct. But not only the shape, the color, too, takes part in it. Thus the color of a black woman's skin generally does not attract a white man. I believe that the visual sense is very important. One might perhaps object that the visual sense is one that develops very slowly and that sight, for example, appears only gradually. However, when we consider that in human beings it is only comparatively late that a discernment between man and woman may be made, and that the impulse urging to sexual contact appear only at an age when the sight has already been fully developed, we shall not be able to contest the possibility that the visual sense plays a leading part. I believe, though, that other senses, too, are of great importance, for example, the auditory sense. A woman with a deep bass voice, who is otherwise delicately built, will repel the man. In my opinion an important role devolves to the auditory sense. The influence exerted through the hearing is much greater than is generally assumed. To this I would not only attribute the triumphs which women with a beautiful singing voice have won in the world of men, but also the observations made on blind people, to be mentioned again later on, as well as the numerous other every-day observations. It is similarly to be assumed that the sense of touch in some respects, also, complements the visual sense. But the tactile sense is only secondary after contrectation has already been released. The question of the sense of smell is a more difficult one. Most men I have questioned could not give me any information about their conscious olfactory sensations which could contribute to a differentiation. These observations, however, as well as those of men who were apparently excited by the sense of smell, contain sources of error, inasmuch as olfactory sensation may operate without the person in question being conscious of them. And on the other hand, the belief that one questioned has been excited by the sense of smell does not prove the case to be really so. It may happen again that the sex instinct takes place through one sense organ but the same object may be stimulated antipathetically by other sense organs and when so stimulated by those other senses, the sex instinct is consequently extinguished. This was the case for example in the following observation with regards to the olfactory sense:

Case XIII. This case refers to a highly tainted individual, abnormal in many other respects, who, until the present, has been completely impotent and who ascribes it to olfactory antipathies. This man, 36 years of age, gives me the following information: "Towards some persons I have an unconquerable antipathy when in direct proximity with them. This antipathy is not always felt in connection with the external appearance of the person. It happened frequently that the face and the expression of a woman pleased me very much but not her immediate proximity. And I have made the observation that my antipathy was tied up with the unsympathetic smell. However much Jäger may exaggerate in this respect, he is undoubtedly correct. I have often convinced myself of it. Formerly, I used to approach

girls mostly in answer to direct or indirect encourage-
ment. But then, at my attempt to have sexual intercourse with them, the foul smell would prevent it. This
took place even before I had read anything about the
subject. Twice the following took place to me: When I
was lying in bed with a girl and was about to lift her
dress, I perceived a smell like that of polishing-wax, so
that in horror, I had to let her go. When embracing a
girl I sometimes received from her hair an unpleasant
smell like that of rancid oil. When I danced with young
girls they emitted a revolting smell like that of the
"place" itself, by your leave. Yet, sometimes I perceived nothing of the kind, but rather complete absence of smell. Very rarely, however, I thought I scented
a very lovely smell, without on those occasions having
or seeking an opportunity for investigating my potency.
I often went to dances merely in order to investigate
what effect the smell of a woman would have on me. It
seems that even then I almost always felt an antipathy."

The olfactory sensation always prevents the person
in question from having an erection, at least as far as
his own observations are concerned. In the preceding
case it was olfactory sensations which exerted a great
influence on the person in question. In the following
case tactual antipathy had a similar effect.

Case XIV. Mr. A. T., 24 years of age. One of his
mother's brothers had been epileptic for years and died
in a condition of weak-mindedness. The patient's father
had never been with a girl until the age of 26, when he
married. This was because he had a very pronounced
sense of shame.

A. T. has been masturbating from the age of 12 to 16.
His first sexual excitements came at the sight of female

figures from the Greek Pantheon. There wasn't any thought of touching the figures. Such desires came upon him though when he was 14 years of age. The female bosom at that time was the only part that excited him. Later the voluptuous thoughts decreased and he began to masturbate less frequently and only when he became excited by some incident. It naturally happened when his older comrades would tell each other exciting stories. The thought that gave him most pleasure at the time was to imagine himself pressing the bosom of a beloved being against his own breast. From his eighteenth to his twentieth year sexual excitement became less and less frequent. The thought of coitus, cropped up in him, but very seldom. His strongest excitements came from risque stories or when he had been looking at piquant pictures presenting women. Sexual excitements, at any rate, were comparatively infrequent, occurring at intervals of eight to fourteen days. Sometimes at night A. T. would be so much tortured by voluptuous thoughts that he spent many sleepless hours and was able to sleep only after masturbation. Pollutions which had formerly been more frequent at the age of 20 to 24, occurred about every fortnight, and strange to say, always on Friday nights. In the proximity of prostitutes he became generally excited, that is to say, not only sexually. These excitements often became so extreme that he actually began to feel unwell. He felt an uncomfortable feeling creeping up his stomach and no matter how little he had eaten or drunk before, he often felt like vomiting in their presence. After which he usually had voluptuous torturing thoughts, which finally were put aside by masturbating, as already mentioned. A. T. did not find any pleasure in masturbation. He merely practiced it in order to rid himself of suffering. The ejaculate was usually very considerable. This was followed by a deep and dreamless sleep.

Pollutions occurred, also, occasionally from his twenty-fifth year until the present. The general excitement in the presence of prostitutes has remained the same. He experienced both a sympathy and a revulsion towards them at the same time. During this time he has always been near women. The sight of their low-cut breasts excited him sexually, but such excitement passed away quickly. At night this was always followed by a pollution connected with a dream of a female person. Sometimes, however, pollutions without voluptuous dreams also occurred.

What is most conspicuous in A. T. is his absolute aversion to contact with a person of the female sex. Not only coitus, but also the thought of kissing a woman or even of touching her by the hand is repulsive to him. This fear rules him and he is afraid that it will keep him from all sexual intercourse. He cannot tell how his aversion to contact had come about in him. He is not in the least homosexual. He is quite friendly to his acquaintances and has no desire *de toucher* or similar weaknesses.

Through methodical and continuous hypnotic treatments it was possible to rid the patient from these feelings of aversion to touch woman, and to follow his serious thoughts of marriage, where previously any contact with a female had been impossible, in spite of the fact that he had heterosexual inclinations. It was possible through methodical suggestion not only to remove all fear of touch but also to make the patient sexually potent. At first the erections were weak, but in time they became stronger and stronger.

William James assumed the existence of an instinct of isolation in human being. Among other things he bases it on the hesitation most people show if they have to sit down on a chair which has been warmed by the pressure of another person's body. If there really is such an instinct of isolation then its effects, at any rate, are usually nullified by the sex instinct. In like manner, it may also affect the sex instinct.

I hope that the question of what sense organs play the main role can best be answered by gathering information about the sex instinct of persons who lack one or several of these sense organs. Of special interest is the sex instinct of blind persons. It seems to me that inquiries about the blind will furnish more exact material regarding the importance of the sense of sight for the sex impulse. I believe that my inquiries, though of a somewhat negative nature, will not be without some importance. In the case of the visual sense we have to consider that it only functions to make us aware of forms and colors. The forms may also be perceived by the sense of touch combined with the muscle sense or the sense of motion. If we could thus exclude the sence of touch in the blind for the distinction between the sexes, we would have proofs that the consciousness of form differences is not absolutely necessary to induce the heterosexual impulse. I have been assured that passionate love affairs frequently took place between a blind young man, X., and a blind young woman, Y., without their having touched each other. Apparently only

the sense of hearing and of touch could be made use of
by these two persons and it would apparently also be
impossible in this case for the blind man to perceive
the stimulus of the female. However, this cannot always be eliminated. For though the two had never
touched each other it is yet possible that X had received
some knowledge of the form differences of man and
woman from other persons and that he filled in the form
of the girl through association with the other sense impressions of the woman. With the aid of his previous
tactual perceptions he might thus have perceived the
shape of the girl without ever having touched.

I have also been informed by a person versed in the
nature of the blind that the olfactory sense plays a large
role with them. Blind people unconsciously put their
heads close together when they talk to each other, without touching. Possibly the sense of smell also aids the
blind in the differentiation of the sexes. So it is not
impossible that in the sex instinct, too, the olfactory
sense plays a more important part. At any rate, the
main question to me seems to be whether the perception
of form differences between man and woman in blind
persons is a preliminary condition for the stimulation of
the sex instinct.

Unfortunately it is very difficult to make exact observations in this respct, for the following reasons:
First of all it is possible to test the importance of forms
for the sex instinct only in dealing with persons born
blind. It is true that inquiries also refer to such persons who had gone blind in their infancy, and who we
may regard as having been blind. But the second condition would be that such persons shall never before their

sex instinct is awakened have perceived the difference between man and woman through the tactual sense. Only if in spite of this the sex impulse in its normal direction were awakened in such persons could it be proven that the perception of form is not an absolute condition for the release of the sex instinct. Most blind people, however, up to a certain age have been brought up at home. They have heard references to man and woman. Thus, when a blind person, in a concrete case, cannot distinguish between man and woman through this sense of touch, but rather through his sense of hearing, one may consider that in the blind the form is important. It is generally attested that hearing will enable the normal blind, if he is not fooled on purpose, to distinguish very easily and with great exactness between man and woman. As in normal persons, the activtiy of the imagination immediately supervenes in those people deprived of one of their senses. Such activity is unconscious most of the time. At the very moment when the blind man, confronted with another person, perceives whether it is a man or a woman, he also complements the form through the aid of memory images, which of course, are derived from the sense of touch.

It is therefore not easy to ascertain in the blind which sense plays the dual role in sexual selection. It is usually assumed that the sense of touch acts as a substitute for the visual sense and that the blind becomes cognizant of forms by means of it, whereas, the normal person becomes aware of forms through the sense of sight. Teachers of the blind, however, state that lay persons err in regards to this point; that the sense of touch does not replace the visual sense to the same degree as is frequently assumed; rather, that the auditory sense plays the main role. Thus Heller, writing about the formative elements in the blind, states: "Those who are not close to the practical problems involved in the education of the blind will regard it as self-evident that the tactile sense, so often and so fondly designated a substitute for sight, as well as the formative elements derived from it, have a natural preponderance over the auditory perceptions and the formative elements derived from these. Or, at least, that they point to the direction of the psychical life of the blind. This is by no means the case and there is an abundance of facts proving that in the first stages of the development of the blind the two fields in his formative elements may exist together without being interrelated, if the wise direction of the education does not bring it about in the blind. Not touch but hearing is the primary conscious sense perception and thus is the formative elements transmitted through the sense of hearing which exert their influence on the thought and emotions of the blind child whose mental life is being awakened."

From the above it might perhaps be concluded that sex differentiation in the blind takes place less through the sense of touch than through that of hearing. It is a fact, though, that blind persons are capable of distinguishing between the two sexes. It is also a fact that the sex instinct of blind persons is often very pronounced so that asylums for the blind have sometimes been confronted with serious disturbances of discipline because of it. This does not, however, answer the question which of the senses plays the main role in sexual differentiations. For it is possible, in view of the fact that the

sex instinct first appears at a time when imagination
has already complemented the sensation and enabling it
to transmit auditory stimuli to the sense of touch, that
sense impressions are received only through the auditory
sense and that the sex instinct is released through a secondary activity of the imagination, through an imagination producing old memories of touch. In that case it
would again be form differences that would play the
chief role. At least this seems quite possible. Nevertheless, it is probably true that the differentiation of
forms in man is not necessary for the rousing of the sex
instinct.

In the animal world, to be sure, the part is played by
other sense perceptions which have nothing to do with
the distinction of form. Later, I shall take up this point
in more detail. I shall only mention here that among
mammals, the eye of the mole-rate is covered by a layer
of skin and the animal is thus prevented from perceiving the form of the individual of the opposite sex
through the visual sense. It is remarkable here that in
the mole-rate it is not the tactual sense but the sense
of hearing that perceives the opposite sex.

Up to now our inquiries have been only negative. We
have seen that blind people complement the forms
through experience and imagination; from this observation one might easily deduce that in man the differentiation of forms is preliminary to the rousing of the
sex instinct. Nevertheless, the following is to be considered. The tactual sense may indeed instruct us regarding the forms of man and woman; although, in reality the sense of touch can never replace the sense of
sight. Each sense organ has its own specific impres-

sions. The perception of forms received through the
eye is essentially different from the perceptions through
the sense of touch. This may best be seen from the observation that persons without experience may easily
mistake a form received through the sense of touch for
another object perceived through the visual sense. And
then, we must also consider the fact that in the normal
sex instinct color also plays an important role—the color
of the skin, of the hair, etc. A white man will be attracted to a black woman only in rare cases and only
after he had become used to her. At least, there are
quite a number of men who have no impulse towards
them. However, these differences in color which are
of great importance in normal man are totally lacking
in blind persons. That the blind may sometimes hint at
another person's color of skin or hair cannot change in
the least this fact. The concepts "brunette," "blond,"
etc., are missing with these persons and consequently
they must also lack sensations connected with the perception of color. From this we may draw the conclusion: That the means of sexual differentiation which
seem to be the most important are not absolutely necessary for the stimulation of the sex instinct. We may
make the same observations also, in the case of the
absence of any of the other sense organs. I have made
inquiries regarding the sex instinct of the deaf and I
never heard of any cases of aberration of the instinct
of the least importance for our consideration. There are
people who from their early childhood lack the sense of
smell. I have had occasion to speak to one of them. He
showed no aberration of the sex instinct. As a physician, much in contact with such persons has informed

me, no one without the sense of smell has ever complained to him regarding its influence on his sex impulse. I am not informed as to whether the want of the sense of touch has any influence on the instinct. However, inasmuch as the tactual sense is apparently only of secondary importance in persons otherwise normal and since the sex instinct makes its appearance long before sexual contact takes place, this defect may easily be disregarded. Similarly we cannot give primary importance to the sense of taste since it participates in sex long after the first awakening of the sex instinct, in kissing, at most; we might thus assume by analogy that none of the senses are a preliminary condition for the arousing of the sex instinct.

From all of which it follows that no single sense organ, regarded as of chief importance in the sex instinct of human being, is absolutely necessary for the stimulation of the sex impulse.

Any one of the sense organs may be missing without the sex instinct showing any qualitative aberration. However, since we must assume that the heterosexual instinct like the other instincts may arise only when various external impressions are produced on the individual through various influences even though he be unconscious of these external impressions;—that is since these impressions are distinct, we may draw the further conclusion that several sense organs participate in the sex instinct of man. At any rate, we may explain it best by saying that any one of the sense organs may be lacking without changing the direction of the instinct. For it may be regarded as an impossibility for one organ to take on the various activity of another one missing, (*e. g.,* the eye), if it does not also support the eye under the normal conditions to distinguish between external objects. It is impossible to assume such a capacity in the blind and at the same time deny it in normal human beings. At most one might speak of an increased activity of the other organs in the blind but not of a new activity of the same.

Though I mentioned at the beginning of this discussion that a single sense impression is sufficient to release the sex instinct in a certain direction it does not follow that a single sense perception really does bring about the sex impulse in man. As we have seen, various sense organs participate in the instinct and various impressions are exerted on each sense organ, *e. g.,* the facial expression and the forms of the breast on the eye. I, therefore, consider it likely that numerous sense impressions, whose external sources are different in man and woman, induce the sex instinct.

Let us assume then that various preceptions set the normal sex impulse of man into action. Several of these perceptions operate on each sense organ. I shall divide them in accordance with the sense organ to which they belong and designate them as A, B, C, D. Let us assume that perceptions A and B strike the sense of sight, C the auditory sense and D the olfactory sense. Then the release of sex instinct might take place as a result of perception A as well as of perception C. Thus each of these perceptions must have the same capacity for reaction.

Experience further shows that though certain sensory stimuli may be capable of awakening the sex instinct, the impulse towards the sex act may disappear if other stimuli are not in sympathy with first one. A few examples will elucidate this point.

A huntsman goes into the woods and imitates the call of the female deer, the doe, in order to awaken the sex instinct of the male deer, the roe-buck. The roe will follow this call, but the moment he sees the huntsman he will surely take to flight. For the voice it heard was merely one perception, let us say perception C, which indeed could awaken the sexual instinct. In order to permit the real performance of the sex act it would be necessary for all the other perception, A, B, C, to establish the truth of the call, sense C perception. This, for example, would be the case if the roe-buck should see the doe from whom the call originated. However, when it perceives that the call has been uttered by an individual not belonging to its own species, the roe will not express any sex impulse toward the latter. Of course, at the sight of the huntsman the instinct of flight is also added. But there can be no doubt whatsoever even in the absence of the latter, that the roe will not be induced to perform the sex act with the huntsman from whom the imitatory call of the doe had come.

Let us consider another case. Any man with a normal sex instinct will feel himself drawn to a woman with a beautiful face. Assuming that the woman's body is covered with unsightly hair, the uncovering of her body will quench the sex impulse of a normal man. This ensues because the sense impression A, which stands for the perception of the face through the eye, is not in sympathy with the second impression B, that of the breast. Instead of a soft feminine body, he perceives a hairy more masculine one, so that the second impression is not

B, but B_1. Finck speaks of the panaceas against love and in that connection mentions a procedure which has already been advocated by Ovid, who in this respect will surely be regarded as an authority by everyone. Ovid counsels lovers who would be cured of their love to scrutinize the features of their loves with the utmost severity. ''Ask of her that she talk when you know that she has no skill in the art of conversation, that she dance though you know of her deficiency in gracefulness, that she tell merry tales when you know that she has bad teeth.'' These remedies rest on the assumption that a disharmony will be created not suited to lover's mode of reaction, *i. e.*, when the stimuli A, B, C, D, are suited to the mode of reaction of the man it should be pointed out to him as boldly as possible that one or several of these stimuli do not stand the test of scrutiny so that his entire reaction complex may no longer be directed towards the female in question.

Should the sense impressions, not in conformity with the whole, fail to reach the consciousness of the individual so that he never learns about them, they will, of course exert no influence upon him. Thus, when he never learns that the girl's body is covered with thick black hair, his passion will not be extinguished, but will remain sufficiently active through the sense impression A. We sometimes come across such cases. There are a large number of male prostitutes who have feminine features and who dress like women in order to attract men. As soon as the victim observes that he is dealing with a man, his passion will die down. He will not have the impulse to perform the sex act with the other man. However, if he should fail to notice it, and he, somehow, is misled, it is possible that his passion should remain warm. The very same is true of those instincts which are misled by a sense deception, but which function well after an animal becomes aware of the deception. Thus geese and hens will sit on white stones shaped like eggs, fish will be baited by insect-like objects, and blue-bottle, deceived by their smell of carrion, will sometimes lay their eggs into the blossoms of Stapoli. Similar sense deception also occur in bees as was long ago observed by Dzieron and Berlepsch. Also, as in spiders, who may be deceived by a small ball of cotton and which they will carefully tend as though it were a little pouch of eggs. The strange profession of male prostitution has been built on the tendency of the instinct in men to be led astray. These male prostitutes, who because of their feminine features or because they developed them, will attempt to lure men to come with them. They are frequently homosexuals and as their own impulse is usually directed towards intercourse with normally inclined men, not with other homosexuals, they will do everything possible to attract such normally inclined men. They thus kill two birds in one shot, so to speak. For they not only earn money but also have sexual gratification. Let me cite here a few examples of such men, a number of whom I had occasion to observe.

Case XV. Mr. T. R., 31 years of age, artist. His mother is still living, his father dead. He has no brothers nor sisters. He can give no positive information regarding mental or nervous troubles, suicides, drunkenness, in his family. As far as his father is concerned he suspects that he, too, had been homosexual. He presumes this from the many stories his mother told; according to which his father had frequently brought young men to the house.

From his childhood T. R. had an inclination toward men. This tendency he first became aware of at the age of seven. When he was a child he liked to dress up in girls' clothing and play with dolls. At school he was called a "sissy" because he would only play with girls. At 14, when living in a city in central Germany, he was one day addressed by a man while walking on the street. He was asked to come along with this fellow. He went to his house where they both masturbated each other. This was the first sexual act which T. R. performed. On that occasion he had both an erection and an ejaculation. He cannot state, however, whether the fluid ejaculated had been semen. Shortly afterwards he took to art. One day while somewhat drunk he was accosted by two men who asked him to come up to their room. He was there seduced to passive pederasty and abused by both men. T. R. believes that he had felt pain the second time, but he cannot remember very well. A short time after, he was used for immoral purposes by an officer who had taken him up to his rooms. T. R. has occasionally continued these practices further. At a private masquerade ball which he recently attended he came dressed up as a woman, as was his custom on such occasions. He was actually taken for such and much admired. Finally a man came up to him and proposed to him in no uncertain terms. When T. R. openly confessed to him that he was a man, the other person would by no means retire. On the contrary, he said that it made no difference to him, and they should stay together. Consequently they performed *immissio* in os and pederasty, T. R. taking the passive part. Pederasty, of all acts, he likes best, while fellatio as a whole is displeasing to him. He has no strong sexual libido, and performs sexual intercourse only seldom. Usually when he takes a passive part in pederasty he almost always imagines himself to be a woman. The thought of being a woman also occupies him in day time. Often it is not even necessary for his partners to touch his penis with their hands, for the excitement during passive pederasty is sometimes sufficient to cause a flow of semen.

Several times T. R. has had intercourse with men who did not at all suspect that he was a man. Since he himself had an inclination towards men who were not perverse he had to dress up in woman's clothes and appear as a woman. He very much liked the idea of being mistaken for a woman on the street. He would go with them to a hotel. When asked for exact details how he performed the sex act he said that it was performed by introducing the penis of the other into his mouth. Or he placed his hand between his thighs and in this manner encloses the other person's penis. Through his woman's dress he has already come in conflict with the law. He was convicted to 14 days in jail for gross misdemeanor since it is forbidden for men to be dressed in women's clothes.

T. R. had never as yet found any sexual gratification with a female. He had tried it several times, having been first induced to it by his two friends, who knowing of his propensity, had told him to go to a woman. He did so, but he did not feel any excitement, not even having an erection.

Sometimes he has erotic dreams at night accompanied

by pollutions. On those occasions he dreams that he is really a woman and that he performs coitus like a woman. Now and then the content of these dreams change somewhat, but they are always of a perverse nature.

T. R. can sing falsetto very clearly. Two years ago, it is true, he suffered with his voice through a cold. All kinds of local treatment have availed little, as staying in different spas. Previously, as he stated he had a purely feminine voice so that no one could suspect his identity. He does not whistle, nor does he smoke, except sometimes in fun. He drinks beer, however. He likes sweet things very much, though not so much recently as heretofore. He also likes to do woman's needlework. He likes to do crochet work, mends his own stockings and also sews his female clothes, which he wears to masquerade balls. He learned sewing from a relative who was a seamstress.

Dr. Flatau's examination of the larynx shows a strongly developed Adam's apple and perfectly masculine condition as a whole.

Case XVI. Mr. P. B., 30 years of age, artist, a male prostitute. He looks very much younger than his age indicates. He is himself aware of this and is vain enough to understate his age. He comes from a small town. There he attended school and at the age of 14 came to live with an uncle in a large city. He was to learn a trade there, but did not like staying on one place. He, therefore, left his relatives and finally came on the stage as a lady-comedian, after having for a short time studied the art of the theatre at an institute.

P. B. is the son of an official, his father had died of

pneumonia, he had been hot-tempered. His mother is dead, too, and is said to have died of some affection of the chest. She had often complained of headaches, had sometimes suffered from vertigo for days at a time and could not see for some time. These three complaints are said to have occured at the same time to her. Most probably she was suffering from hemicrania with visual disturbances. As far as his relatives are concerned no hereditary taints can be established.

At school he had an indefinite yearning for men. When he used to take walks with his father he would always turn around to look at big strong men. As a child he had no inclination towards young boys. He had observed the first sign of this inclination towards men when he was ten years of age. He never played with other boys, only with girls. But he had never played with the girl's genitals. What he liked best was to play the "father-mother-baby" game on those occasions, even though girls took part in the game he would always play the mother and a girl would have to play the man. P. B. began to play with his genitals at the age of 12. He recollects that at the time a large structure was being built in his home town at which Italian workers were employed. Several of these lived at his father's home and among them one to whom he always felt himself attracted. The Italian of large and strong build wore a thick moustache. He was always kind to P. B. but not seldom drunk. It was especially on those occasions that P. B. would come over to him and take hold of his genitals. The Italian let him do it and always joked about the boy's genitals. Finally they did it almost every day. P. B., however, did not as yet have any seminal flow, but he did have

erections. He performed the sexual act with the other
one in bed without any clothes on. Intercourse consisted
merely in mutual masturbation. When this affair with
the Italian had come to an end P. B. felt very unhappy.
''For a long time I did not associate with any one and I
imagined myself all alone in the world and very unhappy. Whenever I saw two men walking together I
envied them their happiness.''

Later he began to associate with a waiter, Mr. S. This
happened when he was about 16 years of age. While
having intercourse with this man, P. B. had an ejaculation for the first time. He and the waiter used to sleep
in the same bed almost every night for several months.
P. B. believes that S. had performed sexual intercourse
with him only to please him for S. was not homosexually
inclined and had never asked him for money. Every
time he asked him to come with him the waiter tried to
persuade him to go to women and not to associate with
him any longer. Intercourse consisted in P. B. touching S. in every possible way, which gratified the former
very quickly. He especially emphasized his ejaculations
which ensued very quickly. He believes that it was sufficient for a man to be near him who excited him sexually
for erection and ejaculation to take place immediately.
This might occur even several times a day, sometimes
even as high as seven or eight times. This rapidity of
ejaculation had always existed and still exists at the
present time. He has only to think of the genitals of a
man sympathetic to him for ejaculation to take place.
After associating for a few months he and S. parted
company. After having affairs with several men he
made friends with another artist with whom he prac-

ticed active pederasty. This act satisfied P. B. completely and caused him an extraordinary orgasm. He could
never be induced to be an active partner in pederasty.
Active pederasty he had learned from the other. He had
never thought about it. He has never felt any pain in
active pederasty. After a time he was induced to become
the passive partner. They made the attempt but the
act was very painful to him. Both of them, were gratified because while the other performed pederasty on
him he was also masturbated by the other. It was at this
time that he noticed himself suffering from shivers in
his whole body. His legs would begin to shake and
would sink down under him. Consequently he discontinued his sexual practices for some time, ascribing to
them the cause of his nervous ailments. Afterwards he
became acquainted with another man with whom he had
sexual intercouse too. He again tried pederasty but soon
discontinued it finding more pleasure in mutual masturbation. In this act it is necessary for P. B. to touch the
other man's thigh with his genitals.

At the present time he has a strong attachment, "But
when I see a handsome fellow I will run after him behind my friend's back." The present friend is 23 years
old. The latter previously had relationships with girls
but only seldom. At present he had nothing to do with
girls. Nevertheless, P. B. believes that his friend, whom
he also supports, is not an urning.

P. B. has a great partiality for heterosexual men. He
had several occasions of having intercourse with them,
when he walked about the street dressed as a woman to
lure men. In order to avoid the suspicion of being a
man he would tell the victim that he had his menses so

that he cannot perform the act in normal fashion. Intercourse would then take place by P. B. introducing
the man's penis into his own mouth. He also assures
me that he deceived men in another manner. He maintains that by telling bold lies and diverting the other's
attention through continuous talk, men may very often
be fooled. He also, mentions a method by which he de-
ceives men, namely, by enclosing the man's penis with
his hands. In his excitement the other one will not observe anything. He also maintains that he can dissemble
his voice so that it is mistaken for that of a woman. It
is true that he is adept at this, as I have myself found
out. He always knows how to extricate himself from a
difficult situation when he is suspected of being a man.
On such occasions he will neither go to his own rooms
nor to those of the other persons, but will somehow
manage to convince his partner that he can only satisfy
him in a different way. His usual contrivance on such
occasions is to promise to take his partner to his own
rooms, and then to explain that he had moved in only
lately, that there were some people in the house at the
time who would notice their coming in and who would
make some trouble for him with the landlord. He then
tries to excite the other man's libido, so that he will be
satisfied with any form of gratification. Then they usually take a cab where they perform the act. P. B. playing
with the other one's penis.

At the age of 21, P. B. also had relationship with a
girl, who was infatuated with him. They were often together; but he did not find any satisfaction in it. On the
first nights in which he was together with the girl, no
sexual intercourse whatsoever had taken place between

them. Later erection took place only when she fondled his genitals for a long time while he at the same time thought of a man. He always imagined that he had performed the act with a man. The more he was together with the girl the quicker the act came off. Habit possibly helped him along. After some time, however, he began to loathe this intercourse with the girl and he therefore put an end to it. He had no sexual intercourse with any other girl.

As a child P. B. had never taken part in wild games of boys. As already mentioned he preferred to play with girls. He especially liked to play with dolls and to cook. The latter is still his favorite pastime. He smokes only very seldom because it makes him nauseous. He drinks only light beer, and is indifferent to other alcoholic beverages. He whistles only badly. As a whole he shows many feminine movements. He wears a wig, most of his hair having fallen out. Dr. Flatau's examination of the larynx shows the Adam's apple to be well developed and as a whole he shows masculine laryngeal conditions throughout. When he does not dissemble, his voice is that of a normal man.

From the discussion we have obtained the following results: In man several sense organs are capable of releasing the impulse towards the opposite sex; as a primary importance in normal human beings is the visual perception. The olfactory sense, too, perhaps plays a more important role than is commonly assumed, the various odoriferous substances emanating from man and woman being a stimulus for the opposite sex. In as much as unpleasant odors may check the impulse it does not seem possible a priori that sympathetic odors, too, should play a part. In addition to these we also have the auditory sense, and the sense of touch. Almost nothing is known about the effect of the gustatory sense. It is also difficult to decide whether the tactual and auditory senses are themselves normally capable of exciting the sex impulse. At any rate, we have seen that the several organs complement each other mutually, as in the deaf and blind.

Something else to be taken into consideration is the fact that innumerable impressions impinge upon each sense organ. Let us assume for the sake of illustration that the four sense organs (eye, ear, nose, touch) each perceive two perceptions: AB, through the visual sense, CD through the auditory sense, EF through the sense of smell, and GH through the tactual sense. Each of these perceptions whose source is in woman may then cause such a reaction in man that his sex impulse towards woman will be released, even when only one of these perceptions takes place, through the activity of his imagination—often quite unconsciously complementing the missing sense perception. However, if after the perception of H, one of the others, *e.g.*, B, should be lacking, then the sex instinct will not be aroused. This is so when a man is attracted by the face of a male prostitute but is immediately repelled again at the sight of his masculine body. The same trial may be followed through in a similar way not only in single perceptions by the same sense organ but also in perceptions by different sense organs. From this it follows that A, B, C, D, E, F, G, H, stand in a definite relationship to one another, or rather, that the modes of reaction which follow upon ABCDEFGH, stand in a real connection with each other.

This connection is partly acquired, partly inherited. Though it is true that much is complemented in life, nevertheless, we have to consider the influences of heredity here too. An example from the animal world will show the connection of the perceptions of two sense organs. The stallion becomes sexually excited by the odor of the mare in heat. In addition he is also excited by the sight of the mare. At least this condition is preliminary for the mating instinct. When the exciting smell comes from an animal other than the mare the stallion has no impulse to cover the latter when he perceives it. Thus in the breeding of mules, the stallion is deceived by first allowing him to get excited by the smell of the mare in heat and then substituting a she-ass so that he shall not see it. Inasmuch as the animal does not perceive the deception the act occurs as though he saw the mare, *i.e.,* the mere odor of the she-ass excited him so that he covers her. What happens to the stallion is what in a sense happened to Jacob when his father-in-law placed Leah into his bed instead of Rachel —a deception which Jacob discovered only in the following morning. If the stallion should perceive by his sight that a she-ass has been brought to him contrectation would be put to an end. Here the perceptions by two sense organs complement each other. The reaction to each of the perceptions is contrectation. However, since the latter finally lays claim to the actual or the illusory presence of the source-stimuli for both sense organs, it follows that there must exist a connection between the reactive capacities towards olfactory and visual stimuli. And, inasmuch as we know that in the stallion contrectation is inherited not acquired, and that he

recognized the species "horse" and its sex by means of these two named sense organs, not through instruction but through heredity, we must regard this association between the reactive capacities as inherited. Since we are dealing here with unconscious processes it is difficult to conceive this as an inherited association. Perhaps an example might clarify it somewhat. When we think of a consonant chord the sensation of harmony appears to us as an inherited mode of reaction. Similarly the reactive capacity towards every single tone is inherited. It is not mere chance that certain chords strike us as pleasurable, while others give us a feeling of displeasure. It depends rather on internal relationships which exist between the reactive capacities towards the various ones. So let us think of these chords now striking one organ, the ear, as being divided and so striking several organs. This will then better enable us to conceive the inherited reactive capacity of man towards stimuli of the opposite sex as an integral complex of individual reactive capacities. We cannot establish what the nature of the inherited disposition towards these reactions is, yet, we may assume that it has its anatomical basis in the nervous system, though in itself it is unconscious.

However, we may very well compare this disposition with inherited dispositions towards other reactions, *e.g.*, instinctive actions; but we shall not bicker about whether they are to be designated as congenital, unconscious, or inherited, ideas. We have already referred to inherited ideas and I will repeat again that we shall not quarrel about the question whether one is to regard unconscious purposes in instincts as unconscious ideas. Whoever

lays great weight on unconscious purpose will, for example, see such purpose in the migratory instinct of
birds, where the seeking for better food conditions in
far-off countries is to be considered. In the sex instinct
this unconscious idea of purpose will correspond to reproduction through coitus. And now we come upon a
different meaning of "unconscious ideas." The above
mentioned couples of the various reactive capacities
must have an anatomical basis in the brain, as already
mentioned. However, we can have no clearer conception of it nor of its psychical equivalent. We can only
say that in man the reactive capacities towards the various specific stimuli of the woman, and in woman the
reactive capacities towards the various specific stimuli
of the man, represent a complex of reactive capacities.
Now this complex of reactive capacities towards specific
stimuli emanating from the opposite sex (when we regard
it as inherited) may also be regarded as an unconscious,
inherited psychical process. One may go further even and
conclude that the idea of the other sex is inherited or unconscious. I shall not dispute this concept. One should,
however, not misunderstand it, as it is only necessary
that the reactive capacity be inherited. In a similar
manner instincts have been called inherited memory. Inasmuch as the concept of "memory" is very commonly
connected with something else, namely, with the trea-
sury of consciously accumulated ideas, which may later
be reproduced, the word "memory" like the word "idea"
may not without further ado be applied in this sense.
In order to avoid any misunderstandings, I will talk only
of reactive capacities. Among other reasons I have also
made mention of this because Wilhelm Haacke in his

interesting work also makes reference to sex instinct. He speaks of an olfatory memory, of auditory memory, of visual memory by which he designated the capacities acquired through many generations, producing the release of the sex instinct.

In regards to these reaction complexes we have further to consider that it is not necessary to regard as inherited the whole complex of reactive capacties, which the individual may express later. On the contrary, excitations through certain sense impressions may also be added as a result of acquired associations. Often one cannot determine where the two meet. Experience, however, shows that stimuli which at first have no effect whatsoever may gradually produce it. I have already referred to the possibility of a primary effect of the olfactory sense. Many who have experienced love will surely have convinced themselves of its secondary importance. After the inclination has already been deeply established every stimulus which emanates from the beloved person will be regarded as excitable, such as the perspirations of the skin coming from her, objects that belong to her, etc. Nevertheless there are a definite number of inherited associations among the various reactive capacities.

It is true that in general the latter complexes are the same in the individuals of the same sex in each species. But they also show certain individual differences. In some human beings, furthermore, they seem to be less sharply developed than in others. In the following chapter I shall go into further detail regarding such incomplete reaction complexes. However, let me mention here that some sex perversions probably rest on these in-

herited and incomplete complexes of reactive capacities.
To bring an example: let A be the impression of the
features,B, that of the rest of the body of Y, striking
the visual sense of X; let C, D, be other sense impressions which under normal conditions lead to sexual stimulations. Let us further assume that only the reactivity
towards A, C, D, is inherited. When perceptions ACD
takes place it is of no importance to X whether B (feminine body) or B1 (masculine body) is present in Y, the
object of X's sex impulse. Here we might include some
cases of psychosexual hermaphroditism, in which, for
example, the sight of the face causes excitement. While
the normal man feels himself attracted to a feminine
face, but is repelled when he perceives that the feminine
face belongs to a man, there are sexually perverse persons who feel no revulsion under such circumstances.
This results from the fact that in psychosexual hermaphrodites the reactive capacity B is not included in the
inherited complex. It will therefore be of no significance to him whether or not masculine or feminine
stimuli (B or B1) are added to the sense impression A,
the feminine face. It is my opinion that in this way
many a sexual perversion will best be cleared up. Some
examples might serve to illustrate this discussion.

The following case concerns a man with psychosexual
hermaphroditism. He is excited only by boys from 13
to 18 and by mature female persons. In him olfactory
sense plays certain roles. He himself is entirely of a
masculine build.

Case XVII. Mr. S. T., 22 years of age, student. His
father died of apoplexy, his mother is still alive and in
good health; but she is nervous and easily excitable and

pensities. One cannot safely ascertain whether there is common exciting cause in the whole of J. K.'s condition, whether it depends on the woman being spellbound or in a submissive state. It is only to be pointed out that certain conditions which are in part psychical exert a sexually exciting influence upon him. Among these are to be reckoned a certain helplessness in the object of his love. It might well be due to this that pity so very often is a source of sexual excitement.

Case XVIII. Mr. J. K. 24 years of age, is said to come from a healthy family. He is a neurasthenic and so distracted that for years he has been unable to do any work. In his own opinion this neurasthenia is due to his masturbatory practices. His inclination is directed towards boys. We shall see, however, that it is connected with peculiar complications. The first appearance of homosexual sensations, as he says, occured in his fifth year. He remembers that at this age he had a strong inclination towards another boy while attending kindergarten. But he does not recall whether the genitals played any role in that connection. No masturbatory practices as yet took place. At the age of eight, however, he experienced a pronounced excitation in the genitals when he thought of a boy whom he had befriended, after having been seduced to the practice of masturbation by a boy of his own age. He has continued these practices quite regularly up to the present. At the age of 13 he had made an attempt to discontinue this habit but his will power was so weak that it was quite impossible for him to do so. The youngsters to whom J. K. feels himself drawn must be of a fine build and beautiful face. They must not be less than 6 nor more than 14 years of age. Whenever he sees or thinks of a boy sympathetic to his desires he would like to embrace him, kiss him and practice mutual onanism with him. As a matter of fact, he has not practiced mutual masturbation more than twice up to the present. Once with the school-boy above-mentioned, at the age of seven and the second time when he was 14 years of age with another boy whom he loved very passionately.

Otherwise J. K. practiced masturbation by himself. In this connection he usually saw in his imagination a man and a woman performing coitus. Hereby the woman had always to be in a position of constraint. He had an especial pleasure in imagining Zeus performing coitus with one of the many maidens he had seduced and forced to lie with him. Or that one of the boys beloved by him performed coitus with a girl. J. K. also found a certain pleasure in thinking that he had sensual delights with the boy he loved.

Seven months ago, J. K. consulted a naturopath, who advised him to practice coitus. Following this advice he went to a prostitute. He was then 24 years of age. He was sexually potent that time, but only after exerting much strength and much power of imaginations. He imagined the sex act between a man and a woman as he often had done in connection with masturbation. The second and third times the performance was much easier and the fourth time it was not necessary to imagine anything. Beginning with the third attempt there cropped up in him a certain impulse towards women; erection took place without the aid of the imagination and a long time before the coitus. In the first place his homosexuality diminished so that he thought himself normal again when he performed coitus for the sixth time. But his neurasthenic complaints did not leave him. He had the misfortune of catching gonorrhea at this sixth coitus and it made its appearance with numerous complications. The regular treatments lasted for about three months and the homosexual symptoms returned in their fullest extent. This occured fourteen days after the last coitus without his having at all masturbated. Four weeks after the last sex act when the gonorrhea made its appearance he had to masturbate frequently for weeks at a time because his sexual excitement was very great.

After three months the gonorrhea was cured and J. K. could again attempt coitus. In the subsequent two months he performed it ten times without the least improvement to his psychical conditions. The homosexuality and the neurasthenia continued as before. At the time he had practiced coitus he had not masturbated, but as the new heterosexual intercourse did not improve his condition he has given up all hope of ever getting well.

The following case also concerns a man who is attracted only to men without beard and then also to semi-mature girls, but the homosexual element is the **stronger**. It is remarkable, at any rate that he is attracted only to such female persons whose breasts are not fully developed. Unlike many other cases, he is not indifferent to their bodily construction, while the contrary, J. K. likes a somewhat masculine body in the female person. We have here then a mode of reaction, AB., in which A would represent feminine features and B a masculine body, or at least not a typically feminine one. No other stimuli besides those operating on the eye can be ascertained. At any rate, we have here a very clear mode of reaction to feminine stimuli in spite of the strongly developed homosexuality. This is the case in regards to the stimulus which is exerted by the face. The fact that all signs of beard-stubble must be absent in a man to attract him, or that at most, only a light down is acceptable, show that in the masculine L. H. the reactive capacities are not those of a normal woman. On the other hand, other feminine qualities in a man repel him. Equally well pronounced is the lack of the normal reactive capacity towards the stimuli of the feminine body. At all events, we have here an aberration from the normal reactive capacity of the man as well as that of the woman. The normal complex of reactive capacity is disturbed.

Case XIX. Mr. L. T. 28 years of age, had a higher education; shows slight hereditary taints. One of his uncles is epileptic. To his knowledge there are no cases of homosexuality in his family. His father died from old age several years ago, but had still been potent in his early seventies. His mother is still alive and in good health. L. T. makes a masculine appearance throughout, has a normal growth of beard, powerful voice and a low masculine timbre. He likes very much to sing and has a bass voice. In his other habits he does not show anything feminine. He is fond of several sport activities, especially rowing. He is not very fond of alcoholic drinks and drinks only very little. Occasionally he drinks a glass of beer but without much pleasure. He likes to smoke. He dresses very simply. There are no signs of feminine vanity.

His appearance is normal. The body and the genitals are covered with a rich growth of hair; but sometimes in homosexual intercourse he has a deficient erection so that he has a premature ejaculation as soon as their bodies come in contact with each other. His change of voice occurred at the normal age. He whistles well and is fond of whistling, especially when alone. Though he knows how to dance he learned only because it seemed proper for social reasons. He has never found pleasure therein, nor does he have any interest in music.

In regards to other qualities, L. T. says that he is rather a good cook. He believes, however, that this has some relation to the fact that he is a gourmet and is thus more interested in the preparation of foods. He is also interested in hunting and politics.

In general L. T. is taken for a very frank person and yet he believes himself to be the most refined and slyest of liars as soon as the conversation turns to sex. "How often have I regaled the company with the story of adventures of a heterosexual nature which I have never lived through! No famous coquette was unknown to me, the most refined method of gratification is not new to me. In short, I acquired the reputation of a veritable Don Juan among my friends on account of my lies. I would tell obscene jokes. I had an extensive talent for fabrications of this sort. I myself never began a conversation but when the topic was brought up, I showed myself as a man. Because of these lies, I was never suspected of being homosexual."

L. T. complains much of headaches and other neurasthenic troubles. Suicidal thoughts are strange to him, yet he has only very little joy of living.

Up to now he has never had occasion to have intercourse with persons other than those standing socially below him. He believes that he always feels such a revulsion towards the persons in question that he would pay them doubly in order that they disappear as quickly as possible.

In his childhood, L. T. had much occasion to play with

boys and girls. At first, as a result of a conversation with his schoolmates and also as a result of being often in the company of his sisters' girl-friends, he had the desire to see the genitals of a girl. In order to reach this point he would wrestle with these girls. He would try everything possible to reach this goal. For example, he would ask these girls to walk up the stairs or to climb up trees. As far as he can recall no reaction took place then. At the age of 15 a school friend seduced him to the practice of masturbation. He attempted it; but even in spite of an effort lasting for a quarter of an hour he failed to induce an erection. Similarly the attempt of a waitress to have intercourse with him remained fruitless. He could not get an erection. At the age of 16 he went to live in a boarding-school. Suddenly, without any seduction or occasion for it, he began to feel a strong friendship for comrades sympathetic to him. Tall, dark-eyed fellows especially attracted him. When he was in his room with one of his friends, he would always try to kiss him upon the lips. But at first he would only do so when his friend fell asleep on the sofa, which usually happened in the summer. L. T. does not believe that he would have been able to satisfy his desire when his friends were awake. One night, when he was 16 years of age, he dreamed that a friend was lying in bed with him and that he pressed this friend to his heart and that he kissed him passionately. This dream occasioned a voluptuous feeling such as he had never before felt. It was followed by his first pollution. He sought the beautiful sensation that he had experienced in his dream and in the dull light of the night-lamp he regarded the features of his sleeping ideal, a boy of about 16. Rubbing his penis with the bed-linen he began to masturbate.

For several months L. T. gave himself up to these masturbatory practices, without the intervention of his hands. He also practiced it every evening. After some time he had to do a great deal of school-work. He did not go to bed before twelve o'clock, having at the same time to rise very early, so that he had very little occasion to masturbate. During his two last years at the high school, he was entirely free from this practice. When he went to the university he found his first opportunity to perform coitus between the thighs. He did it with a boy of 16 who was a male prostitute, who in L. T.'s eyes appeared like an ideal lover. But in the complete passivity, L. T., failed to find what he sought for in this young man who sold himself for money. Nevertheless, during his years at the university he allowed himself such intercourse at the rate of two to three times weekly and though he did not find what he desired yet after each performance of the act he felt satisfied, strengthened and better inclined for study.

During his college years, L. T. had often accompanied his comrade to the brothels and had also made fruitless attempts at coitus with girls of from sixteen to eighteen. Since no erection took place, these attempts ended in ejaculation between the girl's thighs, while he imagined to have intercourse with a boy. He could never achieve an immission of the penis into the vagina.

With older women who were provided with well developed breasts, etc., L. T., could not have any ejaculation even with the aid of his imagination, for a fully developed woman repelled him as much as a fully grown man, no matter how handsome he might be. His inclination is essentially restricted to youths of 16 to 20 whom he supposes to be sexually potent. The main condition is that they have a tall, powerful body, a youthful, unshaved face. He is attracted by a flimsy down on the upper lip. On the other hand, he has no liking for any man, no matter how handsome he might be, if he already shows traces of beard. His chief pleasure, he says, lies in stroking the yet soft or sparsely downy cheeks.

"The young men with whom I go around must have a soft and fresh skin and their faces must be intelligent. I find great pleasure in upperclass men from the high school, though, as yet, I have not had any opportunity to have sex intercourse with them. Nay, I must avoid their company at all costs in order not to be tempted to seduce them in my uncontrollable urge. I always take pains to be as uncongenial as possible in the company of these youngsters. As soon as these fellows grow up I still hold their friendship, for as soon as they no longer attract me sexually my behavior towards them becomes totally changed. If these persons would only know how hard it had sometimes been for me, when they were of a certain age, to behave properly in their presence, how painful it was for me not to tell them of my gnowing love for them! Due to these inner battles with myself I feel that I have grown to be an old man psychically."

The mode of gratifying his love has remained the same for L. T. He restricts himself to performing coitus between the thighs, and whenever possible, in a well illuminated room, so that he may be enabled to view the features of the person giving himself to him, and to cover this person with kisses. He obtains the greatest pleasure by mutual friction of the bodies, causing erection and ejaculation, but this happens only seldom.

"Such an occurrence is the cause of great joy and happiness in my dull days." He does not find any pleasure
in any form of gratification, nor does he believe that any
other form of satisfaction existed for him. Mutual masturbation or being masturbated by another person is
extremely unpleasant to him, and as a whole, being
touched in his own genitals by anyone, no matter how
sympathetic the other person might be, is utterly revolting to him. Nay, it may even result in complete impotence.

"In some foreign city," L. T. relates, "out of despair
for not being able to find any suitable person, I had to
be satisfied in practicing mutual masturbation with a
young fellow. And after all kinds of artifices used by
this quite experienced boy I did achieve an ejaculation,
but without feeling any satisfaction in it. I felt quite
disgusted when it was all over and even up to the present time. Although I might be suffering very much from
sexual excitement, I never could make up my mind to
repeat this experience. In another city I often sought
gratification in friction of the penis which was practiced upon me by the members of the male demi-monde
with whom I became acquainted, but it was never successful. On the other hand, a brief and intimate embrace on the part of the same fellow was capable, when
we were naked, to induce a complete and satisfactory
ejaculation in a few minutes and without much effort.
I have never tried pederasty because it makes me sick,
I am convinced, however, that should I find an ideal
young man, who would perform coitus between the
thighs out of love for me I would also permit him to
perform active pederasty upon me out of gratitude."

L. T. has had many occasions to find young men who

sold their love for money. But the very thought that it was a matter of money with them prevented him from really feeling satisfied and has destroyed his fondest illusions. In spite of many efforts he has been unable up to the present to discover any other young men who would be congenial to him and who is similarly disposed. At least, he did not find any of the right age he desired.

"From the very beginning all signs of effeminacy in the young man of the male demi-monde have repelled me. A falsetto voice, especially has been repugnant to me. Contact with such persons even brought about complete impotence of coition. As a whole, feminine airs and graces in a man have always repeplled me."

At the age of 24, L. T. completed his studies and went to live in a city in Austria. He has made a name for himself in the field of science and received many honors. He is very much engrossed in his academic profession. "I have also achieved economic success, in short, all external conditions which would qualify me to be the happiest of men, if it were not for this curse of homosexuality which oppresses me. An evil fate which compels a free and open man to go through life a hypocrite and a liar, forced to renounce the happiness of founding a family."

L. T. is very much liked by ladies. He is a great friend of children and when he is in their presence he doubly feels the want of a family of his own. His friendship to persons who do not attract him sexually is confident and constant.

There is nothing feminine in his habits and he believes that only one quality, at most, points in that direction, namely his bashfulness. Though he practices sex intercourse only when completely naked and in a well-lit room, yet, undressing in the presence of the other person is always displeasing to him.

For the last few years he has had occasion in a town near his domicile to practice sex intercourse frequently with a young man upon whose discretion he could rely. Previously, though he had many occasions to, he had never asked the person in question to do the act with him. But after having been exposed to many attempts of extortion on the part of other young men, he changed his attitude of reserve and finally performed coitus between the thighs with this fellow. "The person in question gives in to my wishes only reluctantly and merely out of thankfulness and devotion, and for shame I cannot look into his face for several days afterwards. Often I have succeeded in restraining myself for weeks in order to keep away from him, but then a moment comes upon me when I must go to see him and ask him to lie down with me. A few embraces and kisses are sufficient to bring about ejaculation and orgasm and cause me the greatest pleasure. This will strengthen me for weeks and enable me to find joy in my work. I shrink from asking him to perform the act with me, as I know that he does not like it, for he is completely heterosexual. I always hope that one day I should be able to free myself from him and that 1 should perhaps rather have intercourse with a homosexual. It is in fact displeasing to me that the person in question should please me merely because of his attachment to me. The greatest pleasure to me, however, would be if I should be able to become normal myself, to be a happy husband and father, and to be able to look back with horror upon my earlier sexual sensations."

In the last few years L. T. was able to repress his rather strong sexual impulses by vigorously practicing gymnastics. He gratifies his sex only about once monthly. He fears that his social position would be endangered if he should cause any suspicion and this makes him proceed with the greatest caution.

In the last few years his dreams have been exclusively of a homosexual content, but he recalls that before the onset of puberty they had been heterosexual.

"My 'dread of women' is apparent only in relation to intercourse with completely mature women. However, if her breasts are not as yet developed, the features still youthful, and the behaviour that of a flapper, then I have an affection for her and even a vague sexual inclination. But many attempts in that direction have failed and only with the aid of homosexual imaginings was I enabled to perform coitus between the thighs, while the erection was too weak for immission of the penis. I admire a beautiful and clever woman as anyone else would; I like to hold a conversation with her, from time to time to let drop a few gallant words, but I am never stimulated sexually."

In the following case, too, we shall be dealing with psychosexual hermaphroditism and with an inclination which mainly expressed itself in a distinct preference for the feminine face. Here, too, the face of both girls and boys cause sexual excitement, but apparently more so in the case of the latter.

Case XX. Mr. B. L., 23 years of age, philologist. In his early youth there were signs of a perverse sexuality. His favorite occupations were always those associated with the house. His behaviour as a whole had very little of the boy in it. Up to the age of ten he used to play with dolls and would bemoan the fact that he was not born a girl. When he was 13, he had his first sexual excitement with a school-mate, by means of coitus between the thighs. From that time on the two would come together several times weekly. This continued until he was 15 years old, when he had his first intercourse with a girl. This lasted for some time, but at the same time, he also continued his practices with his school-mate, the latter affording him more pleasure. During coitus with girls he would always imagine his partner a boy. Between 18 and 20 his relations were exclusively with other boys and only afterwards did he resume his intercourse with girls and that only sparingly. In Berlin where he went at the age of 21 he learned of the wide extent of homosexuality, which until then he had considered a unique and personal experience. He began to visit male prostitutes and took them to his room, until he became acquainted with a young man with whom he had a relationship lasting some months. Suddenly, however, his beloved fell in love with another male, and he had to console himself to this loss. After some time, at the age of 22 he came upon a young man of 16, whom he still sees. They are both happy.

B. L. loves only young men of 16 to 19, without beard, with fresh, somewhat feminine, faces and strong bodies. The figure of a handsome boy in the street will immediately move him sexually. He is passionate in his expressions of love, jealous, and knows no bounds in his pleasures. With his present lover he has intercourse daily and sometimes even several times daily. Till now he has been unable to discover whether or not his friend is also homosexual.

In the following case, too, we are concerned with a

sexual excitement aroused by immature males. Also, there is present a slight inclination towards immature females.

Case XXI. Mr. D. T., 23 years of age, has a brother who seems to be normal sexually. One may assume, at most, that the latter is suffering from sexual heperesthesia. Otherwise, too, there are certain hereditary taints in the family of D. T. He has practiced masturbation from his 15th year from one to two times weekly. He does not recall having conjured mental images while so doing. Later, when he was 20, he had an inclination towards the female sex. All in all, he has performed coitus three times, each time ending in a flow of semen. Although he had a feeling of orgasm, it was not very strong. His homosexual inclinations appeared somewhat later, a few months after he began his heterosexual practices. He is especially attracted to young men between 15 and 22, and is especially fond of them when they do not as yet show any traces of beard. Altogether he has gratified himself twice by means of mutual masturbation. He also masturbated once a week, on the average. Since the age of 20, he has always imagined a male individual during the act. He cannot say that he has a disinclination towards the female sex. But he believes that his inclination to women grows constantly weaker while that towards men grows stronger.

In his childhood, D. T., behaved more like a girl, being usually in the company of girls and playing with them. He used to play with dolls and do needlework, etc. He never had any sexual dreams.

For a long time he also had other ideas. He had the desire to swallow his own urine and semen and, as he stated, he has several times eaten pieces of chocolate damped with urine. But he does not recall whether it was in any way connected with sexual sensations.

Another patient whose history I am about to relate also belongs to these psychosexual hermaphrodites. He has hereditary taints. His sexual life is somewhat complicated. He not only shows heterosexual and homosexual inclinations but also masochistic ones, experiencing a sexual excitement in his own maltreatment. He has had bisexual intercourse, *i.e.,* with male and female persons, performing normal coitus with the latter. Olfactory sensations, also, play their part in his case. His inclinations towards men, which is of main interest to us here, is directed towards individuals who have only a sparse growth of hair. Otherwise his homosexuality is very pronounced. It is the more masculine qualities which excite him in man. He is not repelled by a moustache. Soldiers, for instance, have a certain effect upon him. Thus the complex of reactive capacities is not so clearly connected with certain feminine qualities, as in feminine beardless face in other cases. On the other hand, it is to be noted that a hairy body, as is proper to a normal man, is repulsive to him.

Case XXII. Mr. C. H. is a physician. The family has marked hereditary taints. His father is dead. He was an epileptic. A brother of his father had for a long time been suffering from paranoia, characterized especially by a marked eroticism, though in normal health he had been to all appearances a very conscientious and moral sort of person. The marriage of his parents was a happy one. His mother died of phthisis. She was very hot-tempered, but reserved in the presence of strangers. Though one can not establish the existence of any sexual perversions; psychical abnormalities have also been observed in his brothers and sisters. On his father's side one can also prove hereditary taints, nervous and mental conditions.

As a child C. H. was wide-awake and spright. He was very shy in the presence of strangers. His fellow students did not like him. He was considered a spoiled child and was always said to be telling things about people. C. H. fails to see any reason for this suspicion and believes that it was caused by the fact that he liked to get away from his comrades and be with grown-ups. He could get along better with girls of his own age than with boys. He from early youth harbored suicidal thoughts, without at all being able to assign any reason for them. He believes strangely enough, that this could be done by holding in the breath, and for this reason often made such attempts. These attempts were made when he was eight years of age. From early childhood he had been suffering from palpitation of the heart which makes its appearance at the slightest emotional excitement.

At the age of seven, he was sent to a spa because of his nervousness. It was then that he had his first experience of a sexual nature. He recalls that he often used to run from the baths to the promenade to sit down on an out-of-the-way bench because workers often passed by there. Here he used to imagine the pleasure of being fastened to a tree by one of them, usually by a vigorous young man, to have his mouth gagged and then be thoroughly beaten on his naked buttocks. He can still recollect the lively and exceedingly pleasurable sexual excitement with which he used to await the passing of someone to whom he could impart his strange desire, though he did not understand it then. He would sit as if glued to the spot, for hours on end, without being able to gather enough courage to acquaint someone with these desires. The picture of the person in question is still distinct before his mind's eye. He cannot state, though, whether he had a particular person in mind. This person was supposed to wear heavy boots, linen working clothes, and a slouched hat. Such were the clothes that he often used to see there. C. H. was not as yet conscious of the sexual basis of his desires but soon after he began to masturbate. One day, in his effort to inflict some bodily pain on himself, he began to wind a piece of string around his penis and then attempted to urinate. The pain caused him to remove the thread immediately. At that time he had not as yet come upon any sort of sexual gratification.

His first voluptuous sex sensations came when he was eleven. He got the feeling while climbing a pole in his gym class at school. Thus he first began to masturbate in this manner. He would seek the aid of a horizontal bar or a railing. He practiced masturbation very frequently, even daily. His sexual desires were always very strong and though he has made several attempts to free himself from his vice, he has failed from want of willpower. C. H. cannot recall whether during masturbation there were any mental images before him, nor of what nature, if any. He is sure, however, that at the thought of being beaten on his buttocks, he has always experienced the sexual sensations above mentioned. This strange condition still prevails. He does recall that in the last few years those ideas have somewhat waned. Previously he, too, showed an inclination to tie some man to a post and to strike him on the naked buttocks. Even at present, before being beaten, he has the urge to tie his companion, to gag his mouth and then whip him mercilessly. C. H. believes, however, that the desire to beat another first plays only a very subordinate role. His only purpose in beating him so mercilessly is to bring the other into such a passionate rage that he will return the whipping with greater zeal. Early in life, when he had first begun to masturbate, he was aware of its wickedness. At that time he would think continuously of suicide because of his failure of self-control.

"Of course," says C. H., "I don't believe there was much danger in these thoughts because I was too cowardly to carry them out. It is true that before my fourteenth year I often thought of doing away with myself. At fourteen I was to be confirmed, so that I might still go to heaven. I felt that after confirmation all my sins would be counted against me. Strangely such reflections bothered me very much, although, as a matter of fact, I was sceptical about religious matters. I wanted to commit suicide before my confirmation, in case my religious beliefs proved to be false. From my 15th to 17th years I again contemplated suicide. However, I would always arrange it so, that I could change my mind at the last moment. In an attempt to hang myself, which very nearly proved fatal I had a very strong sexual excitement. After which I suspended myself for seconds at a time. These attempts always ended in masturbation."

In his 16th year he had an affair with a servant-girl in the house. She was of the same age, pretty and of a fine figure. They associated with each other almost daily for a year, but it never reached the point of coitus, partly because the girl feared the consequences, and partly because of his failure to reach the necessary stage, probably due to impotence caused by his previous masturba-

tory practices. At the present time, C. H. thinks that
in reality it was because he did not place himself in the
correct position for performing coitus, and thus did not
succeed in introducing his penis. It is true that intromission was rather difficult since the girl had not as
yet been deflorated. At ther daily meetings, C. H. tried
to excite the girl by touching and rubbing her genitals.
Only later did it become clear to him that he really masturbated the girl. This toying was usually followed by
attempts on his part to perform coitus, which, however,
were never successful, and sometimes they even resulted
in ejaculations. When the latter did not take place he
would masturbate immediately afterwards. Once he permitted the girl to masturbate him.

In his nineteenth year he made the acquaintance of a
governess. She was 18, had a fully developed figure
and was very voluptuous. C. H. tried to make the girl
fall in love with him and he succeeded in this attempt.
Although the governess was much more accommodating
than the servant-girl, he was never successful in performing coitus. In this case, too, he believes it to have
been due to his incorrect position. The fear of alleged
impotence might also have contributed to this inability
to perform coitus. When he was 23 years old, however,
he quickly succeeded in performing coitus when he visited a prostitute, who explained the correct position to
him. C. H. also found gratification in performing coitus
with the governess. He did not love either of these two
girls, but they were not repugnant to him, including his
reaction to the prostitutes. And as a matter of fact he
desired coitus with them very eagerly. But when he was
satisfied sexually, that is when he had achieved ejaculation, the thought of coitus was loathing to him. He does

not know how this thought came to him; for the repulsive odor which he has lately perceived in the prostitutes, and which is so repellent to him had never been perceptible in the two girls.

When he was 20 years old he entered the University. There he was a member of a club which enjoined upon its members to refrain from sexual intercourse. Later, at 23 when he had left the association, he had during the period of four years, performed coitus with prostitutes, about twelve times in all. These were always successful but did not give him pleasure. In particular, the smell of these creatures caused him to draw back and the loathing became so very real after the act that he was never capable of performing it a second time although he had often made up his mind to do so. It took sometime for an ejaculation to occur, especially lately. Besides he was always more exhausted after the act, than he had ever been after masturbation.

C. H. took an interest in girls when he was 15 years of age, and upon two occasions in the last four years he has had a lively interest in them. These emotions were decidedly amorous. But there the sexual element was very much in the background. "While a smart soldier or any other handsome young man can bring me to the point where erection takes place immediately, I have never observed any such feeling when with girls. What drew me towards them was their friendliness and modesty. If I had observed in them any signs of sexual excitement I would not have been pleased. I also believe that my attachment could not last long. My relationship to the two girls with whom I had had sexual intercourse was of quite a different nature. In their case I sought sexual gratification, otherwise I was quite indifferent."

His reaction to men were quite different. Aside from
the incidents in the bathing-place, he does not recall how
he reacted to men when he was at the age of 13 to 14.
However, he remembers quite well his sensation during
his 14th and 15th years. At that time he had several
school-mates and acquaintances for whom he had a very
peculiar and often quite passionate preference. He was
also conscious of the sexual basis of these attachments,
and for this reason he was always afraid lest other people knew of it. Thus he never spoke about his sexual
reactions to any of his friends, nor did he ever attempt
anything with them. On two occasions he had almost
been on the point of betraying himself; once in his student days after an excursion and a bout of heavy drinking he and a friend went to bed together. He became
so excited sexually that he could not sleep the whole
night. He believes that his friend had noticed his excitement. "However, it was either not quite clear to him
what was the matter with me, or he purposefully let it
go by." The two have never spoken about the matter,
although they associated with each other quite naturally
thereafter. C. H. loved another friend so passionately
that he would go to his house of nights and sit beneath
the garden window just to be near him. Here, too, he
used all possible precautions so as not to betray himself.
Thus he always showed himself indifferent to him. He
was greatly hurt when his friend associated more with
other fellows than with himself. This attitude could
sometimes make him jealous.

"I do not know how I should have practiced sex-inter-
course with a friend of mine, if I had the opportunity
to do it. My dearest wish was to be changed into a woman
and to perform coitus with him. I have often mastur-

bated with this idea in mind, and since its fulfillment was
impossible, I used to imagine myself in the role of a passive pederast while masturbating.''

Besides the two friends above-named, C. H. was
sexually excited also by other men. They had to be
strong, of a fresh and healthy complexion, have only a
moustache, and altogether a sparse growth of hair. Soldiers especially, but also workingmen wearing linen
trousers, could excite him sexually. Their social rank
did not concern him much. C. H. often frequented the
bathing-places in order to look at the naked figures and
at the genitals. On the whole, he does not find pleasure
in anybody at all. There have only been very few exceptions to this. A man in uniform will prove especially acceptable at all times. ''The reason that strong young
men of the lower classes play a greater role in my imagination than those of the higher classes is merely because the former are much more accessible.''

When he was 26 years of age he used to be shaved by
a 17 year old barber's apprentice. As the latter was
very handsome, C. H. developed a strong desire for him,
which has led to sexual intercourse. After inducing an
erection on the young fellow's penis he desired him to
perform pederasty on himself. But the heavy pains
caused him to desist. After this he first masturbated
the young fellow and then himself. The smell of the
semen, however, caused him such a sickness of the stomach that his love for the young man ceased at once. He
tried to masturbate him again later on but the affair
was unsuccessful and too long. He did not even permit
the boy to masturbate him. Another time in a tipsy condition C. H. again took a young man to his rooms but
dismissed him because he found him too filthy. And

once when he was sober he induced a young man to strike him and afterwards try to masturbate him. But again the process seemed endless, while the odor nauseated him to such a degree that he had to desist, so that he would not even let himself be masturbated by the other.

Lately C. H. came upon the following scheme for combining the homosexual and heterosexual. As the result of several days drinking he was not feeling quite well. He was very much excited sexually. In such a condition he desired to see a prostitute. But before he did so he met some man he knew who aroused him to even greater desire. Under the pretext that the latter should point out the house of a certain prostitute he induced him to come along. When they arrived at the house he finally had the man perform coitus with her in his presence. This excited him to the utmost so that he immediately had intercourse with the same prostitute, which caused him great pleasure.

C. H. has made frequent attempts to rid himself of the habit of masturbation. But he never succeeded in abstaining for more than four to six weeks. Yet on several occasions he was able to restrict its frequency so that he would practice it only once or twice a week for a long period of time. But this restriction took place only periodically, especially during his hours of study when he would be variously diverted in the company of his friends.

Previously he sometimes used to practice masturbation in such manner that he would sit down on the narrow-shaped corner of a sofa. By pressing against the penis he would try to prevent an ejaculation. He stated that in this manner his orgasm was greatly enhanced.

When masturbating he permits ejaculation to take place only from time to time. When it does take place, he maintains, it is only to prevent pollutions at night. Often he resolved to consult a physician in an attempt to be cured of the habit. But these resolves were never carried out. And once when he did consult a physician he did not have the courage to disclose the secrets to him. In his embarrassment he asked to have his lungs examined. He hoped that the physician would discover his anomaly without his own disclosures, and would question him accordingly, but he left without having accomplished his purpose.

Previously C. T. had frequent pollutions. He would sometimes dream of having coitus with women, but often dreamed of naked young men. At an earlier period he used also to dream about boys, with whom he would wrestle, the boys seizing his penis and he seizing theirs. He would be surprised that even in his dreams the penis of others felt exactly like his own. Surprised because he had always believed that his penis must look different on account of his sexual debaucheries. On many occasions he was conscious that he was dreaming and sometimes he tried and successfully to dispel the dream-picture in order to avoid an ejaculation in bed. The pollutions occurred very quickly without causing a great orgasm. When he found that he could no longer prevent the ejaculation he would dream that he was trying to prevent the soiling of the bed by holding the prepuce in his hand. Very often, of course, he convinced himself on awakening that this had not happened. Sometimes, however, the pollutions actually took place according to the dream. Pollutions which had been quite frequent in former years now occur only very seldom. Sometimes in his determination not to give in to himself and, as he says with great success, to prevent pollution, he would wind a thread around the penis below the testicles. He does not recall quite distinctly whether intercourse with women in his erotic dreams predominated over that with men. But he believes that the latter were the case. He is quite certain of this as regards the near past. As a whole the quantity of semen has largely diminished in the last few years so that he was suffering from atrophy of the testicles.

"I am well aware of my predicament, of the danger of losing my social position, of my very livelihood. However, I find no strength to fight my impulses. All my good resolutions were always broken. I do not place much faith in the possibility of being cured, yet, only a cure can save me. For sooner or later my activities will in the end be discovered. My outstanding mental quality, and the one which has enabled me to overcome other bad qualities, or at least to place them in the background, has failed me totally in this respect. I have always been without energy, lazy and cowardly. But with the aid of boundless ambition I have managed to appear to others a man of energy, diligence and courage.

"As far as my own judgment of my condition is concerned, I must say that for a long time I have been clearly conscious of suffering from my sexual anomaly. It is true that I did not distinctly understand certain aspects until after I had read of similar cases. This occurred about three years ago. Nevertheless, it is sometimes not quite clear to me what my reaction to women is. Perhaps my reaction is stronger or at least was previously than it now appears to me most of the time. Perhaps my present aversion to heterosexual intercourse is due to the fact that I think only of prostitutes and am afraid of becoming diseased. It may be that I would not experience such aversion as I do in the presence of a prostitute, if I were to meet with some decent women. I cannot, however, be too sure of this especially since intercourse with the former occurred so long ago and revealed to me my shortcomings.

"As regards the moral judgment of my own sexual impulses and activities I am of the opinion that the former, of course, are not criminal. For I have not willed them, but rather possess them against my will and desire. And in general, the activities of my sex impulse is nobody's business unless I were to interfere with the rights of a third party. As regards prostitutes, both male and female, there is hardly anything to debauch in them, and therefore I regard them without-the-law, which would not be the case with decent women. The latter I must avoid only because I thereby endanger my social position. I know that I must try to discontinue the practice of masturbation because it ruins me in mind and body. My self-reliance and self-esteem are very much lowered.

"I am utterly powerless to suppress my impulses to masturbate. I do regard as moral offences my relationships to the above-named servant-girl and the barber's assistant, for I may have led them on a path which may bring unhappiness to their lives. I consider my sex impulse not a crime but a misfortune. My greatest desire would be to be rid of it altogether. This would hardly be possible through castration. I would gladly undergoe such an operation if it would have such desirable results. For want of something better I would be exceedingly happy if I could at least rid my lust of homosexual intercourse and my habit of masturbation. From the removal of the former the latter would also disappear.

"My ideal is life in a small city unmolested by sexual needs and to be busy with certain favorite studies besides my professional work. I don't believe that I shall ever find any happpiness in marriage, not only for the reason aforementioned, but also because under my own material conditions I would have to stress the point of a rich wife. This alone, I am convinced, would be enough to throw a shadow on the love. Personally I do not consider myself potent any longer, and even though I were, I would nevertheless fear that my luckless morbid qualities might be inherited by my children."

In order that the "divine" interpretation of psychosexual hermaphroditism may come into its own right I shall cite here the serious communication of a psychosexual hermaphrodite who tries to justify his loves as follows:

Case XXIII. Mr. N. S. writes: I am a merchant, 26 years of age, physically normal, and of a masculine habitus altogether. I am in love with both sexes, and it is really the Divine in human beings which attracts me. For is not the divine soul of man destined for immortality, the realization of all ideals. One must therefore love the soul of man. Just as the mysteriously ticking life in a clock beckons the child so the divine soul of man (or female) beckons me. In both I love with the same fervor the thinking, feeling and therefore divinely sacred part.

Human beings form the delight of the Creator, because they are born in His image and are the blessed mirror of His blessedness. So in us too, the beloved person finds an absolute, which is objectively the delight

of the lover, and the realization of his ideals. Children
are the delight of their parents, and that for me is love.
For love is first of all objective, it is a universal truth,
and who would maintain that we should love only the
opposite sex? Well, then, the ultimate consequence of
my ideal love, which I delighted in even as a young man,
is that I also love erotically. One's ideal in human shape.

The real mechanism of the world and ideal perception,
moreover, stand in opposition to each other at the present. While I, in my free and passionate love am too in-
depen lent, too adventurous, too ideal to be able to follow merely the mechanical conception of the procreative
processes. This were, so to speak, mechanical love. For
the latter rests more on the mechanical rather than ideal
cognition, more on lustful physical desires than on the
objective recognition of a pure and ideal loveableness.
(By this the writer means the worthiness of being
loved).

Objectively, for erotic purposes, man and woman are
of equal worth, both of them for the world. Do we not
possess an abundance of ideal love for the same sex,
especially among the male sex. Let there be present
more than a certain amount of ideal love, originally lyr-
ically pure, in a male soul, and erotic love with voluptuous desire is the inevitable result. The love-intoxi-
cated soul can not find other refuge, relief and libera-
tion.

Sensual pleasure, based on exact philosophical relationships, is the goal of erotic love. A young man, too,
is glorious, and I am not such a dullard as not to perceive
it. Him, too, I can love erotically. Man, however, has
developed mechanically instead of ideally. Men are perverse, for they turn their back to the ideal world, while

their eyes look merely towards the mechanical indica-
tions of nature, deducing everything therefrom.

This dual love is the source of all universal love and
goodness, which the world so utterly lacks and which
makes it so similar to a sick-room. This dual love in
time will have to attain to this moral sublimity.

The noblest powers, Oh Plato, are permitted to lan-
guish in our times. A world-redeeming ideal is stigma-
tized! Not only from the preceding considerations, but
from everything that may prove valid I would like to
derive the point of view that pederasty is permitted by
nature, that is by God, that like every other emotion it
is freely given to human beings; therefore rejoice!

Is it permitted less to men than to women? Nonsense,
pederasty is at the least better than masturbation. In
view of all this, I am not inclined to be influenced by the
medical profession. I wish to add further that I have
loved women several times with all my passion and I
preferred women to men insofar as impetuosity and eth-
ical loftiness are concerned. There are a number of
reasons, not known to yourselves, why I prefer pederasty. I finally wish to add: In the fine sentiments one
prefers one's equal!''

The subject in the following case was previously a
homosexual but now is inclined to pederasty.

Case XXIV. Mr. M. K., 23 years of age. He has formerly practiced masturbation quite frequently, and at
the age of 14 showed an impulse towards women and
boys. At present his impulse for the female sex has become totally extinguished and only has feelings for boys
of ten to fifteen. The main condition being that they
are not pubescent. He allegedly practices intercourse
neither with women nor with boys at the present time.

Neither can he tell what manner of intercourse he prefers with boys.

M. K., like his brothers, shows a very sparse growth of hair. In the following we have an example of an exclusive inclination towards the male sex. On being repeatedly questioned, however, the patient believed that he might perhaps like to kiss an immature girl of 15 to 16.

Case XXV. Mr. I. S., 22 years of age. Mother of the patient is a very nervous woman, in fact, one may find in her family hereditary nervous taints. A relative of the mother also seems to be homosexual. I. S. has several troublesome complaints of a neurasthenic nature to make about himself. I shall not discuss in detail their nature. As far as his sexual life is concerned his memory goes back to his seventh year. At that time he liked a boy two years his junior. He used to dream about him and those dreams were of a sadistic nature. He would see himself a rich prince who had the right of life and death over the boy, whom he could throw into prison, but whom he would free again because he loved him. When I. S. became older matters continued in the same way. There was always a boy to whom he felt himself especially attracted. When he was still in the lower classes in high school he read in an encyclopedia that pederasty was prohibited. When he was 17 years old he met the son of an afficial, a boy of rare beauty. I. S. used to give him lessons. He made the acquaintance of the boy's parents and also invited the boy to come to see his own parents. Their relationships lasted for several years. The boy was about four years younger than himself. Indecent acts never occurred between them. Nay, the boy himself had no inkling of I. S.'s peculiar attach-

of my inclination I consider that out of the question. Often I am extremely depressed when I consider the prospects of my future. I know that I cannot make a secret of my inclination towards boys, and that sooner or later I shall commit a wrong. But even the thought of the possible consequences cannot restrain me for long. All these things are quite certain to me but in the long run I shall not be able to help myself.''

In this connection I might point out that certain perverse modes of gratification, which may be observed in homosexuals, are also surprisingly often tied up with sexually immature persons. Sadistic propensities which in the man appear quite often, sometimes refer to maltreatments of woman, and at other times to that of males. In none of the cases which we have come across up to now was there present any sadistic tendencies of male individuals towards a grown-up man, on the contrary, in almost all cases, it was directed towards sexually immature male persons or towards women. In the latter immaturity was not a necessary condition. Let me cite here two cases of sadism directed towards boys.

Case XXVI. Mr. M. C., 28 years of age, has several brothers and sisters who are quite normal. Both of his parents have outbursts of passion. A paternal uncle was insane for several months.

Aside from his sexual perversion patient feels quite normal. Denies suffering from any nervous disorder. Questioning and further investigation failed to elicit anything in regard to this nature. M. C. has erections and experiences sexual excitement whenever he thinks of a boy being beaten, but the boy must be neither too young nor too old. He prefers only boys between the ages of

10 to 15. They must be handsome. Only blows on the posterior excited him sexually, the chief consideration being that the boy should feel the pain greatly. It is of no great importance to M. C. who administers the beating. In his imagination he himself at times administered the beating, at other times someone else. Whether it was done by stick, rod, whip or hand mattered little to him. Stressing only the fact that the boy should feel great pain. Such was the patient's mind even at the age of eight. Up to the present, however, he has never given in to his sexual inclinations, but is dominated by them in his thoughts. When these thoughts become too strong he has to resort to masturbation. He has further observed that periods of great sexual excitements alternated with those entirely free from them. The thought of a beating administered to grown-up men, girls or animals, cannot excite him. Nor can he be excited by the thought of being beaten by someone else. He has tried coitus twice without success. Erection was possible only through vigorous friction on the part of the girl but no ejaculation took place. M. C. has pollutions very infrequently. He cannot recall the dreams in that connection.

Case XXVII. Mr. N. D., 20 years of age, when questioned states that occasionally his parents had complained of light nervous ailments. His brothers and sisters on the other hand were perfectly healthy. This is true of his other relatives. Patient is and has always been of weak bodily constitution, but without any organic defects. In his early youth his health was poor. He suffered much from headaches, especially between the ages of 7 and 10, which recurred periodically. These have now entirely disappeared. Aside from his sexual life he is free from every eccentricity. He is level-headed and of a quiet nature, though when alone he will become sentimental and melancholy. He avoids contact with people. His intellectual capacities seem to be those of an average person.

N. D. is suffering from sadistic inclinationns in connection with homosexuality. This inclination is directed towards boys of between 9 and 15 years and exclusively towards such as are physically strong. Such inclination would disappear if he should assume that maltreatment might impair the boy's health. The punishment of children, administered by others, causes only resentment and pity in him and this even in respect to such boys towards whom he himself might experience sadistic emotions. In such cases, however, he sometimes feels a certain sexual excitement which he resents at the same time. In strange contract with this sexual pr<NA>pensity is the fact that he is good-natured and really loves children. N. D. is very proud of this because he believes children have a fine intuition for persons that mean them well. It is further to be mentioned that even in cases in which he has no sexual thoughts whatever he likes to amuse himself better with boys than with girls.

Patient has never as yet attempted coitus. He is convinced that due to his total indifference to women he would be quite incapable to perform it. Coitus with a prostitute would further be impossible because the very thought of such a person is repugnant to him. His aversion towards the female sex is so pronounced that he would not even associate with girls socially. As a consequence he is regarded as a misogynist. No one knows the real reasons.

His condition became clear to him about two years ago.

It is true that previously he was surprised that in contrast to young men of his own age he had no need for sexual intercourse with women. But he did not give it any further thought and as a whole he was never alarmed about the relationship of the two sexes. He had not the least inkling that his own sex instinct had been awakened a long time since expressing itself sadistically.

He believes that he can follow back the first traces of his malady to his ninth year. At that time he began to masturbate without having been seduced to the practice. While masturbating he would think of boys of the same age naked and defenseless and tortured in the most cruel manner. He cannot recall distinctly the clearer details but he still remembers that he imagined kings and princes from the fairy tales who would torture some boy. In general, he believes that present sadistic inclinations are of a milder nature than they were in his childhood. But his ideas remained unchanged for a long period. While at first they would pursue him only at night, they occurred in daytime, also, with the onset of puberty. These thoughts disturb him in his work and even force him to interrupt his work in order to masturbate. About two years ago his sex instinct reached its acme. Since then it has abated somewhat, so that he has peace at least by day. He believes, nevertheless, that on account of masturbation his capacity and diligence for work have suffered a great deal.

Gradually his sadistic thoughts concentrated upon the idea of a boy whom, while masturbating, he would always imagine maltreating. On the one hand whenever he sees the boy he has the desire to press him to himself, to stroke him, etc. In this connection he is especially excited by this boy's thighs and his chin but not by the genitals.

On the other hand he has the desire to torture the boy. Now and then this boy permits himself to be tied up naked by N. D. and to receive a fierce beating. This results in N. D. getting an erection. He says that he could never resort to real maltreatments as he imagines it while masturbating, even though he had the opportunity of indulging in it. Such was the state of affairs three years ago. He then became acquainted with a second boy ten years of age. He developed a great liking for the boy and the latter, too, as he states, is very fond of him. In his relationship with the boy his sexual proclivities were very much in the background. He has also, as he believes, produced a very good influence upon the boy. He is not so much excited with this fellow as he was with the other. It was usually sufficient to fondle him. However, when N. D. was upset by his sadistic feelings the boy was very accommodating, knowing that the duration and temper of the beatings depended on his own will. N. D. would never force the boy to submit to them since the boy's love had become indispensable to him and he would not destroy it through maltreatment.

N. D. has linked his affection for the two boys in the most peculiar fashion. While masturbating, he would imagine that the second was witness to the scene of torture in which the first was the victim. He also would like to tell the second of the cruel and fictitious punishments he administers on the first. This was to him what obscene talk was to a normal man.

The belief that for the sadist the really exciting thing is the feeling of unlimited power over the beloved person, may be confirmed in the case of N. D. The binding and the desire to humiliate the two children are distinct proofs of this. The maltreatment, according to N. D., is not a means to an end but for the purpose of humiliating the boys, the reaction becoming greater if the subjects were unwilling to bear the tortures.

N. D. nevertheless feels extremely unhappy, although, he does not conceive the whole extent of the loss in his deficiency of a normal sex instinct.

Thus N. D. went in for medical treatment. The strength of his sex instinct varies. At times it is very slight, then at times it is very strong. Medical treatment has improved him. Psychical masturbation decreased considerably, although physical masturbation continued.

The two boys referred to formerly were the centre of his sex life. Later, however, his attitude toward one of them changed. Sexual excitement began to play a minor role. He needed the boy's friendship more than he desired him for sexual purposes. He would suffer terribly even at the slightest cooling of the boy's affections. In this respect a change has taken place. Their friendship became strained without N. D. feeling as hurt as he surely would have felt at the beginning of their friendship. A still further change may be observed in that he could find gratification with boys in a manner corresponding coitus while masturbating. For the time being he can easily suppress this desire. At any rate, the sadistic impulses have clearly receded.

At first he showed himself only passive and neutral in regards to women. He had no desire to perform coitus. Medical treatment, however, brought about a certain change insofar as his former aversions towards sexual contact has given place to a certain indifference. N. D. comprehends what an effect the sight of a beautiful body exerts upon a man. He feels, however, that some reaction is lacking which ought to release the sex impulse.

After having undertaken a long journey, on his doctor's advice, his sexual state changed even further. Far from his customary surroundings and from his everyday life through which his force of habit had made him surrender to his inclination, he became diverted by the impressions of nature and perhaps also by a physical exertion. Thus his condition improved even more. It is true that his perverse inclinations during the journey appeared but they were only transitory and moderate in strength. At times he would even observe that he was bored by dwelling on such thoughts. The inclination to gratify himself with boys in a manner similar to normal coitus did not occur either. His former passion for one of the boys has cooled off more and more and has almost disappeared. A lasting separation at the present time would hardly affect him. A thing he would have considered impossible a few months ago. He feels vaguely that his homosexual sensations are slowly approaching their death. On the other hand, however, a desire for women does not clearly appear, except in one case, when he made the acquaintance of a beautiful girl of 16 who was already quite mature. He very much liked to associate with her, for he felt himself attracted to her not only psychically but also sexually. But he felt the sexual only "inwardly" and not in a manner that would make itself perceptible in his genitals through a reflex action. He cannot say what attracted him to the girl. He believes it was more the spiritual fervor, her naive emotional nature that was perceptible in the girl just as in the boys, and which was the real stimulus. Formerly N. D. had been so unhappy, as he always repeated, that he had a strong desire to die. For he felt that his per-

verse nature would condemn him to a solitary life and
that the evil habit of masturbation had robbed him of
the best dower that nature had provided him with, which
were energy and work. How could he consider himself
very lucky unless he would be able to lose the impulse to
masturbate even though he might not feel sexually normal otherwise? At any rate, N. D. thought so at the
beginning of the treatment. He was treated by me for a
long time; his neurasthenia being especially considered by several methods. It proved successful in
repressing very considerably his perverse idea. Distinctly heterosexual love sensations were partly awakened, it is true, as a result of external and favorable circumstances.

N. D. made good use of the opportunities for diverting
his mind through sports and physical exercise. These
bodily activities as well as much staying outdoors tended
to stifle his perversions considerably. It is true that
from time to time he continued to masturbate, but only
very seldom. He further observed that its harmful consequences entirely disappeared. When, after some time
he began to neglect his physical exercises, his sexual
sensations again increased.

After a period of time N. D. sent me the following communication: "The most important thing is that I have
been completely cured of my passion for the above-
mentioned boy. I believe that I have observed a slow but
sure cooling of my passion. This cure has gone so far
that at present such love seems incomprehensible to me.
Nay, I believe that such an attachment would be impossible for me in the future. Of great benefit to me was
the occasion I had of being together frequently with a
young lady I have already mentioned and in retaining

my interest in her. My attachment for her became deeper and the leave-taking which I have delayed for a long time has become quite difficult for me. She, too, has a liking for me."

When we consider the preceding examples we may observe, with the exceptions of cases XXVI and XXVII, a common characteristic, that of an existence of an inclination for both sexes, with a preponderance for the male sex. Case XVII shows especially a similar urge towards female persons. It is further remarkable that in all of these cases the men to whom the subject in question feels himself attracted sexually at all events must have any one of several feminine features. In most of the cases the beard must be absent, or the face must have a girlish appearance, while in one of the cases (Case XXII) only the body must not be covered with hair and a small moustache is not considered repugnant. When I take into consideration further case-material, most of which I am not including here, we must conclude that analogous cases are abundant, that is, one may observe in men very frequently a strong though varying inclination towards both sexes. In the man thus loved certain qualities are required which usually are regarded as feminine. It follows, from this, that on the one hand we may not speak here of a real inversion of the sex instinct in the sense that the subject feels like a woman. If this were so he would have to feel himself attracted to completely mature men without being repelled by a hairy body or by a bearded face. A thoroughgoing examination of my case-material convinces me that as a whole the number of men who feel themselves attracted to their own sex, and who periodically show an inclination towards females is great. But the opposite too, namely, that men who are usually designated as completely heterosexual have gone through this or that episode in their life in which they felt themselves attracted to their own sex. In most of those cases, however, certain feminine qualities are required to exert a sexual attraction, as in the above mentioned cases. Certain qualities are required in the woman which the sexually attractive female does not possess under normal conditions or again, the presence of both of these factors. In such cases there is often an inclination towards sexually immature female persons, as we have seen in Case XIX. The breasts, for example, must not be developed. I believe that we must consider these cases on the basis of our preceding considerations about the complexes of reactive capacities. The simplest case would be when a girl-like face is requisite and when it is of no consequence whether this face goes together with a masculine or feminine body. We have here an incomplete reaction complex, in which, as already considered, assuming A to stand for the feminine face, B for the feminine body, and B_1 for the masculine body, we not only have the reaction complex AB, and not only the reaction complex AB_1, but either the reactive capacity A alone, or AB and AB_1 together. When we further observe cases in which the subject feels himself attracted only to such female persons who have not as yet matured sexually, who have no breasts, we must assume that he is endowed with a heterosexual reactive capacity. But this complex of reactive capacities is not normal. The subject, *e. g.*, is not excited through stimuli emanating from the sexually mature woman, but through charms which are a part of the female who has not as yet reached sexual maturity.

In those cases in which young girls with undeveloped

breasts exert the same sexual stimulus as boys, we must assume that there is present a modification of the complex of reactive capacities. The men who excite the persons in question are not such as will excite women under normal circumstances, nor are the women such as will excite men under the same circumstances. I might say that in such cases there exists a complex of reactive capacities, which viewed from the standpoint of normal man and woman, is to a certain extent negative. For the person in question feels himself attracted to women with undeveloped breasts while typical feminine qualities hinder the stimulus. Such stimulation is also brought about by typical masculine qualities. It is not children who excite him sexually but persons who have outgrown childhood, though they have not as yet reached complete puberty.

In many similar cases where men show an inclination towards immature female persons, we find that these men are also excited by certain male individuals who have not as yet overstepped the stage of puberty. In this connection the subject, it is true, shows homosexual inclinations, but the complex of reactive capacities is not the same with him as is normally the case in woman. For under normal circumstances she feels herself attracted particularly by sexually mature men. We shall find here a great number of different types which I cannot treat here in fuller detail. I only wished to point out that the normal complexes of reactive capacities may be seen to have numerous deviations in many persons. In many such cases it cannot be determined whether these deviations are caused through heredity or whether through conditional circumstances, nor do we know what has been added to the inherited complex through associations during life. I would like to remark at this point that the psychical qualities of the person exerting the stimulus play no less a role than the somatic qualities. Another factor that might perhaps be of importance in such inclinations towards sexually not quite mature persons is their innocence, which exerts such a strong sexual stimulus upon many without the subjects being aware of it. The psychical qualities, too, need not be the exclusive effect of either an inherited disposition or of influences during life. Both of these factors work together. I shall return to these matters when I shall consider the question of habit.

What I wished to point out was the fact that the heterosexual complexes may present numerous disturbances without the necessity of there existing a complete inversion as we are familiar with it in pure homosexuality. And, as already mentioned, there may occur numerous variations in this connection, inasmuch as certain masculine and certain feminine qualites may combine with each other as stimulating factors. In general we may say that transitional states may exist between the typical feminine sex instinct directed towards completely mature males, and the typical male sex instinct directed towards completely mature females. When we glance at other literature on the subject we shall observe as a matter of fact, as already remarked, that the inclinations towards not completely mature men is an unusually frequent occurrence. We may observe the same as far back as in ancient Greece. Thus Antinous, the beloved of Hadrian, is often represented with thoroughly feminine features. It is on this point that Ulrich presents interesting details in his ''Memnon.'' He also mentions that Ganymede is almost always represented as quite a young

an almost childlike boy, although Martial ascribes a
downy beard to him. In the Orient, as I have been well-
informed, homosexuality is with uncommon frequency
directed towards boys. That both in ethnology and in
history we may see examples of men showing love to
castrates probably rests on the fact that some men are
attracted sexually by a blending of masculine and feminine qualities or by the absence of masculine and feminine qualities respectively. I have already mentioned
above that women, too, had intercourse with castrates.

At this point I might also state that there are females
who are not attracted to sexually mature males. Such
cases have been published by Aniel, and also by Magan.
The latter mentions the case of a woman of 28, who
had an inclination towards her small nephew, only two
years old. Similar cases were described by other authors. And in like manner as we find men who love others
possessing feminine qualities, we also find women who
are attracted only to other women possessing masculine
qualities. Occasionally such a woman also reveals an
inclination towards men. The following case will illustrate this point.

Case XXVIII. Miss F. C., 36 years of age. Her
parents are dead. Her father was an official and was
said to have neither a nervous temperament nor to have
suffered from any physical diseases. He died of decrep-
titude. Her mother died of pneumonia. Miss F. C. is
familiar with her parent's relatives. She often visits
her brothers and sisters, some of whom are married and
have children. F. C. does not know of any nervous ailments or similar affections in the family.

Until her sixteenth year she attended the local school
in a town with a population of about five thousand. In

her school-days she liked to play both with boys and with girls. She was a very ingenious child and felt no passionate attachment either for boys or for girls. She can still clearly recall all those of her school-mates with whom she associated very innocently. She liked very much to play with dolls. She began to menstruate at the age of 13½, while she was still attending school. At this period also occurred her first sexual excitements. She only remembers that at the time she felt vaguely some sensation in her genitals. She did not masturbate. None of her comrades spoke about it and she had no inkling of the existence of such a practice. She cannot give any closer details about herself in that period of her life.

She was well brought up at home. Her step-mother, who took up her education after her mother's death, was always kind to her. After confirmation she left her parents and her home town and accepted a position in a larger town. When she was 16 and still a virgin she was placed in a brothel by a procuress. Everything seemed to have been pre-arranged. By means of showing her beautiful clothes, linen and other similar things, it was possible to make her accept such an engagement. This occupation, however, proved to be only a ruse. The further experience of Miss F. C. is not of great interest to us. She spent several years in a brothel. She succeeded in leaving it, usually a very difficult matter, through the aid of the family who paid off her debts. It is a well-known fact that the debts the girls contract in a brothel are the chief means of keeping them there. In the brothel, of course, she had intercourse with men. She also believes that at the time she very much liked the sex intercourse with certain men. She had no special inclination towards any one man. Several times she was the passive partner in cunnilingus with certain males.

While in the brothel she associated with another girl who had been there a long time. They used to sleep together often and occasionally practiced mutual cunnilingus. F. C. maintains that intercourse with the girl very soon began to cause her a certain pleasure, brought about especially by the local physical titillations. When she came out of the brothel she went to live in Berlin and there found a position. Very soon afterwards she procured herself a girl-friend. Whereas in the brothel she usually acted as the passive partner in cunnilingus she began to practice it actively with her girl friend. She lived with her for two years, after which they separated. F. C. found another girl friend with whom she has now been living for the last four years. At present she practices various forms of sexual intercourse. Most of the time she is passive in cunnilingus, but at times she is also the active partner. Whereas she had felt no especial attachment to her friend in the brothel she states that she had immediately shown a great affection for her present companion. Her present friend is more masculine, her breasts are not fully developed, which makes her more pleasing and attractive to her, since she prefers girls who are masculine. She is, for this reason, especially attracted to girls with closely cropped hair.

As already mentioned she had permitted a man to perform cunnilingus on her when she was in the brothel and the act had satisfied her. However, she is more gratified when a woman fondles her organs. Except when in the brothel she has never been gratified in normal coitus. She maintains that she has never felt a stronger inclination towards men and she deduces this fact from the observation that she had been too much excluded from the company of men at the time when her sex-instinct was awakened.

Miss F. C. is almost never gratified in her dreams. The few erotic dreams she can recall now, referred to the sex act with girls and at other times with men.

F. C. neither smokes nor drinks. She appears much younger than her age. Dr. Flatau's examination of her larynx shows purely feminine conditions.

The following case is very similar.

Case XXIX. Miss P. T., 26 years of age. Her parents have been dead a long time. All her brothers and sisters are dead. Phthisis being the cause in all cases. P. T. too gives the impression of being physically weak. Her face is remarkably unsymmetrical, her left side being sunken in. Nervous diseases are said not to have occurred in the family.

When questioned how she came upon sexual intercourse she states "I had no relatives, and lived on my income in a home where prostitutes were kept. There I observed what was going on and a man who made my acquaintance had an intimate relationship with me. What made me accept him was the interesting life and also the money he offered me. This affair lasted about a year. Occasionally he gratified me sexually. Nevertheless, the pleasure I experienced was not very strong and especially not immediately after defloration." When questioned further how she had parted from this man she answered: "He had been living beyond his means and had embezzled some money. He wanted to give me a good time and I really did have it without knowing how the money had been procured. One day he suddenly disappeared and has not been seen since. He came of a good family and was a merchant. Later I accidentally found out from people who knew him why he had disappeared from Berlin.''

When asked how she first came upon intercourse with girls she relates how one day she made the acquaintance of a woman, Miss Y., and that she has thus been led to this form of intercourse. ''It was Miss Y. who asked me to do it. She was a handsome girl and I liked her very much. We have lived together for several years while at the same time I made my living as a prostitute. I learned about homosexual intercourse only shortly after the affair with my lover was ended. My relationship with the woman lasted five years. I have never associated with other girls behind Miss Y.'s back. Finally she left our common domicile and made a new acquaintance. Miss Y finds absolutely no pleasure in men. She always used to tell me she could never touch a man. She comes from a good family, but her parents are dead. Intercourse with Miss Y. consisted in mutual cunnilingus. The active and the passive roles were interchanged. At first my friend, Miss Y., used to be the active partner in cunnilingus, but very soon I, too, did it on her. For the present I prefer active cunnilingus. I cannot tell what in the genitals of the girls really excites me. I cannot tell whether it is the odor, but I believe that it is greatly due to the sexual excitement of the other girl in cunnilingus. Active cunnilingus merely serves to excite me sexually; gratification often follows afterwards through being masturbated by my friend.

''However, I have also found gratification in passive cunnilingus. Since a few months ago when I separated from my second friend, I have had no other intimate friend. I am a frequent guest in homes where homosexual girls meet in Berlin, and associate with different ones at a time. I prefer girls built like Miss Y., *i. e.*, girls who have masculine features. Feminine behavior in such girls repels me. I could never associate with a really feminine girl.''

As regards her erotic dreams, P. T. can not recall whether such dreams have ever gratified her. It is true that she has often been sexually excited in her dreams, but she has never found any gratification in them. She has also dreamed of sexual intercourse with her first friend, but it did not go beyond that. She alleges that she has never dreamed of sexual intercourse with men.

Dr. Flatau's examination of the larynx shows no deviation from the feminine type, no trace of an Adam's apple, etc.

Up to now I have intentionally refrained from referring to psychical importance of the sense impressions received. Of their importance I am thoroughly convinced. It was only in order not to bring in too many complications that I at first referred the direction of the sex instinct to the stimulation of certain sense organs without considering whether the stimuli go through a psychical elaboration or not. I am of the opinion, however, that in man the psychical elaboration of the sense impressions received plays an important role, a role which may be observed in everyday occurrences. It is due to such psychical elaboration that sexual excitement will take place in a man and a woman long after a conversation. Every one, according to his own individuality, will elaborate the impressions received in a different manner. This will easily explain the numerous differences in the individualizing direction of the sex impulse which has its highest point in love. The face is the mirror of the soul. What exerts an especial influence is the manner in which the features are expressed in conversation or after being together for a long time. Also the speech, the mouth, and the sound of the words spoken. The great influence that a feminine singing voice exerts may best be explained through its psychical effect. "The voice which is at the same time both organ of speech and the means of expressing our thoughts, is alone enabled to combine sounds with words, and to place music in the service of poetic art. Whoever prefers soulfulness and fullness of expression in music will give preference to the human voice, this most flexible of instruments flowing from the spirit." This does refer only to the singing voice. The same thing is true of ordinary conversation. And just like the voice, which after all consists merely of movements, so also all the other movements in her face, her body act as stimuli for the sex instinct of man. It is the psychical elaboration that is essential for the release of contrectation. It is quite the same with the stimuli that the man produces upon the woman. It has often been maintained that woman is much more influenced by stimuli of a psychical nature. The stimulus which "redcoats" exert upon women rests, I believe, upon the psychical elaboration of the sense impression, the woman becoming cognizant of that which most stimulates her sex in the human and animal world. It is not the colors the soldiers wear which is of effect here. Servantmen and telegraph messengers, too, wear colorful clothes without exerting this influence. In the animal world an essential role is played by courage and in the sacrifice of life itself in the struggle of the males for the favor of females—the stronger male obtaining the fought-for prize. And it is assumed that in the animal world, too, the female is mostly excited by greater strength. This may be also accepted in the case of man and to this fact at least may be reduced in part the stimulus the soldier exerts upon woman even though she may not be conscious of its mode of operation. Let me remark, however, that other factors beside this psychical elaboration play their role in the stimulation of the "uniform." It is possible that the tight fit of the uniform and the resulting throwing out in bold relief of the bodily form exerts a sexually stimulating influence, and this is further proven by the fact that the sexual libido of many women with remarkable frequency is directed towards lackeys, grooms, etc. In vaudeville theaters and circuses we may best observe what strong excitement women experience at the sight of acrobats, gymnasts, etc., and their snugly-fitting tights. Nevertheless, I believe that we can say that some sense impressions at any rate can only exert an influence through a psychical conception and elaboration.

We may see that not only the sense stimuli in the stimulated person B undergo a psychical interpretation but also how he is enabled through these sense stimuli to draw conclusions as to the psychical qualities of A, the source of these stimuli. This deduction may be either conscious or unconscious, nevertheless it plays a very important role. For it is not only the physical qualities belonging to A which exert an influence upon B, but also psychical characteristics, some of which excite the male while others excite the female. The man is often more truly stimulated by a certain reserve and chastity than he is by a woman's forwardness so that we may conclude that there is a psychical difference between the sexes. For the woman is not only not repelled by the male's courage but rather in most cases is excited by it. We know that this is often to be observed in the animal world. The female of the blackbird makes copulation difficult for the approaching male, ever withdrawing from him and sometimes even repelling him by light flappings of the wings. We may observe the same phenomenon also in man. The spermatozoon seeks for the ovum. This is true physiologically, the egg being placed in a definite position, the sperm seeking to penetrate it; but the statement is true also psychologically; the man, the producer of semen, seeking to conquer the woman, the producer of the eggs. Of course there are other psychical differences aside from the reserve of the woman and the aggressiveness of the man. But at this point I only wished to illustrate the essential importance of the psychical concept of these impressions.

Yet, though I hold to the opinion that we must not only consider purely physical differentiation, also that the psychical element is of essential significance here, this does not in any way contradict the inheritance of the normal sex instinct. One might perhaps object that essential psychical differences do not exist between man and woman. I believe that this is an erroneous idea and that as a matter of fact we may differentiate between the two sexes also psychically, as already indicated above. Nor may one object that up to now no typical differences in their brain have been found. One must forget that in spite of the most laborious and significant investigation by numerous scientists our knowledge of the structure of the brain is still in a comparatively very low stage, and moreover, that in general we may not base a psychology of the sexes merely upon the structure of the brain.

Even though certain qualities of the opposite sex have

always served as a means of sexual excitement and differentiation, within certain limits these exciting qualities vary in different countries and at different times.
Innocence, chastity and virginity are in our civilized
society commonly considered means of sexual excitement for the man. We may observe that with some people of antiquity and of modern times virginity is not so
highly prized. In the different countries of the Orient,
in Armenia, Babylonia, Carthage, Cyprus, Lydia, Pales-
tine, and especially in Phoenicia, the defloration of the
virgin was not undertaken by the future husband. For
this purpose she was given to strangers. Thus one may
infer how easy it is for experience to come into conflict with inherited inclinations. Rosenbaum, in his "History of Prostitution in Antiquity," quoting many author-
itative passages regarding these conditions mentions the
causes for defloration by strangers. We have to differentiate between two factors here. One reason was religious, the virginity of the girl being offered to Venus as
a sacrifice and could not consequently be offered to the
future husband. The other reason was the fact that the
blood lost in defloration was considered impure as
that of the menstrual flow. Defloration was therefore
left to the strangers, outside of the region of the temple.
When stimulus exerted by virginity collides with other
emotions, e. g., of religious nature, the reaction to the
sexual stimuli must be modified. We cannot forthwith
decide whether the inherited elements in the complexes
of reactive capacities is modified through such viewpoints in some people, or whether a change in this inherited element's is made by such viewpoints. I believe
that in the same manner in which sexual excitement differs in man and in apes, so also there are differences

within a race and in different individuals. This probably refers both to physical and to psychical stimuli. These differences in races and in individuals are, however, not merely dependent upon the influences during life. Inherited race peculiarities also play a major role here. "Not only physical virtues but also primordial race tendencies and many other unknown and implicit motives make and form man what he is, here and now." (Franz Engel). It is certain however, that influences during life are not without their effect here. It is probably due to this in part that love shows so many differences among the various nations. Stendhal, in his "Physiology of Love," has discussed love as it has been observed in various nationalities and at different times. He states that for the Frenchman the most flattering thing is to conquer and not to hold. It is due to this that the French prostitutes are so charming, the Spanish so insignificant. In France, this author remarks, a prostitute may make a man as happy as a decent woman can. In England, he says, the chief pride of the husband is the modesty of his wife. But the society of his wife very soon becomes a burden to him and as a result we may see that rich Englishmen, bored at their home, will rather undertake a four or five-mile jaunt under the pretext of necessary physical exercise. The Spanish are the personification of the Middle Ages. The Spaniard is not as yet familiar with an immense number of truths, e. g., that his neighbors possess a childish vanity. The love of the German is considered to be a virtue, as an outflow of Divinity, something mystical. His love emotion is not even vivacious, impetuous, jealous and tyrannical as that of the Italian. It is more deeply felt. Love in the United States is said to be without a passion that may give pleasure. Habituation to the reasonable is common in that country so that a crystallization has become impossible.

When we go back into the history of former centuries we may again find numerous differences in regards to sexual stimuli. In the age of the Minnesingers submissiveness to woman was considered the main quality and virtue in a man. The necessity for servility is the more remarkable since it was frequently married women who thus exerted their influence; that is, women whom the lover could never hope of possessing. It is an error to assume that the goal of the man in all cases was to marry the woman he loved for it is exactly this form of love that seems to me to have been characteristic of that time. Of course, one must not in such cases forget that generalities may not be deduced from single cases. Still this form of love seems to have played quite a prominent role among the ruling classes at the time of the Minnesingers. It is true that in France, at least, the conditions at the courts of love, above described, lasted only through its first period. At some later time the French husband laid no more claim on the constancy of his wife. The lover usurped the former's rights.

Just as the psychical qualities of the opposite sex serving as sexual stimuli, differ in various countries and change at different periods of history, we may also observe this difference and change in physical qualities. We have already mentioned that the black man prefers the black woman and a white man a white woman. It is also a matter of certainty that in the course of time the concept of beauty has undergone many changes and considering the closeness between beauty and sex stimulus we cannot ignore this point. That the idea of the beautiful has changed may be seen from the representations in art and poetry. In order to cite an example I shall only refer to the female bust. The elevated position of the breasts in antique art stands in opposition to their lower position as represented in Correggio's "Danae." And though according to Brücke we must take this to be an exception yet we may observe that this lower position came more into the foreground and may be found very often in the paintings of the German renaissance school. I should also like to point out that in antique sculpture we very frequently come upon women types. Venus, for example, never appears as a young girl, but always as the type of young woman. In what other ways these national differences may be expressed may be seen in the so-called épaules tombantes (drooping shoulders) which in France have for centuries been considered a sign of beauty. Mignard's famous picture of Maria Mancia in the "Old Museum" of Berlin, and many other paintings, especially in the Louvre, leave no doubt about this fact. Another example is the crippling of the feet of the Chinese women. Exner, in his description of Chinese life, describes how this crippling takes place, the bandaging of the girl's legs beginning at the age of six. A fashionable woman's shoe must be no more than three inches in length and in order to achieve this end the growth of the feet is hindered through bandaging by means of cotton bands, pressure and pulling. It is not known what this crippling of the feet is due to. Some would like to refer it to the desire of the husband to prevent the wife from walking too fast and thus made her feel the strength of authority. We, in Europe, on the contrary, would find no stimulus in the crippling of the feet. Nay, it would be repugnant to us. This illustration was intended to point out the differences in regards to the means of sexual excitement among various nationalities. A phenomenon that is analogous to the wedging in the feet is the effect of wearing a corset. For most men a narrow waist-line in woman, a waist that stands out in bold relief against the clothing and the lacing of the corset, is no doubt a sexual stimulant. It is well-known that transformation in the female organism may take place, as a consequence. At any rate, we have here another ideal of beauty than that which is represented in the antique statues. It has often been pointed out that the Venus de Milo shows not the slightest trace of the so-called "wasp's waist" and the other statues, too, for example, in the Venus de Medici, the opposite of such will be found.

That the idea of masculine beauty on the other hand depends not only on the complexion of the skin but on other factors too may be seen in the fact that the beard is worn in different styles among the different countries of the world and from the fact that some races show a sparse growth of beard altogether whereby such means of differentiation is removed.

Cordier pointed out that beauty is not the property of this or that race. Every race differs from all others in the beauty proper to it. The laws of beauty are then not general. They must be studied specifically for each and every people. It goes without saying that besides such sexual beauty there are also ideas of beauty regarding other objects such as the beauty of animals and of inanimate nature.

But in spite of great differences in this respect among various nations and different times there have always existed certain qualities which have differentiated man from woman and which may well be regarded as a lasting sexual stimulant. No matter how much the requisite spiritual and bodily qualities of the opposite sex might have changed during the courses of centuries in the countries of the world in spite of the fact that certain differences might have taken place in regards to the physical stimuli, the general bodily formation of the female sex has always been a stimulant to the man and general masculine bodily formation to the woman. In this connection we may assume that in spite of all variations certain reactive capacities in the sexual life have always been the same.

I shall not go into further details about the particular psychical differences of the two sexes. For the eternal feminine will always remain that which will attract the man; and I believe that we must regard the capacity to react to the eternal feminine as inherited in the human sex instinct.

And the fact that reactive capacity may to a certain extent be modified through habit, through influences during life, does not contradict the idea of inheritance. I have already mentioned that a white man will not usually be excited by a black woman and yet we know that white men living in the colonies for lack of their kind, will feel themselves attracted to black women.

That habit may contribute to the development of the instinct may be seen in the attempts of breeding animals. Thus while a male canary will very easily be induced to copulate with the female of the species, we find that usually it will refuse to copulate with birds of another species. Still it is possible in a number of cases to induce it to copulate with the female of a kindred species. One must conceive this in such a manner that the two species at first have sexual inclination for each other

but that with the provoking of detumescence, contrectation, too, is modified in accordance with the existing situation. That this capacity varies in different animals may
be seen from the fact that some of them will not under-
any circumstances copulate with animals of a different
species.   Others again can accommodate themselves
perfectly, the copulations resulting in hybrids. We are
indebted to Adolph and Carl Müller for more detailed
information on the subject, especially regarding the
hybridization of canaries with kindred breeds. In this
connection, however, it must be remarked that the sex
instinct of caged animals shows certain deviations.

Numerous observations have been published about
the intermarriage of different races. Eduard Westermarck has compiled a great number of these in his work
on human marriage. It is usually assumed by the adherents of teleology that the sterility of children resulting
from such mixed marriages is foreshadowed in the
mutual aversion of such races to each other. Since procreation is everywhere willed by nature, races whose
hybrid offspring cannot reproduce their kind, will not
attract each other. The contention that such half-breeds
will become sterile must, however be qualified inasmuch
as such cross-breeds may at least have fertile offspring
by marriage with either one of the pure races. More
and more it became the standpoint that half-breeds are
sterile only among themselves as in the case of the he-
mule and the she-mule which may, by way of exception, reproduce themselves in the first generation. But no matter what happens to the further offspring, it cannot be denied that often there is no sexual
sympathy between races far removed from each other.
And Westermarck justly points out that sometimes this

lack of affinity between different races is the result of differences in interests, concepts and habits. It may actually be observed that when races are in close proximity numerous intermarriages with fertile offspring finally do take place. In such cases habit has played a not unimportant role. A white Caucasion will certainly not prefer a black woman when other, white women, are at his disposal. But in the end habit is so strong that as a result we may observe half-breeds all over the world at the present time. Nansen reports that hardly any native Eskimos are to be met with in Greenland at present. In South America there are a great number of half-breeds, the offspring of Anglo-Saxon and Negroes are very common. It is not of any importance to us whether the intermarriage of these cross-breeds is fertile or not. I merely wished to point out that habit is a very important factor in the sex instinct. One should not assume that I consider everything the result of heredity.

We can observe the workings of habit in everyday life. Husband and wife gradually get accustomed to each other and upon this fact, in the end, rests the institution of marriage. Very often a third person cannot understand how a man can continue having intercourse with his no longer young wife and yet we find this condition to be quite frequent in married life. For a gradual habituation of one to the other has set in, and expresses itself in an ever continuing accommodation of the two partners to each other, just as the two persons have grown old only gradually.

Something very similar must have happened in the case of evolution. Let us assume the gradual transformation of one animal species into another one. This transformation was brought about by way of many, many intermediate stages. For inasmuch as an individual of one species will only rarely unite with an individual of another, we must assume that in the process of evolution a similarly gradual habituation of the transformed individuals must have taken place. Let us assume, to choose a crude example, that a certain species of fish has gradually been transformed into a mammal. The males of the specific species M must therefore have gone through numerous stages before they were finally transformed into male mammals. Let us further assume that several of these stages of the male were represented by M_1, M_2, M_3, M_4, etc., until finally the male mammal M_{10} was developed. Let us assume, in the same way, that the female W has gradually been transformed into W_1, W_2, W_3, etc., until it became W_{10}, or a female mammal. The intermediate stages then must have gradually habituated themselves to one another sexually, for M_1 would not seek to unite with W_{10} nor M_{10} with W_1. The intermediate species, standing close to one another, must have sought to unite with their own kind preferably. We may therefore establish that there was a gradual habituation of the inte. diate species to one another.

In respect to the inherited sexual reactive capacities the animal world shows the same phenomena that we have found in man. But, in accordance with their lower psychical life their sex instinct will, of course, express itself in a different manner. Animals with but few exceptions always feels themselves attracted only by others of the opposite sex but of the same species, because their inherited reactive capacity consists in responding to such stimuli. In every animal species, as already indi-

cated, other stimuli than observed in man play the role.
Most likely several of the sense organs participate to a
greater extent; others may be weaker than in man.
There can be no doubt that with many animals the sensations play an important role. In birds the sexual
importance of the sense of hearing has been established.
Jäger, who ascribes so much importance to olfactory
stimuli, stresses the fact that in sexual love of man too
the olfactory peculiarities of man and woman are different and that they have a very peculiar significance for
the mutual attraction of the two sexes. This author
cites many examples from the animal world to illustrate
the importance of the odoriferous substances. He mentions a communication by Fritz Müller referring to the
odors of butterflies. According to him certain spinners
will find the female merely through their sense of smell
even though the female be completely hidden by the
trunk of a tree. At first the male butterfly will fly in
any direction whatsoever but as soon as it has come
up to about 20 to 30 yards of the female it will suddenly
change the direction of its flight and fly in direct line
towards the trunk of the tree. As Jäger stresses, the
sense of sight cannot have been responsible for the
attraction. And if this is really so, the most probable
assumption would be that the sense of smell has exerted
the attraction. At any rate, we have many other examples showing the considerable importance of the sense
of smell in copulation. It might be mentioned here that
some male insects are able to find their females although
they have been closed up in a box. Though the female
is not visible the male will fly over to seek for and to
copulate with it. Here, too we must assume that it was
mainly the sense of smell that guided the male. It is

also well known that the musk-deer and the beaver at
the rutting season secrete a substance which has the
power of attracting the female animals through its strong
odor. No one of our modern women using musk will
want to be reminded that it is derived from the musk-
bag near the sexual orifice of the male musk-deer. The
animal secreates that substance only when it becomes
sexually mature. Similarly the beaver secretes castoreum
at the period of heat.

It is possible that in some species of animals differentiation takes place through the senses which the
human sense organs are no longer able of producing,
considering that some fish resemble one another viewed
superficially by our own weak sense of sight which fails
to perceive differences between them. And assuming
further that the sense of smell can hardly guide these
fish in water, and that the voice can play no role in
their lives, we shall have to conclude that the male must
be able to recognize the female through sense impressions which escape us, and which most probably work
through the visual sense. In other cases, the differences
between the sexes is very pronounced, e. g., in the case
of the lion, the lion and the lioness being clearly dis-
tinguishable. We always have to bear in mind that
sense impressions which are perhaps absolutely incapable of differentiation in human beings play a sexual
role in animals. This is true also outside of the sphere
of sex as may be observed in the case of highly developed
insects where one individual will readily recognize another. On the other hand, even the greatest efforts of
man will not enable him to distinguish between individuals, say, of an ant colony. At all events, we may
assume that every species shows a certain reactive capac-

ity to react to sexual differentiation; that each species has its peculiar reactive capacity, and again, that each sex and individuals of each sex are characterized by an individual reactive capacity. In man this individualizaton is most highly developed. Just as two persons do not resemble each other entirely so there will also be differences in sexual reaction even though common characteristic features are to be assumed in general, as has been proven in the preceding discussions.

The discussion in this section should first of all serve to oppose the objection of many who deny the concept of heredity in the direction of the sex instinct, *i. e.,* the objection that when one assumes the direction of the sex instinct as inherited one must also assume that significant impulses and ideas are congenital. Disregarding the error that is often evident in confounding the concepts "inherited" and "congenital," we have also seen that if one is to accept the concept of heredity in the direction the sex instinct takes, ideas may not be either inherited or congenital, but that the inherited quality might merely be the different reaction to the stimuli emanating from man or woman.

One might object, however, that this is altogether no proof of the inheritance of the direction of the sex instinct. I shall therefore attempt to find another means by which to prove my contention. As a starting point let us take the theory of descent or rather Darwinism. considering the great importance which the latter has acquired we shall have to investigate whether its followers must not of necessity regard the sex instinct in man as an inherited function. Moreover, in view of the fact that Darwinism has very often been badly confused with the theory of descent and that the real principles of the former have not been sufficiently separated, we shall first of all have to go into a discussion of these principles.

Many writers before Darwin had already assumed that the various animal species are divided off from each other by sharp lines, that they have not developed singly, and independent of each other, but that some species are descended from others, and that man, too, has descended in a similar manner. Darwin tried to point out the reasons and the principles underlying this descent.

First of all, Darwin, of course, had to adopt as one of these principles the transmission of qualities from parents to offspring, a principle which has been accepted long before him. What Darwin added were the different laws of heredity. It is possible for parents to hand down qualities to their male and female offspring. There are other qualities, however, which are inherited only in *one* sex. Thus the sex glands, the primary sex characteristics, are inherited by one sex, male in the sons, female in the case of the daughters. Similarly, the secondary sex characteristics are inherited only by one sex. As a result we have the development of the beard in the male offspring, and of the breasts in the females. In this connection it is impossible for the mother to contribute in part to the inheritance of the male characteristics. The son may have a beard whose color is that of his own father's or the color of maternal grand-father. To these secondary sex characteristics also belong the psychical qualities. As I have stated above, the normal instinct itself is also to be reckoned among the secondary sex characteristics.

Another chief principle of Darwin is that of variability, the change ability of individuals and species.

That is, individuals may to a certain extent, change through external conditions. These changes are transmitted to the offspring, and the influences of the external condition makes itself felt in the same direction in the offspring as in the parents. The changes may then become more and more pronounced so that new species finally develop.

Before I proceed into Darwin's principles of natural and sexual selection, let me say something of the influence of heredity on the development of the direction of the sex instinct. We assume the transmission of the qualities of one sex to the offspring of the same sex, as we have stated above, since we may directly conclude on the basis of the laws of heredity that heterosexuality is inherited. According to Darwin, all activities exercised through many generations finally appear as hereditary even though they were originally acquired during life. As an example, let me remind you of the beavers constructing their dams, etc. That instincts may likewise be inherited by one sex may be seen in the fighting instincts of male animals. It is true that the heterosexual direction of the sex instinct is a quality adhering to both sexes, but, of course, it is of a different nature in both sexes. The impulse of the woman towards the man, and vice versa, is a quality which corresponds only to one sex, so that the mono-sexual inheritance of the impulse above discussed must necessarily be accepted. One may voice the objection that this does not agree with the theory of Weismann, according to whom qualities which have been acquired are not inherited. Apart from the limitations which this theory has already undergone, and which Weismann himself has admitted, we have also this to consider. We are unable to establish altogether whether the normal sex instinct has been acquired during life or whether it was not present immediately after birth, at the very moment when the sex glands were transferred to different, sexually differentiated individuals. We do not know under what conditions it has first made its appearance. This opinion will be justified in the face of all conclusions which have been drawn from the theory of Weismann. But aside from this the following consideration about natural selection, upon which Weismann has placed very great importance, will, I hope, also satisfy his adherents.

According to Darwin natural and sexual selection are the main factors which assured the retention of the changes. Let us of all consider the natural selection to which many are inclined to ascribe changes which Darwin himself has traced back to sexual selection. A preliminary condition for natural selection is the struggle for existence. "Just as the animal breeder will look over his cattle and permit only the promising animals to copulate so also may a sifting selection take place in Nature—a singling out among the various forms, only those fit for the living conditions surviving. What produced this sifting in Nature is not the choice of a breeder but the struggle for existence." (Eduard von Hartmann, "Truth and Error in Darwinism"). In these few words Hartmann formulates Darwin's theory of natural selection. Adherents of this main principle of Darwinism must conclude that the development of the heterosexual impulse is a necessary consequence of natural selection. There are many objections to the Darwinian theory of selection which we cannot discuss in this volume. At some future date I hope to write a work on this subject. As we have seen above, the development of the young in

the mother organism represents the highest stage of evolution. But even the fertilization of the egg-cell in the maternal organism and the subsequent development of the young outside of the maternal organism, as in birds is already a comparatively advanced stage. At any rate, this form of reproduction is by far more advanced than fertilization outside of the organism. It is to this form that we have to ascribe the gradual evolution of copulation. This took place long after the differentiation into male and female sex glands had already been affected. It facilitated the meeting of the two sex glands in the mother organism. The latter could be secured best mechanically through the adaptation of the external male and female genitals to each other, as may be observed in mammals. When we proceed from the point of view of natural selection we will see the cause of the gradual change of the locus of development and fertilization in some external influences. The most common assumption would be that the eggs fertilized outside the body were destroyed by external enemies, stranger animals or climatic conditions and consequently the species in question was forced to find some concealed and protected shelter for fertilization. Some fish find such protection in artificial grooves. The trout digs a cavity with its tail and there deposits its eggs. The perch fastens its eggs into plants, pieces of wood, stones, etc. The salmon deposits its eggs in a groove which it covers after fertilization. The stickleback builds an artificial nest which it secures with some adhesive material. After the animals have in this manner continued to deposit their eggs in concealed and protected places the locus became changed even further. The egg and the sperm cells no longer came together outside of the organism.

The fertilization of the ovum by the sperm cell took
place in the mother organism itself. We cannot tell in
what species this first took place in a way that this stage
was not again lost. But we are probably correct in assuming that it first occurred in fish, for we sometimes
find their locus of fertilization to be within the mother
organism. This is the case, for example, in viviparous
sharks. What makes the assumpton even more probable that such manner of fertilization is a protective
measure, is the fact that some male fish carry the eggs
in their mouth where they are hatched. We can only
surmise through what influences the female became the
bearer of the fruit. At all events, this method of reproduction and development may best be understood as a
protective measure for the developing young who are
thus protected against external enemies. This is also
corroborated by the fact that among lower animals there
is, in most cases, a quick separation of mother and
daughter organism, unless the latter is the result of a
budding or a similar process. In the higher animals, on
the other hand, the mother continues caring for her
young for a long time only abandoning it when it is
capable of maintaining itself independently.

The higher we gradually go in the scale of evolution
the longer the helplessness of the young—a phenomenon which may most clearly be observed in man. Caterpillars which have just crept out of their eggs can feed
themselves immediately. No parents, no relatives look
out for the newly-born individual. Fish which have just
left the egg feed for some time upon the vitteline sac
which has remained attached to the shell after its being
burst open. Afterwards they move into places where
better food is to be found. Here again the parent ani-

mals are no longer concerned with their offspring. In mammals matters are different. In the case of birds the young are for a long period fed by the parents, that is, until they are capable of maintaining themselves. Afterwards, however, the parents no longer care for their offspring. In other species the parents and their offspring stay together for a year. The long duration of helplessness shown by the newly-born human individual is only seldom to be met with in the animal world. Every newly-born child would starve to death if it were left to shift for itself. It does not possess sufficient capacity for locomotion, nor adequate development of the sense organs. But we may observe alongside this deficiency of the newly-born also an increased care of the family for the offspring. It is partly due to this that we must ascribe the intimate family life such as is found among human beings. We know that nowheres in nature are useless functions to be met with. Useless activities must disappear. Both Darwinists and teleologists will agree in the question. If the newly-born could feed itself and fight its own battle through life the care of the parents would most probably diminish. The two stand in cross relationship to each other. The greater the capacity of the offspring to maintain itself the less the parents' care.

This care for the newly-born is the highest degree of protection for them. The mother organism carries the fruit to full maturity, whereas in the lower organism the eggs are left to shift for themselves. External dangers induced the animals to change the locus of fertilization. This occurred long after that period of evolutionary history marked by the meeting of two animals for the purpose of reproduction. But no sooner had external dangers induced the animals to transfer fertilization and maturation into the internal organism, than a corresponding transformation of the organs had also to take place. Through heredity the new organization had to be transmitted to the offspring. But not only the organs must be inherited; the offspring must also inherit the same urge to fertilize the egg within the mother organism, unless opposing factors stand in the way. For, since this process afforded the greatest protection, it is to be assumed that the eggs fertilized outside the organism were destroyed, and that finally only such offspring as had been developed in the above manner were born. Through a continued summation of the process this form of fertilization must have become established as an instinctive activity by way of heredity and natural selection. Individuals born outside the mother animal reached their full development less and less frequently until they finally died out completely. Other instincts, too, are supposed to have been developed in the same way.

A close glance at these last considerations regarding the relationship between natural selection and the normal sex instinct and we will discover a surprisingly close analogy between sex instinct and the secondary sex characteristics. This has already been referred to. We shall have no further scruples pratically from the point of view of evolution in regarding the sex instinct as a secondary sex characteristic based on natural selection, just as Darwin has established it for numerous physical qualities.

In opposition to Darwin, Weismann, as everyone knows, maintains that acquired characteristics are not inherited, if the germ-plasm is not changed at the same time. But even Weismann is of the opinion that when in the struggle for existence bisexual reproduction has become a fact, it must be retained, and that those individuals which abandon sexual reproduction must perish. Sexual reproduction permits the offspring to adapt themselves to external conditions better than uni-sexual reproduction. It is only through a binding of numerous hereditary tendencies, as in sexual reproduction, that variations in multi-cellular individuals can be produced, so necessary for adaptation. We must therefore agree with Weismann that sexual reproduction is necessary to the preservation of the species. Science actually proves that this opinion is justified. Even a hundred years ago Sprengel, writing of the reproduction of plants, expressed the opinion that nature does not intend that androgynous flowers should be fertilized through their own pollen. What Darwin, Häckel, Weismann and others of our own contemporaries sought to establish are truths which have been held many decades before. The theories of Sprengel and of others, however, gave rise only to teleological interpretations. But it is not a vital matter how we conceive the origin and the cause for bisexual reproduction. Since fruitful offspring in animals and in man could be produced only when the male copulated with the female, the instinct of performing coitus had to be transmitted to the offspring, for the inheritance of qualities takes place through *one* sex only.

In like manner it may be explained why different forms of bisexual reproduction occur in the lower vertebrates. We have already seen the different behavior of fish, many of them depositing their eggs in certain places to be fertilized by the male sperm. The male merely follows the female in order to fertilize the eggs. In order to achieve this purpose the male will battle off rivals in order to prevent them from fertilizing the female. The young cannot develop from the eggs unless they have fertilized. They will quickly disintegrate if fertilization does not take place immediately after being deposited. That is to say, only such offspring can be produced which have inherited the urge of the parent animals to copulate and to fertilize in the manner described. Of course, we cannot always explain why the mode of fertilization of a particular animal species shows a certain variation from that of another; why the river-lamprey holds fast the female while both empty the germinal material; why some fish thrust themselves out of the water during fertilization, belly to belly, at the same time, depositing eggs and sperm; why some sea-fish perform fertilization in such a manner that the female swims at a higher level while the male is lower down, the eggs being dropped into the region impregnated by the males. As we have said, some details are not entirely clear. But since the offspring of every species will develop only when the eggs have been fertilized immediately after being extruded—a great number of the eggs, as is well known, serve as food to other fish— only such offspring will be developed which have inherited that mode of fertilization.

It is not to be supposed, however, that these considerations regarding natural selection will fully explain the rise of contrectation. Darwin has very cautiously steered clear of explaining the origin of the instincts. We shall have to uphold the same attitude of caution regarding contrectation. Let us assume that at some past time there were two individuals, A and B, who were capable of reproducing themselves asexually. Let us further assume that at the same time there were two other animals of the same species, M and W, which reproduced sexually. In accordance with the principle of natural selection we concluded that the offspring of A and B will have perished because only *one* hereditary tendency was present in each offspring. In the struggle for existence the asexual offspring had to perish, consequently; on the other hand, the individuals brought forth sexually, that is to say, the offspring of M and W, lived on because they were better endowed in the struggle for existence due to the fact that in them two hereditary tendencies were blended. This does not, however, explain how the impulse of the two individuals, M and W, originated. For though in connection with natural selection we may assume that the impulse has further developed in the following generations, it does not explain how the first traces of the instinct appeared. This gap in the argument of natural selection can not be pointed out too sharply in order that other attempts at explanation be not neglected by over-estimating the proofs of natural selection. This not only refers to the the sex instinct and to other psychical qualities, but also to physical ones. The theory of variability or changeability which Darwin and his followers adopted as their method of explanation, is quite correct, but its real causes have remained entirely unexplained. In regards to variability one must assume that under certain conditions certain changes took place in the organism and that these changes were reproduced and cumulated in their further course through the generations. The real reasons for the development of the variations are not in this manner explained. And as this remains unex-

plained for the present we cannot regard as explained
the first appearance of the instinct of mating during the
history of evolution.

We may assume that the sex instinct of man and
woman as well as that of higher animals is only a means
of bringing together two cells, the sperm cell and the
egg cell. How this process came about as a whole was
in part discussed in the first chapter and partly in the
last few pages. But we cannot ascertain what the details
about this development were. I believe, however, that
we may readily assume that the sex instinct did not
originate directly from a conscious urge. In respect to
the migratory instinct of birds it is assumed, as already
described above, that at first these birds had flown to
remote regions in order to seek for food—this might
have been an intelligent act—and that this quality had
been inherited by the offspring. Natural selection then
stepped in allowing only those animals to survive and
to bear offspring which performed that activity, *i. e.*,
migrating. Through a further pairing of the animals
an ever increasing prominence was given to this instinct.
Wundt, moreover, justly remarks that other attempts
at explanation do not contradict this theory of original intelligent activities.

Transfering these considerations to the sex instinct
we are dealing with the question whether or not the sex
instinct, to which corresponds the instinct of reproduction, has originally arisen from an intelligent activity.
He who upholds the standpoint of evolution cannot very
well assume that the conscious purpose of reproduction
had originally produced the sex instinct. In the entire
animal world, in their opinion, coupling of animals can
never have served this conscious purpose. Later, it is

true, when man had reached a certain degree of intelligence, the sex instinct was recognized as such an intelligent activity.   But it must again be stressed that the sex act is rarely chosen as a conscious means of reproducing.

We have seen that the development and the heredity of heterosexuality appear to follow necessarily from the basis of natural selection.   A further principle of Darwinism is sexual selection.   This depends on the advantages that certain animals have over others of the same sex and the same species in relation to reproduction exclusively.   Several male stags woo the same female. They fight for her and the strongest carries away the victory copulating with the female.   Since only that male reproduces which has been best endowed in the competition for the female the offspring inherit only the most valuable qualities, inasmuch as the males with the inferior qualities have perished in the struggle and never succeed in copulating.   Added to this is the fact that the female on her part chooses her mate.   Peacocks unfold the splendor of their plumage in sight of the female in order to excite her.   The pea-hen selects one of the males, giving preference to the more beautiful one.   This, too, has the effect of bringing about the reproduction of males with the more valuable qualities only.   It happens that as a result of an excess of females or for other reasons weak males are sometimes enabled to perform copulation.   For example, while two stags or salmons fight for the female, another much weaker rival may copulate her.   This, however, is only a rather rare occurrence; for, in general, the offspring in such cases will be less endowed, inasmuch as inferior males, with rare exceptions, will usually copulate only with inferior females. Wallace and others have opposed sexual selection as a principle of explanation. Groos opposed the theory of conscious choice though holding fast to the idea of unconscious preference of the females for the well-endowed males. Many have denied the importance of selection by the female and have reduced every thing to natural selection. I will not enter into a dispute about this question. However, if sexual selection is an added factor it must clearly refer to the inheritance of the direction of the sex instinct. We merely have to uphold the idea that the impulse of the male towards the female is inherited by the male and vice versa. The question of the reproduction of males having no impulse towards the female must be excluded for only those males endowed with such impulse are engaged in the struggle for female. Only in man may we observe sometimes males lacking the sex instinct wooing the female for material or other reasons. In animals this phenomenon is entirely absent. Of many homosexuals it is, of course, maintained that they have a numerous offspring. But, in general, it must be assumed in the case of man, that only those individuals possessing the normal sex instinct will reproduce. Sexual selection in man then plays a like role as in animals and contributes to the heredity of the direction of the sex instinct.

The direction of the sex instinct from the point of view of sexual selection is as important as the sex glands. Just as copulation will fail in males devoid of testicles so also, will there be no copulation when the impulse towards the female is absent. The male will not participate in the competition for the female. Though the possibility cannot be excluded that these males, too, will participate, yet, generally speaking, they show a want of pleasure in it, so that we may leave them out of our discussion altogether.

We may thus see that as soon as the normal sex instict has made its appearance not only natural but also sexual selection are concerned with the transmission of the qualities. This principle of Darwinism, then would also argue for the heredity of the heterosexual impulse.

It will then be seen why it is important that animal mating first took place as a result of the sex instinct. There can be no doubt, in view of the well-known facts of heredity that the normal sex instinct as a secondary sex characteristic had to be transformed into an inherited quality after having been present in millions of generations. As I have already mentioned, the opponents of the inheritance of acquired characteristics will find no offence in this conception, for the "omnipotence of natural selection," on which these writers rely so much would also argue for heterosexuality as an inherited quality.

———————

Before I proceed any further with this discussion let me cite the communication of a homosexual, which will tend to show that homosexuality does not in the least exclude marriage and reproduction. This man's detailed information about his family are the more valuable inasmuch as he is a man of science. His recital, of course, does not contradict the conclusion drawn above, *i.e.*, that generally only normal men participate in the competition for women. As a matter of fact there are psychosexual hermaphrodites who feel themselves attracted to both men and women. Pure homosexuals, too, are known who marry and reproduce out of selfish reasons. But the rule is that heterosexuals predominate in reproduction. This is true more of man than of woman.

Case XXX. Mr. P. L. writes: I am 33 years of age, a university instructor, and have many brothers and sisters. Consumption prevails in the family. Several of my relatives have already died of this disease.

From the age of five to nine I used to play mostly with girls, because there were no boys among the children of my neighborhood. I played with dolls and often wished to have been born a girl. But this entirely disappeared when I was with other boys. I made rapid progress at school. I graduated from gymnasium at the age of 17 and before I had completed my 21st year I had taken the last of my University examinations.

Up to the age of 13 my true friendships were with women only, but these were much older than myself. They were usually educated women of a literary bent interested in my rapid mental development. When I was about thirteen I became acquainted with a physician whose mother had told me much about her son. He was 37, of a fine appearance with light-gray hair, almost steel gray; his whiskers were of the same color. This man became my ideal. Never before had I known any man who pleased me so much, and whenever, in later years I met a man with similar hair and beard, and of about his own age, I always wished to make his acquaintance. From 13 to 14 my sex organs became fully developed. I occassionally masturbated up to the age of 17 or 18, but have not continued this practice. At the university I sometimes used to sleep with my fellow-students. On such occasions each would insert his penis between the thighs of the other. This often resulted in ejaculation on the part of both. However, I have never loved any of these students. On the other hand, I constantly met with men who atracted me very much. In all cases these were scholarly men. All of them were between 35 and 45 years of age. All had steel-gray hair and whiskers of the same color and all somewhat resembled the above mentioned physician. Such were the men whom I liked. I imagined that I knew them perfectly, that I walked arm in arm with them, that I kissed them. Later I also imagined it delightful to sleep with them. I also associated with men who did not fully correspond to my ideal in regards to age.

I never experienced any love for women, though I was much in their company. Sometimes this aversion caused my friends to taunt me for it. I began to practice my profession very early, and made rapid progress in it. From day to day the desire to find a man whom I could love became more urgent. I would listen to my friends' talk about their affairs with women, how they kissed them, etc. This repelled me very much; for I found it disagreeable to kiss my own sisters. But if one of those ideal men I have described would only allow me to kiss him on his lips, how happy this would make me!

When I was 26 I made the acquaintance of the first man who seemed to love me. This enlightened me about the fact that other men, with the feelings and desires like my own also existed. The man was a very prominent physician, 50 years of age. In the appendix below he will be designated briefly as Mr. A. I knew him for a long time, but not intimately enough. For some time we lived in the same city. One day when both of us were in another city he wrote me a letter asking me to come to see him in his hotel, saying that he had to give me some information about a common friend. I accepted the invitation and that same evening went to see him in the hotel. We had dinner together and then we retired to his room. Though I made several attempts to lead off the conversation to the subject of the letter, I did not succeed. After ten o'clock I finally wanted to take leave of him and to hire a room in the same hotel, for there was only one bed in A.'s room. But he would not listen to me. He insisted that his bed was large enough for two, I should please stay and sleep with him, as he still had to tell me about certain matters. I protested, saying that it would be better if we slept separately; but finally he quieted all my objections so that I stayed with him. My suspicions had already been aroused by his peculiar behaviour and by his persistence. But since I had not before heard about homosexual love, it never even occurred to me that he might have the same feelings as I. I was the first to undress; I lay down on one side of the spacious bed. He followed and as soon as he was undressed he took me in his arms, kissed me and fondled me. He told me that he had been in love with me the very first time he had seen me; that he made many efforts before to meet me, but that I had never responded to his insinuations.

On this occasion I learned at first hand that other men with my feelings also existed. This knowledge was by no means pleasing to me. I began to reproach myself, to accuse myself for never having sought intercourse with women, thinking that sexual intercourse would surely have prevented my unnatural desires from developing. I then decided to depart from A. as soon as possible, and to find a sympathetic woman with whom I might have

intercourse. I actually did succeed in this purpose: she
was attractive and conformed to my expectations and
easily gave in to my desires. Sex intercourse with her
was not difficult for me. Ejaculation occurred quickly;
in about three hours I performed the act four times with
her. But this kind of intercourse did not afford me any
pleasure. Nine months later I met another woman, Mrs.
B. with whom I began a similar sexual relationship. Intercourse with B. caused me great pleasure. Subsequently I also performed coitus with the first whore.
But it only came off under psychical constraint. I also
had intercourse with other young women, once with a
girl of 21, and another time with a girl of 24, but with
neither of these did I get any pleasure. I concluded then
that it would be impossible for me to find sufficient pleasure in normal intercourse; I reverted to my homosexual
love which gave me full satisfaction. I am really fond
of women, I do like their company and I frequently associate with them; but my sexual love belongs to men
only.

When I compare my own passionate feelings with
those of other men with whom I talked over this subject,
I must conclude that my sex instinct is not very strong.
In the last six years I have made the following observations: At times I experience increased sensual excitements, together with a strong desire to sleep with a man.
This excitement lasts from three to eight days. This
condition is usually relieved by a nocturnal pollution and
the sensation again disappears. These conditions of excitement occur irregularly in intervals of two, four and
six weeks. They fail to appear altogether when I practice sex intercourse every week or every fortnight. When
I have sex intercourse with a man or a woman immedi-

ately after the onset of the excitement it immediately disappears; whereas ordinarily it continues, for about three to eight days, on the average, until it is relieved through a nocturnal pollution.

For some time I made a complete notation of my dreams, for a period of four months. During that time I had 92 different dreams. Some nights I did not dream at all as far as I could remember afterwards; at other times I dreamed as many as five different dreams. During the four months I twice dreamed of performing coitus with women, three times of sex intercourse with men, five times of being together with women without any reference to the sex intercourse or sex organs; twelve times I had had erotic dreams associated with men. During all this time I had no intercourse with women, but five times with men; I also had nine pollutions.

Men of about 35 to 50 attract me most. Once, however, I slept with a man of 28, another time with a man of 29. Both of these, however, already had full grown beards and appeared at least five years older than they were. It is impossible for me to associate sexually with boys or young men for I have no inclination towards them by nature. Old men do not excite me either. Nevertheless, I once had intercourse with a man of over 60, but his features still appeared young and he possessed what I have always admired in a man—beautiful gray hair. I do not like heavy-built men, nor am I fond of big men. Men of medium height are my favorite type. Their hair and whiskers must be of a black color, blended with light gray, or they may also be light blond. But they must not be red-haired. My decided preference is for dark and light steel-gray hair.

Let me stress again the point that the man whom I first

met had also steel-gray hair and gray whiskers. It is an open question what influence this man had upon me by directing my sexual feelings in a contrary path. He was 37 or 38 years old and of medium height. It is impossible for me to have intercourse with an uneducated man. For my aesthetic feelings would be wounded thereby, and I would get no pleasure out of it. My preference is for university and high-school instructors, physicians and lawyers. My first experience with A. took place about seven years ago. Since then I had intimate relations with twenty-six other men. But of these, twenty-six men I loved only three. Mr. C. was my first love. But with him I had no sexual intercourse. We were attached to one another for three years and are still good friends. But we are not in love any more. At that time C. was a widower but he has married since. We rode together, saw one another almost every day. He used to take me in his arms or hold me upon his lap for hours. During these three years there were two occasions when peculiar circumstances forced us to sleep in the same bed. But he never touched my genitals; nor did I touch his. He always wished to hold me in his arms until I fell asleep, but he never proceeded any further. I loved C. with all fervor possible. There can be no doubt of this. His love for me was just as strong. He told me that I was his third love.

I also loved K. but I have no reason to believe that he returned my love. After a year of vain hopes and efforts to win his love I gave it up. I made the acquaintance of N, who is my present love. My love for him is very strong. We are living far apart from each other, but we manage to see each other frequently even at a great expense. We correspond daily and telegrams are often exchanged. Though he is married it is me that he loves most. I am his third "friend." His first love attachment lasted five years. His "beau" was married and about his own age. His second "friend" was a man of 26 and their relationship lasted nearly two years.

I never had any sexual relationship with F., and never really loved him. He liked me very much, and often we used to kiss and embrace each other. But in spite of a few favorable opportunities for it, I never insisted that we sleep together. With three of the twenty-seven men I shall describe below, I never had any sexual intercourse, namely with C., F., and K. Twenty-four thus remain with whom I did perform it. With the latter, B., E., and G., and H., the act was performed in such a manner that each placed his penis between the other's thighs. With A. I performed intromission in the anus, he taking the passive role. The act was not successful when I was the passive partner. With the other nineteen sexual intercourse consisted in fellatio. For several years it was impossible for me to perform it. L. was the first with whom I tried it. D., L., and U., received my sex in their mouth while I masturbated them.

In the following lines I shall briefly describe these twenty-seven men. Of course many more of these homosexual men were known to me, at least 200 of them. I met them in bathing-resorts, in cafes, restaurants, at vaudeville theatres and in many other haunts where homosexual men usually meet. I have traveled much. I have seen almost all countries of the world and have come across many homosexuals and spoken to many of them. In my description of them I shall always mention their ages when I first met them.

Mr. A., 50 years of age, married, has *one* child. He

shows no traces of effemination, except in his gait. At the age of 26 he became an army-physician and remained in that position many years. In the pursuit of his profession he made the acquaintance of many officers who had sexual intercourse with him. He practiced normal intercourse only with his wife but succeeds in performing coitus only with great difficulty, while intercourse with men came very easy for him.

Mr. B., 42 years old, professor, unmarried. He makes a very fine and delicate appearance, dresses very scrupulously and loves diamonds and jewelry. He is very fond of social activities and associates with both men and women. He likes singing and has a fine tenor voice. His first sexual sensation occurred when he was 18. At that time he made the acquaintance of a priest with whom he had sexual intercourse.

Mr. C., physician, 43 years of age. During the time I knew him he was a widower. He had one child by his first wife, and two children by his second. I had no sexual intercourse with him. It was simply love.

Mr. D., manufacturer, 45 years old, single. He often had intercourse with women before he was 18. Then he made the acquaintance of a priest who was married. He fell in love with him and they frequently had sexual intercourse. For a time D. lived in a city of 60,000 population where he knew at least 50 homosexuals.

Mr. E., manufacturer, 38 years of age, married, has *three* children. Before his marriage he never had a love-affair, though he always liked men. He draws no distinctions between the sexes, loving both men and women and having intercourse with both alike.

Mr. F., university instructor, 45 years old, has *four* children. I had no sexual relationship with him. It was merely a love-affair. He told me that he also loved another man.

Mr. G., teacher, 37 years of age, has *two* children. He observed his inclination towards men before his marriage and hoped that normal intercourse with his wife would tend to make these inclinations disappear. Though his marriage is a happy one, he nevertheless fell in love with several men after marriage, and associated with them sexually. His intercourse is with educated people exclusively, and consequently with his colleagues.

M⁀. H., physician, 42 years of age. He is very fond of female society, frequently gives small parties for women, but they repel him sexually nevertheless. He is a man of fine tastes, a friend of music and the arts.

Mr. I., 38 years of age, lawyer, married, has *one* child. He has a beautiful figure and also has a large penis and testicles, which I have seen. Before his 19th year he frequently had sex intercourse with the women-servants of the house. When he was 19 he made the acquaintance of a merchant who fell in love with him. They had sexual intercourse frequently. At the age of 23 he married a tall, well-built woman who was somewhat older than himself. At the beginning his wife experienced pain during coitus on account of his large penis. Even after the birth of their first child these pains did not decrease. Four years later he met a man with whom he fell in love. Sexual intercourse between them took place often. Since then he frequently had intercourse with both men and women. He would find as much pleasure in normal intercourse with women as with men were it not for the fact that his large penis caused the women much pain. At least he thinks that this is the main reason for his homosexuality. He is a man of great passion and performs coitus three or four times every week either with a man or with a woman. He lives in a city of 350,000 population, he is a member of a club consisting mainly of married men of 30 to 60. The club has 50 members, and has beautiful quarters in a large building, consisting of a card-room, reading-room library, music-rooms and various sleeping-rooms for the use of the members of the club's guests. Mr. I. tells me that among the fifty members there were at least eight homosexuals.

Mr. J., lawyer, 46 years of age, married, has two children, both of them dead. In his opinion his homosexuality is congenital. In his knowledge he always loved men more than women. He married with the hope of ridding himself of the anomaly, but all in vain. At first sex intercourse with him was easy, but later coitus became impossible. He cannot induce an erection when with his wife but it is very easy with men.

Mr. K., politician, member of Parliament, married, has *three* children. When he was 19 he fell in love with a man and has been in love with him ever since. Fifteen years ago his "beloved" married. K. was disconsolate and, as he told me, himself undertook marriage for the simple reason that his "love" also was married. The two, however, continued in their mutual attachment and met very frequently. No sexual intercourse took place between K. and myself. His hair is just as I like it. I loved him very much and used to fondle him often.

Mr. L., Baron von, 29 years of age, single. He never loved women, and he finds it impossible to have a normal sex relationship. Nevertheless, when he was 16, he performed coitus with women, and successfully, too. But afterwards he could no longer induce erection. With men, however, this is very easy.

Mr. M., merchant, 34 years of age, single. Before he was 20 he had intercourse with women. He loved many men. He is somewhat vain in regards to dress. He uses powder and other cosmetics. He only loves men about his own age.

Mr. N., 44 years old, married, has *three* children. He always loved men only. He liked to visit the bathing-resorts in order to look at the naked men. Before he married he had relations with three different women. The first five nights after marriage he was incapable of producing an erection nor intromission. Later he was more successful. Several years after the marriage, after the birth of one of his children, he made the acquaintance of a man to whom he became immediately attached. Sexual intercourse between them took place. N. found intercourse with him easier and much more pleasant than coitus with his wife. Since then he has loved men only. He never had any desire to associate with a woman sexually.

Mr. O., 34 years of age, single. When he was 31 he had his first sex experience with a man. Since then he has loved only men.

Mr. P., man of independent means, formerly banker, 35 years old. He has been homosexual since childhood. When still very young his father's coachman gave him his first instruction about it. He likes the company of women, but as far as his sex instinct is concerned, he loves only men—men who are ten to fifteen years his senior.

Mr. Q., a man of independent means, formerly banker, 68 years of age, widower, has *three* children. At the age of 51, after the death of his wife, he had his first love experience for a man—a man of 31. But he had always liked men. From his early youth he always had the urge to look at men's genitals. He loves only men who are from 28 to 40.

Mr. R., musician, 42 years old, single. When he was 21 he fell in love with a married man of 38. Previously he had been surprised when he heard of men falling in love with other men.

Mr. S., brewer, 37, married, has *three* children. Before his marriage he had intercourse with several women. Coitus with his own wife is easy. But he prefers intercourse with men. His chief pleasure is to devour the male semen.

Mr. T., mechanic, 42 years old, single. He tried intercourse with women but felt no pleasure in it. He especially likes men of the age of 50 to 60.

Mr. U., musician, 52 years old, single. He first learned about pederasty when he was still in high-school. He never had any intercourse with women.

Mr. V., opera singer, 40 years old, single. His first love affair was with an officer, while serving in the army. He is a passive pederast, and, as he states, can find only few men who are willing to gratify him in this manner.

Mr. W., artist, 47 years of age, has *one* child. His father has been dead many years. He is quite sure that his father, too, had been homosexual and that he had transmitted it to him. He never had any liking for women. His relations with men he traces to his 18th year. One of these affairs lasted nine years. He married at the age of 44. Though he loves his wife he prefers men. He married in order to put an end to the continual gossip of his friends and relatives.

Mr. X., physician, 28, single. He was never successful in performing coitus with a woman. He tried it repeatedly with several women without being able to produce an erection or ejaculation. In intercourse with men ejaculation immediately takes place.

Mr. Y., merchant, 52, widower, has *five* children. He was 31 when he had his first love-affair with a man. This took place after the birth of all his children. He also liked men previously, even before his marriage. Whenever a man visited him he would sleep with him in the same bed. Several times this made his wife suspicious for she could not understand the reason for it. But none of the men with whom he slept would fondle him or even touch his genitals. Consequently he used to think that he was the only man afflicted with such an unnatural inclination. Then he made the acquaintance of a homosexual in a railroad train. Since then he performed sex intercourse with men only.

Mr. Z., merchant, 39, married has *three* children. He is a Jew. As he says he always loved men and women equally and intercourse with men gives him as much pleasure as normal coitus.

Mr. AA., 44, single. He is a man of wide experience and extensive culture. He believes that his father, too, was homosexual. From his early childhood he had loved men only. He often used to visit the bathing resorts to watch the naked men. His first sexual intercourse with men occurred at the age of 24. The man was a Catholic priest. Since then he had relationships with other men though he finds pleasure also in women.

Of these 27 men 14 are either married or widowers. In all they have 36 children. Not one of these 14 men is childless. Seventeen of the men have finished their academic studies and are practicing their respective professions. Five are physicians, four university or high-school instructors, three lawyers, three musicians, three merchants, two manufacturers, two men of independent means; there is also an artist, banker, politician, brewer and mechanic.

In my opinion, married men are quite as homosexual as single ones. I am personally acquainted with as many as 200 other homosexuals. More than half of them are married. Nevertheless, most homosexuals have hardly if any sexual intercourse with women. Mr. X. is the only man I know who was a total failure when he attempted coitus. He never succeeded in performing it. L. was at first successful, but only for a short time, while T. never tried it. At any rate, I doubt the much accepted theory that homosexuals are without offspring. Every one of these 14 married men had children, and with only two or three exceptions, all married men of my wide acquaintanceship with homosexual, have one or more children. Mr. BB., one of my acquaintances, who is also homosexual, believes that married men who are homosexual, usually have children. On the basis of an extensive list of his married friends he even believes that more homosexuals with children may be found than normal men. But he did not give me any statistical data about this point.

It is surprising that Mr. P. L. should have associated with so many people who in spite of their homosexuality had numerous offspring. This seems to me to be related to certain social conditions which brought him in more frequent contact with married men than with single ones. For, other things being equal, I consider it certain, that homosexual men will produce less children than heterosexual ones. Not only the pleasure of mating with a woman is lacking in them but even the capacity for it. Sexual selection, considered as a separate factor, thus is capable of establishing the inheritance of the heterosexual reactive capacity.

We have seen in the discussion that the heterosexual sex instinct from the standpoint of the theory of descent and of Darwinism must under all circumstances be conceived as an inherited function. Sexual and natural selection do not admit of any other interpretation. But it would be well to guard against onesidedness in interpreting it. The principles which Darwinism adduces in regards to the origin of the species and the descent of man from the lower organism, are yet not calculated to solve the riddle of descent. For the main hypotheses of Darwinism, heredity and variability, have up to now been left unexplained both by Darwin and his followers. Darwinism justly accepts heredity and variability as well established, but does not explain them. Neither Darwin's theory of pangenisis, nor Häckel's theory of perigenisis, nor Wisemann's theory of the continuity of the germplasm, nor the gemmulation theory of his opponent Haacke, have up to now contributed anything essential to the explanation of heredity. Nor can I find any explanation in the writings of O. Hertwig, Brooks, etc., clever though their theories might be. That two sex-cells uniting together will under favorable conditions produced an individual of the same species, is, and for the time being, must remain a riddle, but let us not dwell too long on the negative side of Darwinism. No soner had Darwin investigated the external circumstances through which one species is transformed into another, their relationship to the theory of man's descent from the lower organisms, then others began to ask the further question: Why are the organisms so equipped that they may become changed into different organisms? Up to now Darwinism has not been able to answer this question. It is not surprising therefore that many have sought for an answer in another principle. This principle is teleology. It is true that different writers have also tried to make use of still other principles. Let us refer to the discussion of Nägeli according to whom the chief reasons for variations must be found in internal processes. These internal processes are molecular forces. According to him these internal forces and not external ones as Darwin has assumed, cause the development of the sense organs. This concept of Nägeli which presents a strictly materialistic point of view, may, of course, be confronted by the same question as the discussion of Darwinism. Why are the internal forces such as to cause growth according to definite laws? And since an answer to this question is not forthcoming either, we may not dispute the right of the other conception, the teleological one, to offer its explanation.

Recently Josef Müller attempted to establish heredity on his theory of gamophagia. He assumes with Weismann that the paternal and the maternal germ consist of numerous units in which the hereditary tendencies of both is lodged, and that when these two germs meet a struggle of existence between the different hereditary units take place. This struggle between the paternal and the maternal units causes some to succumb and to be devoured and others to be victorious. These latter determine what hereditary predispositions are transmitted to the new being. That the child in some points resembles its mother and its father in some other details is to be explained in such a manner that now maternal now paternal units are victorious. Müller regards it an especially purposive arrangement for a bond to exist between the organs preventing the formation of mixed forms incapable of functioning, a bond causing the simplest elements of both primary and secondary sex characteristics to suffer the same fate in the struggle for existence during gamophagia. This is the reason why ovaries and penis do not arise from the same germ units, but that ovaries are grouped together with the uterus, the vagina, and the clitoris, and not with the penis, superfluous for its functioning. Müller similarly assumes that when the sex glands, be it ovaries or testicles, develop, a brain corresponding to these sex glands, is formed also. In the case of man, a psychosexual centre in the brain is developed for the control of the sex instinct towards woman and vice versa in the case of man. We need not bring up the question here whether or not the theory of Müller is correct. The fact remains that generally the corresponding sex instinct is developed. Nor does Müller's theory clarify the mechanism of the process. We may at any rate, return to Darwin's principle of natural selection. But even then we would be justified in referring to the teleological principles for the above named reason.

By teleology we understand that concept according to which the idea purposiveness is the formative principle. While some thinkers, among them Anaxagoras, regard Plato as the originator of this idea of purpose in nature, others, the proponents of anthropological teleology, among them the Stoics, recognize the usefulness of certain arrangements for the purposes of man only. In the principle of teleology the main idea is the presence of purpose in the flux of things. It has often been maintained that Darwin gave the death blow to teleology. But this is not so and can never be until Darwinism will be enabled to solve the above-named riddles. The controversy between casuality, the principle underlying modern Darwinism and teleology is of long standing. The objective adherents of teleology, *e.g.,* Hartmann, have with great wisdom sought support for their point of view in Darwinism itself. Leibnitz, similarly, in contrast to Spinoza, expressed the opinion that the universality of cause and effect is inconceivable without teleological assumptions. Other teleologists, again, failed to see any contradiction between this conception and Darwinism.

I consider it superfluous to throw ourselves into this dispute. It is of no consequences for our question whether we recognize mechanical laws in nature or whether we hold to the opinion that a predetermined design rules all events. For Darwinism, too, maintains that everything purposive is retained. What distinguishes his theory from teleology is the assumption that it rests on causative grounds. If the heredity of the direction is considered purposive we may explain it both from the standpoint of teleology and from Darwinism. Accordingly we shall occupy ourselves only with the question whether such hereditary transmission is purposive or not. Our judgment about purpose are often subjective and vary therefore. In regards to the structure of the body, at any rate, purposiveness will always be a point of departure. Organs which serve a definite function are useful. Organs which do not are not useful. The

function of each organ is already determined at birth.
The liver will manufacture bile necessary for digestion,
the kidneys will remove superflous substances from the
organism, the food will be prepared for digestion by
the salivary glands of the mouth. If man were provided
with a mouth, pharynx and œsaphagus and with the
muscles for swallowing food, but with an oesaphagus
which terminated not in the stomach but externally, so
that stomach and oesaphagus were not connected, this
would be a purposeless arrangement. Such an arrangement would still be purposeless if man knew the anatomical structure of the body and perhaps could cause
a connection between oesophagus and stomach through
a major operation. For purposiveness of organization
lies exactly in independence from fortuitous external
influences after birth. The function of the organs should
not be interfered with by such influences, and be of use
to the organism as a whole, the function of the organ
persisting and becoming extinct only with the death of
the organ. Form and function are bound together very
intimately. "In this respect nothing is unimportant,
nothing might have been different than it is. Every
organ, nay, every cell and every part of a cell is predetermined, for the role which it is to play" (August
Weismann). What role reproduction plays in the life
of animals may be seen in the case of those animals who
die immediately after performing the act. Drones, butterflies, ephemeral flies, and some of the grasshoppers
perish soon after they copulate or lay their eggs. The
same may be observed in the river-lampreys which die
after fertilization; also the eels which perish immediately after copulating.

When we regard the anatomical structure of the human body and of the higher vertebrae we may observe that each part points to the acts of copulation. Let us first of all consider the essential part of the genitals, the sex glands. The testicles prepare the spermatozoa and these can be effective only when coming in contact with the egg-cell. The egg-cell is formed in the maternal organism. When we refuse to regard the product of the testicles as superfluous and that the production of spermatozoa is merely a caprice of nature; when we further consider that the sperm-cell has the inherent capacity to form a new individual when uniting with the ovum of the woman, we must conclude that the parents are invested with the capacity to bring about this union of sperm cell and egg cell. Furthermore we also know that for the purpose of the growth of the egg it is not merely necessary that sperm and egg cell meet outside of the human body but that they unite within the material organism. A purposive formation must therefore be supposed also with regards to the intromission of the sperm. The external copulatory organs, of the higher animals, including man, have a useful purpose for the act. In view of the construction of the sex organs there can be no doubt that copulation through the immision of the penis into the vagina, is the most useful method. It facilitates the union of the two sex cells. One might of course imagine a more useful arrangement, *i.e.*, the egg descending lower, or the penis penetrating deeper into the organism of the mother to make fertilization even more certain. But since we must judge the purposiveness of a function, the elements present, and since the structure of the male and female sex parts is not such as to bring about an absolutely certain union of egg and sperm cells, we must be satisfied with that which is purposive under the existing anatomical conditions.

If the sex instinct were not inherited, copulation would depend merely on reflection or experience. Should reproduction, however, be left merely to reflection or experience the possibility of the extinction of the species would immediately be given. Such extinction is even quite probable. There can be no doubt that intercourse would never take place in man as a result of experiences during life. Man's reproducing or failure to reproduce would then be left to accident; if fortuitous conditions were unfavorable for reproduction the extinction of the race would follow. Chance occurrences in one generation would thus destroy the fruits of millions of generations and would endanger the continuance of the race. Whoever recognizes a principle of design at all must regard such an eventuality a contradiction to the purpose of life. For reproduction has always been regarded as the main purpose of existence by teleogists, such as Schopenhauer, Hartmann, et al. We shall hardly find a proponent of teleology who does not share this opinion. The human reproductive and copulative organs have been created for the purpose of reproduction and are adapted to each other. From the preceding discussions it must then be assumed from the point of view of teleology the utilization of the organs for specific purposes was made possible by an inherited predisposition. This is somewhat similar to self-preservation which according to teleology is also purposive activity. If man were endowed with reproductive organs while the instinct itself were to be acquired only through experience it would be the same as equipping him with everything in connection with self-preservation except with a regulating medium for preserving life. Hunger is such a well-known regulating medium warning man that he must eat in order to preserve life. But the sex instinct just as the sensation of hunger is not acquired during life. The sensation of hunger appears in the newly-born immediately without the aid of experience. Though the means of satisfying hunger are not as yet conscious in the child, nature has nevertheless provided it with the means to gratify the instinct. I shall only mention the sucking movements, which Lotze, who maintains that the instincts are acquired, assumes, lead the child to swallow foods to remove the sensation of hunger.

It is true that nature has not endowed the child with the instinct to suckle, to grasp the mother's breast. Lotze rightly remarks that this impulse to grasp the breasts comes only with experience. And one may also conclude that in regards to the sex instinct the impulse towards specific kinds of external objects was not inherited. However, this conclusion from analogy would be premature. At first the sense activity of the newly-born is much too faint to enable it to distinguish between the objects of the external world, such as the milk or the mother's breast, just as the growing boy is enabled to distinguish between the sexes. This deficient sensory capacity in the newly-born is, however, complemented by the instinct of mother-love showing itself in such a touching manner in the higher animals, including man. This impulse of the mother to take care of the newly-born and her capacity of feeding it by means of a special organ, the mammary glands, is a perfect complement to the capacity of the newly-born to preserve itself. Either one of these instincts would be superfluous by itself, since the purposeful cannot go hand in hand with superfluous. The superfluous organ soon becomes extinct or

stunted in growth.   This inverse relationship between
the newly-born's capacity for self-preservation, and the
mother-instinct is quite well founded.   The caterpillar
can feed itself as soon as it has crawled out of its egg;
therefore it needs no mother to protect it.   Without a
mother the mammal would perish.   For this reason the
mother, on the basis of an inherited instinct undertakes
the care of the offspring.

Let us see then whether this reasoning may be applied
also to the question at hand.   When children approach
the period of puberty or when the first symptoms of it
have already set in, they tell one another about sex, the
older children instructing the younger, less experienced
ones, about the significance of the sex parts, and about
the manner in which man reproduces.   The fable of the
stork was long ago declared a myth.   The children gradually discover the truth about the relationship of the
sexes.   Let us then see whether such instruction has any
significance for our question.   We have to consider
whether such guidance afforded to a child during life
is the result of the lesser strength of heterosexuality or
whether, these influences during life are requisite because heterosexuality is not inherited at all.   This question is now to be discussed from the standpoint of teleology.   Such reciprocal relationships are often to be met
with.   To come to the conditions found in the newly-
born, we find this to be true: The more the newly-born
depends on the parents' care the greater that care is;
the greater the care of the parents the less the independence of the offspring.   The so-called "mother's boy" re-
maining longest under the care of his mother, grows up
to be the most dependent of creatures.   He who sets
out for himself early will become more mature in char-

acter much faster. Nevertheless, I do not believe that we can draw such conclusions in favor of the acquired nature of the sex instincts. Aside from the fact that everything speaks against it, one must add also that seduction so common at the time of puberty, are not everywheres observed. What argues especially against this comparison between the instinct of hunger in the newly-born and the sex instinct of the grown-up is the fact that the capacity for perception has been developed in the latter and not in the former. Furthermore, for millions of generations organs for nutrition have been formed in the newly-born, whereas the seduction of younger individuals by older ones is always the result of accidents of life. This would be quite in contrast with the principle of purpose.

This discussion about the sex instinct from the standpoint of heredity and teleology could further be objected to by saying that reproduction in nature is often left to external influences and that incession of an inherited instinct is not therefore necessary. It is true, that plants reproduce by the aid of wind or insects who carry the pollen from the one plant to the stigma of another. In the case of the lower animals, for example, in the infusoria, the union is caused by external conditions, such as water currents. In these cases external rather than instinct is at times sufficient for the animals to reproduce. But we must consider that there is an essential difference between individuals who have adequately developed locomotor organs and others who lack them. Darwin pointed out the close connection between organs of locomotion and sex instinct. According to him many locomotor organs of the male develop merely in order to enable it to seek for the female and to copulate with her, or hold her fast during copulation. It is difficult to believe that this will be perceived as a contradiction to the concept of teleology. Teleology recognizes the purposive utilization of the organs of locomotion as self-evident, for they serve the purpose of reproduction, external, more accidental conditions thereby being superfluous. For, since the organs of locomotion in the higher organisms, facilitate copulation, the necessity of external conditions is eliminated, assuming that the sex instinct in these animals is inherited. Furthermore, the more frequent the transfer of impregnation into the mother organism (the latter also serving the development of the embryo) the more the necessity for the elimination of external accidental influences. The efficacy of these influences is purposive only when the sex cells must meet outside the mother organism or at least not in its interior, so difficult of access. As Darwinism has shown it is due perhaps to this need for protection that the locus of impregnation and development of the embryo was transferred to the mother organism. Whether or not we recognize this theory we cannot deny that a means for bringing together the two sex cells is required, easily attainable in the existing organization. No safer means for that purpose may be found than the individual's inherited direction of the sex instinct. This cannot be contested for only under these conditions may reproduction be removed from external accidents.

It is a common observation that the purpose may be transferred from the consciousness to the unconscious and that consciousness may in the end be filled only with the means to that end. No one can deny the fact that when one perspires profusely the body needs additional water in order to keep the tissues and the blood in a more acqueous condition. A thirsty person drinks enough water until the stomach is supplied with a sufficient quantity of water. This removes the sensation of thirst. But apparently the filling of the stomach with water is not the purpose of drinking. It is such only in the consciousness of the drinker, satisfying him that no additional water is requisite for the proper functioning of his body.

Let me point out another matter analogous to the sex instinct where the consciousness of the means sets in as substitute for the consciousness of purpose. This may be observed in ants described by Pierre Huber, Forel, Lubbock and others. A species of ant, the Amazon ant, *Polyergus rufescens,* falls upon another species of ant, robs them of their puppae, and brings these up to become their slaves. This goes so far as to result in the Amazon ants refraining from feeding themselves. They are fed by their "slaves." Gradually the hosts have forgotten how to feed themselves. The Amazon ants, for example, are very fond of honey. But they cannot feed upon it themselves any longer. It has been established experimentally that these ants will surely starve when they do not have one or more of these slave-ants about them. Even though one place the honey directly in front of their manibles they will not take it. But they will eat when one of the slave-ants feeds it to them. Weismann says that the ants have not lost the food instinct but rather the capacity to seek for and to recognize food. Their impulse of absorbing food is not released through visual impressions of the food itself but through the sight of the slave-ant. In the sex instinct we have a striking analogy to this food instinct of the Amazon ants, the woman standing for the slave-ants and the ovaries for the honey. We may then understand how the instinct towards the ovum is replaced by the instinct towards the woman. According to Weismann natural selection caused these ants to lose their capacity to seek for food. It seems too far-fetched however, to explain the sex instinct in the same manner, *i.e.,* that through natural selection the capacity of the male to become excited by the ovum of the females was lost. Just as the honey will be absorbed only when brought by the slave ants, and not otherwise, so also the woman only, and not ovum will have any exciting effect, at least insofar as the process enters the consciousness. In both cases the object of the purpose causes no direct reaction. This is effected by the bearer of that object, by the slave-ants in the case of the Amazon ants, by the woman in the case of the sex instinct.

As we have seen we must affirm the heredity of the normal sex instinct from the point of view of the theory of descent, from the facts of unisexual heredity, from natural selection as well as from sexual selection and from the standpoint of teleology. Even though teleology and Darwinism are opposed, both nevertheless agree that the organs and functions serve definite purpose. The difference between them is essentially this: From the standpoint of teleology purpose is predetermined. The transformation of the organs is, to a certain extent, only an expedient for reaching the purpose. Darwinism, however, does not recognize the determinism of purpose, but rather considers it merely the consequence of these processes and transformations. But even the most outspoken proponents of Darwinism, agree that under these circumstances the purposiveness of the organs must be regarded as an heuristic principle. In science we may be guided by the existing purposiveness of the organs, though not as yet able to explain such purpose scientifically. In this we may also consider the sex instinct without fearing the contradictions inherent in Darwinism and teleology. We might ask whether we may not argue the inheritance of heterosexuality from certain phenomena observed in connection with the sex instinct.

In the following pages we shall ascertain that a series of these phenomena point unmistakably to reproduction. We shall observe that these phenomena can have their basis only in heredity. Though this will not conclusively prove the inheritance of heterosexuality it will at least make it seem quite probable.

We have seen in the first chapter that the excision of the testicles or ovaries do not permit the development of the sex instinct if the castration was performed early. We have no reason to assume that castration should in itself destroy contrectation. For castration has an effect only on the production of semen or ova. We must assume, however, that inasmuch as castration also effects contrectation, and since education cannot modify this result that a connection must be found between sex glands and contrectation. Those who perhaps consider the direction of the sex instinct to be acquired through fortuitous association, will object here saying that the sex instinct of castrates has been stunted because they were brought into a different environment. This is an erroneous opinion. For animal breeders and others interested in animals have informed me with positive assurance that they castrated mature animals in order that their sex instinct become abated, which they could not achieve in any other manner. Stallions are so impulsive when approaching a mare that she is made uneasy. These stallions are castrated even after reaching puberty because such operation, without of necessity changing the animal's environment, will tend to lessen considerably the animal's restlessness and its impulse to mount the mare. These castrated animals are kept together with others as well as the females of their species during grazing. Yet they will take no notice of the latter. They are bred and kept in the same manner as the other animals who are not castrated. According to all experts who answered my inquiry regarding this question the difference between the two groups of animals is very clear to anyone who will take the trouble to observe it. External influences therefore cannot have any effect on the suppression of the sex instinct in castrates. Castrated animals are neutral with regards to the opposite sex whereas normal male animals will be found to be aggressive. This difference is remarkable in every respect. If it should be further objected that in this respect man cannot be compared to animals. I can only answer that such objection is of significance only to those who uphold the anthropocentric point of view. It was, of course more advisable perhaps for the purpose of comparison to use the example of such animals who live a conjugal life, *e.g.*, storks, parrots; to observe how these animals behave when castrated at an early age; whether or not they show then the impulse towards the other sex. Such experiments would be even more decisive than observation of mammals whose sex rarely posseses the higher psychical qualities for a truly long attachment and pairing as observed in birds. However, I could ascertain only very few details regarding the castration of birds. I could only establish the fact that when castrated cocks are set free they show no impulse whatsoever towards hens. But this is of no significance to us in the present question because the cock is polygamous.

As far as our material goes we may assume that contrectation remains undeveloped as a result of early castration in spite of uniform breeding. This is true both of animals and of man. In male castrates a connection is thus established between testicles and contrectation. From the point of view of Darwinism, then, and also of teleology, both of which stress a purposive arrangement, and the former also recognizing an heuristic principle, we may form the following conclusion. The connection between testicles and contrectation is purposive. When testicles are wanting such purpose is superfluous. Therefore, on removal of the testicles contrectation remains undeveloped. Further observations teaches that contrectation can be purposive only when directed towards the opposite sex, that is to say, when it is heterosexual. For only then may the function of testicles be fruitful. For this reason we must assume also that the normal sex instinct is inherited and not acquired. For the sex instinct is not subject to the accidents of life but to the presence of testicles. Observation of the consequences of castration, in other words, forces us to the conclusion that the normal sex instinct is an inherited function. For if heterosexuality were regarded as acquired how could we explain the absence of contrectation in castrates? If heterosexuality were inherited and it were merely a matter of education whether a person is to incline to homosexuality or heterosexuality, or even perhaps to sodomy or any other perversion, there could be no reason why the removal of the testicles should result in the destruction of contrectation. That the development of the peripheral genitals is preliminary for the development of contrectation points altogether to an intimate connection

between the two. From the point of view of Darwinism
and teleology this inner connection can only be a purposive connection.

On might object here that in persons castrated late in
life contrectation is not inactive. It is true that even
though original source-stimuli of phychical processes
have been destroyed, yet the latter may continue to exist,
and to manifest themselves the stronger the more vivid
the memory is. I assume that contrectation of human
beings after castration is evident to a larger extent than
in animals. This is probably due to man's stronger
memory. It is similar perhaps to the strange sensation
of pain in "parts" of the body which have been ampu-
tated.

That the secondary sex characteristics, *e.g.,* the beard,
will not develop because of early castration, already was
discussed in the first chapter. This observation may now
be applied to the sex instinct. Assuming with Darwin
that the secondary sex characteristics have originated
through natural selection we are unable, on the basis of
our present knowledge to give an adequate reason for
the deficiency of the secondary sex characteristics after
premature castration. If we assume that these sex
characteristics fail to appear because they are superfluous, this would be a teleological explanation and not
a scientific one. For the present we must be satisfied in
assuming that the secondary sex characteristics of the
male during evolutionary history have developed in connection with testicles and that, consequently, secondary
sex characteristics, on the basis of unisexual heredity,
have always made their appearance when the testicles
did. However, the reason for the non-appearance of the
secondary sex characterictics in men without testicles,

does not seem to me to be solved either from the standpoint of natural selection or from that of teleology. For,
inasmuch as male persons with their testicles removed
could not have reproduced themselves, others could not
have inherited their defects in regards to the secondary
sex characteristics. As I have mentioned already the
reason for the intimate connection between contrectation and the sex glands remains unknown. The same may
also be said regarding the inner connection between
testicles and somatic secondary sex characteristics. It
is quite true that this in all is a weak point of
Darwinism. Darwin himself seemed to have recognized
it, seeing the necessity of modifying his main theory.
This weak point is the so-called idea of *correlation,* according to which the different parts of the animal or
plant body do not vary independently, the variation of
one part often causing variations of other parts. Correlation has generally been recognized but has not been
clarified sufficiently. The opponents, *e.g.,* Hartmann, aim
their attack mainly at these lacunae in the theory of
Darwinism.   Haache, similarly, has recently attacked
the pre-formation theory of Weismann. . The non-de-
velopment of the secondary sex characteristics after premature removal of the sex glands must be reckoned another gap which remains unfilled.

There are still other facts that point to the inheritance
of heterosexuality. One of these is the periodicity of the
sex instinct in animals. This phenomenon, too, indicates
purpose and will strengthen then our argument for the
inheritance of heterosexuality. In animals living in freedom the sex instinct is awakened mostly at definite periods. This period of copulation varies extensively.
It depends on the duration of pregnancy in the fe-

male. Copulation, namely, will take place only at a period
when sufficient food for young and old may be procured.
Should the deer mate at such a period of the year that
young would be born in December, it is very likely that
all the young would perish. For in the winter time there
is not sufficient food even for the full-grown animals.
From the standpoint of Darwinism one might assume
that this periodicity of the sex instinct, definite seasons
for mating, is not the result of a predetermined purpose.
Animals who are born at a season of the year when sufficient food for both young and old is to be found, remained alive. On the other hand, animals born at a
period when there was not sufficient food, perished. Consequently only such periodicity was transmitted to the
offspring which resulted in adequate food conditions.

Richard Semon's observations in Australia provide
us with some very beautiful examples of the possibility
of preserving the brood alive, conforming to favorable
external conditions. Whereas the main distinction between the seasons of the year in our own latitudes consists in differences of temperature, such decided changes
between "warm" and "cold," are not observable in the
tropical regions. This change in temperature is replaced
by a rainy and a dry season. In the dry seasons herbivorous animals find food as scarce as animals in our own
climate in the wintertime. Consequently the birth of
the young coincides with the onset of the rainy season.
In one region, however, in Buitenzorg, there is no dry
season altogether, the plants being in bloom all the year
round. Here reproduction is hardly, if at all, tied up
with the seasons of the year.

One might also imagine this periodicity to manifest
itself without the presence of external stimuli, *i.e.,* such

stimuli lying outside of the organism, in a manner like
the period nature of menstruation, which, of course, does
not depend on external stimuli. Or, again, these external
impressions might be regarded merely as a starting
point. This point of departure might operate also
unconsciously or at least instinctively. This stimulus
is supplied by the impressions received by the animal from the environment. Such influences might be
those of temperature or climate, or of the surrounding
flora. Hares usually begin to mate in February; premature copulations with them are explained as due to
mild winters. But matters, are, of course, much more
complicated. We must assume then, that the mode of
reaction causing the functioning of the sex glands in the
presence of certain of external conditions, is inherited.
Contrectation would then be released in the presence
of these stimuli, as under normal conditions. It is self-
evident, of course, that external climatic conditions will
release the sex instinct only when everything in the organism is ready for it. I believe therefore, that such
periodicity, too, has its organic basis in many thousands
of generations during which it has manifested itself. This
basis is nevertheless unknown to us. Such intrinsic basis
is indicated by the fact that in many caged animals this
periodicity has been lost. Yet it has been observed to
occur quite independent of the external conditions the
animals had been accustomed to. However, it seems that
such periodicity of detumescence independent of external
stimuli is not capable of causing the impulse of mating
at all times. Thus, caged animals, especially at the outset of their captivity, show the physical symptoms of
heat, but are unable to copulate. Breeders of wild animals assume that their failure to mate these animals

is due to the fact that the external conditions for copulation are not sufficiently well known. That captive elephants almost never breed is due to the same reason.

In man the periodicity of the sex instinct has been lost to a great extent. It is true that with some people the instinct manifests itself to a greater extent in spring and summer than in the other two seasons. But generally speaking a periodicity like that of free-living animals, is not present. Nay, it is a fact the domestic animals, too, have, in most cases lost this periodicity. No matter whether we place ourselves on the standpoint of Darwinism or on that of teleology, purposiveness must be seen in this arrangement. Man can always procure food for himself, be it in the winter, spring, summer or autumn. The theme of the child's birth, does not, therefore, play such an important role. According to Westermarck, the prevalence of human mating during certain months of the year is due to natural selection. It is well known, at any rate, that certain variations occur also in human beings. But inasmuch as man is able to procure food regardless of the season the periodicity has almost completely disappeared. In animals, however, natural selection is of deciding importance, for the offspring would perish completely if copulation did not take place at the opportune time. In domestic animals the extinction of the rutting season may be explained in the same manner. I do not maintain, of course, that periodicity is dependent on natural selection exclusively. Other factors, too, may be added, which we cannot discuss here in detail. Certain periodical fluctuations in the sex instinct of man may perhaps be explained in a similar way. Some people are entrely free of sexual desires for weeks; their sex instinct suddenly manifests itself very strongly for a few days. The question whether this is analogous to menstruation in woman or whether it is to be observed only in pathologically inclined persons, I shall not here discuss. In animals heterosexuality is thus inherited, in all probability. For otherwise such periodicity would have no reason or purpose. Inasmuch as we cannot agree with an anthropocentric point of view, we must accept the same also in the case of man.

But there are still other observations arguing the inheritance of the sex instinct. Let us consider the instinct of the horse. The mare allows the stallion to mount her until impregnation has actually taken place. Sometimes the animal breeder does not himself know whether impregnation has taken place. But the mare does. For she reacts in a different manner before and after impregnation. It is well-known that a mare does not allow a stallion to mount her after she has been impregnated. Thus one may discover whether impregnation has really taken place. The extinction of the mare's sex instinct at the moment of impregnation must be regarded as a question of cause and effect from the point of view of Darwinism and as a predetermined design from the standpoint of teleology. Both Darwinism and teleology agree in recognizing a purposive arrangement in it. For such an event may be understood only when designed for the purpose of reproduction. It can have been caused only as an inherited capacity. Under these conditions, it would be absurd to regard as inherited the mare's capacity to repel the stallion after impregnation, and her instinct towards the stallion as otherwise due to sheer accidental causes after birth.

Similar observations have been undertaken also on

other animals. The reason for having chosen the horse
as an illustration is that I had at my disposal the most
reliable information, not only in the literature of the
subject but also material supplied to me by animal
breeders. If the above observation leads us to conclude
that the mating instinct of the horse is inherited, the next
question is whether the same is true of the sex instinct
of man. Let me again stress that only those favoring
the anthropocentric point of view will refuse to draw
the obvious conclusion. No one who regards man as a
higher animal and worthy of being the object of scientific
investigation can regard this conclusion as unjustified.
One might object that in woman the waning of the sex
instinct after impregnation has not been established.
It is true that we lack sufficient material to describe the
character of woman's sex instinct after impregnation.
This is partly due to the fact that little is known about
woman's sex instinct altogether. Truth and fiction often
cannot be distinguished. We must as yet disclaim possessing any reliable material on this subject. How widely
spread erroneous opinion about her sex instinct is, may
be seen in the fact that only very recently the idea was
current that in woman the urge to perform coitus was
present to a lesser degree than in man; that many women
lacked both the impulse and orgasm. Yet, in spite of the
scantiness and the unreliability of the material, I shall
nevertheless refer to some information I have received
on the matter. It will at least prove that the woman's
sex instinct is different than that of animals.

I endeavored to get information regarding the question whether in woman, too, the sex instinct decreases
when pregnancy has set in. Many women stated that
they felt when pregnancy had set in but they did not

know how to describe it. Such vague statement must not, of course, be given too much credence. Professor Leopold Landau of Berlin, to whom I am indebted for part of this information, himself places very little faith in their statements, although the women questioned were mostly educated, observant and reliable otherwise. One special reason, according to Dr. Landau, why these statements are of small importance is that some of the women claimed to experience the sensation of pregnancy even during the performance of coitus. It is impossible to accept this as true on the basis of our present knowledge of the physiology of reproduction. Dr. Landau's criticism of the women's assertions is thus quite justified. But even if it were true that these women had the capacity to "feel" when they became pregnant, it would not answer our question whether such knowledge caused the extinction of the sex instinct. No one has ever made such an assertion. I have made careful inquiry of many women as well as of several physicians, but their answers have always been negative; namely, that woman's sex instinct did not undergo any changes on account of pregnancy; at least not during the first months. As a matter of fact, an increase of the instinct was proven in several cases. These observations tend to show that one cannot deduce the behavior of human beings from a study of animals. Let me remark, however, that in animals, too, the above observation is not at all general. Female animals will not always refuse to copulate as soon as impregnation has taken place. Of the many examples at hand I shall only mention the case of a female cat in the Berlin Zoölogical Garden, who, though big with young, yet received the love-sick tomcats. Throwing aside all female pride she permitted herself to be copulated in that condition. The behavior of mares is nevertheless important when desire to make a final judgment regarding the purpose of coitus. One should not forget that in the case of the horse another factor is present. It is a general opinion that the stallion is excited especially by the odor of the mare in rut. Inasmuch as the impregnated mare loses this odor, it may be assumed that the stallion is no longer excited by her. We may thus see that nature has arranged the sex instinct very practically in the two sexes for the sole subserviency of reproduction. It is not well known whether the same thing may be said in the case of the impregnated woman. It should be pointed out that in cases of advanced pregnancy the sexual excitability of the male is decreased on the account of the changes in the woman's body. We must also consider the influence of the growing embryo upon the relation of the woman to the man. Michelet, writing about the consequences of pregnancy, says: "Entre amis, il faut étre vrais. Je dois te le dire franchement, sans détour . . . Tu as un rival—Grand Dieu! Un rival préféré. Elle t'aime et t'aimerai toujours. Mai enfin, prends-en ton parti, tu n'es plus sa premiére pensés." Runge, a German gynecologist, lays especial weight upon this remark of Michelet ascribing it to a sharp gift of observation. One cannot fail to see an analogy between the refusal of the impregnated animal to permit further copulation and the influence of the growing child on the relationship between man and woman.

It must further be remarked that when animals have a free choice they will pair off only with animals of their own species. It is easy to see a purposive arrangement in this, when we consider that most hybrids which are the

off-spring of animals of different species are themselves
sterile. The proponents of teleology, of course, see predetermined purpose in such selection. From the scientific point of view, however, we must ask whether the
cause for this event lies not in the nature of the individuals, in their anatomical structure, in the function
of their organs, and especially in the evolutionary development. It is difficult to conceive this cause of the processes, especially since we know very little about its
psychical basis. The teleological point of view has at
least something in its favor, solving the riddle with use
of a work or design. But this in turn is an unsolved
riddle and does not advance us any further. From a
scientific point of view natural selection is claimed to
be the reason why males always feel themselves attracted
only to the female of its kind. It is assumed, for example,
that the union of dog and a bitch always results in fruitful dogs, while the union of dog and cat produced no
offspring. It follows from this that only such animals
produced offspring which possessed the impulse towards
the opposite sex. Such animals, however, who were
attracted to the female of another species and copulated
with her, could not bring forth any offsprings. So that,
though an impulse towards animals of other species had
really made its appearance, the union had no consequence. Only such animals were born who inherited the
impulse towards the opposite sex of its own species.

We have to consider that in recent times a new interpretation was given to the theory of cross-breeding.
Leuckar has already pointed out in the year of 1853
that the sterility of hybrids is not a general law. One of
our most prominent investigators in this field, Edward
Hahn, has shown recently how important hybridism has

been for breeding domestic animals. The origin of breeding which resulted in the domestic animals is said to have taken place as a result of cross-breeding and furthered occasionally by kindred blood. According to him our domestic animals came to be what they are through this process.

Robert Behla, on the basis of the facts known about hybridism, in his books proposed that experiment be made on the extent of cross-breding of different and remote animal species. He proposes the mixture of the sex glands of a land animal and fish in order to observe the result. He conjectures that beaked animals were the product of the otters and the ant-bears with aquatic birds. On account of the strange shape of penguin and the armadillo, he even proposed the union of fish and birds, of turtle and ant-eater. This union is to be brought about through seminal injections. To most of us such conjectures will seem strangely absurd. However, when a scientist as prominent as Eduard Hahn maintains that hybridism has not as yet been adequately studied, that initial observations have merely passed from one book to another, it will then be admitted that in the future the question of hybridism will become more important than it is now.

We must remark furthermore that in the mating of animals of different species habit bears an important influence. Just as human beings of different races will readily mate when habit has made them more accustomed to each other, so also many animals of different species get accustomed to each other. The fact that a lion will copulate with a tigress only when confined in the same cage, and not in a condition of freedom, is due the fact that normally the animals are isolated and unsocial, resulting also in sexual estrangement; while the two species are forced to accustom to each other in captivity.

Hahn points out a fact, already observed by Darwin, that caged animals will at times copulate with animals of a different species. I am in a position to report a case similar to his, regarding the mating of tiger and lion. In my case a tigress, who would not permit the male tiger to mate with her, allowed a lion to do it. The act lasted so long that the two animals had to be forcibly separated. Impregnation probably failed to take place. My informant, who observed the case, considers it not unlikely that the tigress dropped her young during the night and immediately devoured it. Still, he believes that such supposition is not warranted; that the mating did not result in any offspring. In the menagery at Dreutzberg, a union between a lion and a tigress is said to have been fruitful; also, another time, the case of a jaguar and a black panther. According to Semper, hybridism also takes place between free-living butterflies.

Taking all these things into consideration the fact nevertheless cannot be denied that in a condition of freedom the cross-breeding of animals always occurs only between animals capable of producing offspring; between animals whose offspring in turn are fruitful. In this phenomenon, too, one will, no doubt, perceive a significant purpose of nature. It would be very strange indeed if the sexual attraction embracing only animals of the same species which can reproduce themselves, did not, at the same time, also result in a differentiation into sexes. For the differentiation into sexes is much more important for purposes of reproduction than differentiation into species. Occasionally we do observe offspring of different species, even fruitful offspring;

but the union of individuals of the same sex can never
bring with it such results.

Another factor that argues for the inheritance of
heterosexuality is the development of contrectation
mostly at the time of the maturity of the sex glands.
Several exceptions to this rule have indeed been mentioned. The more common even, however, is the con-
currence of these two phenomena. At any rate, the two
events are not far removed from each other in most
cases. When the testicles begin to mature and to secrete
semen, when the pubic hair begins to appear on the genitals, when the male larynx becomes larger and the voice
deeper; a sexual inclination to the opposite sex also
makes its appearance. In the beginning, perhaps, that
inclination is rather vague and unsteady, but soon it
takes on a purely heterosexual character. What is especially characteristic in this respect is the fact that in
many cases of homosexuality before the onset of puberty
or during its first stage, heterosexuality will make its
appearance after puberty is more advanced.

Natural selection will explain why contrectation and
detumescence appear almost simultaneously in most
cases, or rather, why contrectation becomes clearly dif
ferentiated only when the testicles have begun already to
secrete a sufficient amount of semen. The premature
arousing of contrectation is purposeless, for copulation
would then be without issue. Similarly, the premature
detumescence would also be purposeless, for without the simultaneous appearance of contrectation no offspring can result. Deviations from these rules may be
explained as the influence of civilization upon the instinct.

All these last mentioned facts point to the purposiveness of reproduction, dominating very largely the various phenomena of sex. We have seen that in most animals the sex instinct manifests itself periodically at a definite season of the year. We have found this to be a purposive arrangement, for otherwise the offspring would perish. We have seen that the females of some species will not permit copulation after impregnation, and that they then fail to secrete the odoriferous substances causing sexual excitement in the male. We have found that certain analogous phenomena may also be observed in man, such as the rivalling of the growing child for the mother's love, though this takes place only when the mother has already become aware of the developing embryo. We have seen that animals almost always mate only with animals in a union which will result in fruitful offspring. We have also recognized this to be a purposive arrangement. We have also observed that generally contrectation appears at the same time as the maturation of the sex glands. In view of all these considerations it would be absurd to assume that all aspects of the sex instinct are designed for the purpose of reproduction, resting on a hereditary basis, but only the impulse towards the opposite sex is accidental, caused by any influences whatsoever during life.

I have intentionally refrained to go into further details regarding the question whether detumescence, too, is inherited. There can be no doubt whatsoever that man's urge to ejaculate when the genitals are congested is an inherited quality, observable not only in man, but also in animals. Trustworthy observers, as already mentioned, have reported cases of bulls, stallions, monkeys, and dogs masturbating; even the case of a trained tomcat who used tame rats to titillate its genitals. Erection following the charging of the seminal vesicles, as well as ejaculation resulting from friction of the external genitals, are inherited reflexes whose anatomical basis we know is located in the lower spinal cord. It is certain that detumescence in man is based on heredity, the filling of the vesicles with semen causing a strong feeling of displeasure as well as the urge to remove such displeasure. If another individual cannot be procured for this purpose, mechanical friction will be performed instinctively by the male in order to remove the tension. The trial-and-error method will also be used. Matters are somewhat different in the case of woman. On what specific peripheral stimuli the arousing of the detumescence in woman rests has not been clearly established. It is ascribed to the filling of the glands of Bartholin or to the activity of the mucous glands of the uterus.

We have seen thus that both detumescence and contrectation rest on an inherited mode of reaction. Both components of the sex instinct must be regarded as inherited functions, whose activation merely requires a definite development of the perceptive powers. It does not follow, however, that all details in the sex instinct are inherited in the same degree. I have not as yet discussed the question whether heredity manifests itself also in the impulse to perform cotius, or whether mere contact of the male and the female body will satisfy that impulse. We know that the man who feels himself attracted to a woman through contrectation will at first be satisfied merely by conversing with her, then he will exchange light bodily contacts with her, then he will kiss her, and finally general bodily contact with erection will take place. As is generally the case with young people, pressures and comparative light embraces alone may cause ejaculation, especially when the young man and the girl are not as yet clearly conscious about coitus. In itself, the bodily contact, belly to belly, face to face, is an act one is most readily inclined to perform on account of the structure of the body. The male organ will come into contact with vagina and finally, as a result of mutual activity, the male will form an urge to introduce his penis into the vagina. When this stage of the activity is over and the penis is in the vagina, the subjective feeling of pleasure will be at its highest. A factor which is then added is the woman's excitement. It is, of course, well known that the woman enhances the male's pleasure and that without this accompanying pleasure on the part of the woman the sex act would not be completely gratifying to the male. However, when the woman experiences no adequate pressure and excitement in her own genitals she will fail to become gratified. Thus, considering that two are necessary for the act, the man will be gratified fully only when the woman is. How far the inherited element in coitus is of effect also in the female may best be seen in animals. One may observe female mammals in heat to stand with their hind legs spread wide apart, ready for the male to mount her. Only when the act is over do they assume their normal posture. It is true that matters are not seemingly the same in the human female, as will be discussed in the next volume. We must keep in mind that sexual anasthesia plays an important role in woman.

But disregarding such cases for the present, it must be stressed that mutual gratification presupposes the adaptation of the two partners to one another. Gratification, therefore, should not be too quick in the one, and too slow in the other. Many an unhappy marriage is the result of insufficient adaptation between husband and wife during coitus. Very often the man is excited much more quickly than the woman and often completes the act when the woman is just beginning to experience the pleasure. The following case, a case of pathology, concerns a man suffering from hyperthesia of the sex instinct. His wife could never gratify him. It will be observed that other factors have played their part, too. Such cases of insufficient adaptation of the sexual processes in man and woman are not rare at all; but they have not as yet been sufficiently discussed.

Case XXXI. Mr. S. L., 36 years of age, married nine years. Patient came to consult me on the question of his sanity. His chief complaint was the extraordinary violence of his sex instinct. He wanted to ascertain whether he was suffering from a nervous disease, or from a mental abnormality, or from a moral defect, perhaps. He used to masturbate frequently for many years. At present he is compelled to gratify his sex instinct daily, some time several times a day. He chooses ordinary and mutual masturbation for various reasons. First of all, coitus is altogether displeasurable to his wife. Though she finally does become gratified, the act takes a very long time. In addition she suffers from a disease of the uterus, and consequently is obliged to wear a pessary. Sexual intercourse, it is true, has not been proscribed to her, but she finds no gratification in normal coitus with her husband because she requires much longer stimulation than he does. He himself can be excited sensually as soon as he sees a girl whose appearance may in any manner please a man. Consequently he indulges in sexual acts with women, but he permits them only to masturbate him.

When further questioned he states that his parents are separated. He believes that the separation is due also to his father's hyperesthesia of the sex instinct. Patient had pollutions occur when he was 14 years old. At the time he dreamed of another young man. Formerly he could be excited sexually by boys; but at present sex contact with men repels him. He frequently performed active cunnilingus with females, but found no gratification in it. As he states, he only did it "in order to be through with it."

It should be mentioned that a few months ago patient was gravely wounded in a fall from a platform, which allegedly brought with it concussion of the brain and loss of consciousness. But this is not said to have caused any change in his sexual behavior.

S. L. makes a remarkably depressive appearance. He ascribes it mainly to the strength of his sex instinct which he is utterly impossible to satisfy in a normal fashion.

———————

Quite apart from the question of mutual gratification there is quite a difference in man's sensation, too, whether his organ is enclosed in the tightly-fitting vagina or whether it is merely placed against any part whatsoever of the woman's body; for in the former case the excitement is greatly increased, the moist warmth which surrounds his organ causing him a much more pleasurable sensation than any other form of contact with the woman's parts. The adaptation of the penis to the vagina is then the most essential requirement. Both parts have been formed for each other. When the penis is erect and the two bodies in close and intimate contact, its direction corresponds perfectly to the direction of the vagina.

The latter observation might cause one to object that the performance of the act itself depends on trial-and-error methods, or on experience. I believe, indeed, that this objection is justified. It is quite possible that though in animals the movements requisite for the performance of the act are locomotor complexes, in man they are the result of trial-and-error movements. But, in the last analysis, such movements may be observed also in many other processes, which, though inherited, yet require such trial-and-error movements in order for additional processes. To cite an example: Young guinea pigs will lick any object presented to them, no matter whether these objects are bitter, sour or sweet. But food tasting sweet will be preferred by them from the very outset. A few days after birth they already have the capacity to differentiate between the different tastes, so that their sense of smell alone will enable them to pick the sweet stuffs from all the others. These animals have tried out all tastes, so to speak, until they have discovered what gives them the greatest amount of pleasure. Similarly, we may imagine that in coitus, too, all positions have at first been tried out until finally that position which afforded the greatest amount of pleasure was discovered. That ideal contact, because of the structure of the genitals, of the nervous system, and of the sensitivity of the parts, is the position of the penis in the vagina.

And just as the guinea pig prefers the sweet substances not because it has learned from experience but rather because it possesses an inherited disposition which enables it to recognize the sweet foods from all others through its sense of taste, so also is coitus chosen as the ideal form of contact. That the greatest pleasure is afforded by introducing the penis into the vagina rests on an inherited disposition. Trial-and-error methods may at first be required, but these are later dispensed with. What is sought is a contact which affords the greatest amount of pleasure, on the basis of the structure of the genitals. The two partners are gratified only when their genitals come into a more and more intimate contact. The seeking may sometimes take a long time, but finally the male will find the introitus of the vagina. A proof of this may be seen in the coital play of animals whose first attempt at coitus sometimes fails. It may be observed in monkeys, dogs, horses and birds. But in spite of such initial failures the animals are at last able to perform the act perfectly. It is well known that direction and instruction will tend to make the performance of the act easier. It is quite common for the animal breeder to introduce the penis of the male into the vagina of the female to secure the success of coitus. No one will maintain that the animals themselves would have failed to perform the act perfectly well. Human assistance in the copulation of animals is only resorted to in order to prevent fruitless ejaculation in the case of breeding prize dogs or race horses.

It is my belief that in animals the instinctive move-

ments are of a much more original nature and much
more ingrained than in man. It is well known that young
animals perform covering movements already a few
days after birth. Switz reported the case of young ante-
lopes. It is true of dogs, horses, goats, and monkeys.
Still it should be mentioned that young animals perform
also mounting movements not corresponding to their
sex. I possess reliable information about such behavior
in the case of young female monkeys, she-goats, bitches,
mares and calves. This will be easily understood when
we consider that before puberty the secondary sex characteristics are only partially developed and less sharply
distributed between the two sexes. When animals grow
mature they perform the mounting movements without
any guidance, their roles being clearly given. It seems,
then, that in animals the motor complex necessary for
coitus is more intrinsically hereditary than in man.

We have seen above that animal love-plays, to which
the mounting movements must be reckoned, and which
serve the purpose of the coital act, must be regarded as
a preactivity of the later-to-be-awakened sex instinct.
And though it must be assumed that these coital movements, in the animals observed, rests on an inherited
mechanism and not merely on the imitation of the movements of mature animals, we cannot draw the same conclusion in the case of man. At least, I do not know that
such coital movements in its original character has ever
been observed in children, unless it was the result of
seduction. I know of children who imitated coitus perfectly; girls even, who when young, played ''father-and-
mother'' among themselves, and later became homosexuals. But such children, most likely, have been seduced
to imitate these movements.

Delage, on the basis of observations, established the fact that young pigeons copulate more readily when they see the example of the mature birds, than when they are left to themselves. He believes that the same may be said of those more mature males of mammals who seek out young females, and vice versa, so that one partner in each case has had sufficient experience previously. But he adds further that young animals who have not been incited to perform coitus through the example of more mature animals, will nevertheless mate with other young animals and be able to perform it perfectly. Delage maintains that this cannot be established in the case of the other instincts; that in the sex act we are concerned with a reflex act. He is inclined to assume an inherited capacity. It is my belief, however, that the transition from the reflexes to the instincts is much too gradual to enable us to make such a sharp distinction. Besides, it is also less advisable to include it among the reflexes rather than the instincts. That the coital movements in man bear less of an ingrained hereditary character may be due to the fact that man wears clothes.

This prevents him from perceiving those organs through which the instinct to perform the coital movements are released, as is the case in animals. The influence of civilization upon the activities of the normal sex instinct will be discussed in the next volume.

I believe that if man were left without the instruction of his fellow-beings in regards to the sex act, he would be forced to resort to trial-and-error methods to achieve intromission. Such intimate contact would at last be reached because it afforded the greatest amount of pleasure.

To be sure, there are several objections to these con-

siderations. One of these objections is based on the
fact of the presence of the hymen, hindering intromission and forcing the penis to be turned aside. This objection must be put to a serious test. It seems to me
that if the trial-and-error methods should be followed
through in the above manner the hymen, too, will not
represent an insuperable obstacle; at least not to the
male with a well-erected penis. We have seen that as a
result of the intimate contact of the two genitals, the
penis will at last reach the region of the vagina. At
this point no one is present to instruct us about the
nature of the hymen; that it, too, may be vanquished. I
admit that this is not quite so simple. Let us assume
that two individuals, a male and a female, have grown
up alone on an island without receiving any instruction
regarding sexual matters. It seems difficult to believe
that the two individuals will finally be able to perform
coitus in view of the obstacle of the hymen. Yet, difficult though this may be to conceive, it seems to me to be
the most probable assumption to make. I shall again
cite the example of higher animals, some which also
possess a hymen. We know that monkeys captured when
young sometimes, though very rarely, reproduce, or at
least copulate often. We must assume, therefore, that
they finally achieve intromission on the basis of an inherited impulse. Without regarding the question as having been answered that two persons would at last reach
the point of performing coitus, if in the manner of Adam
and Eve they were left to grow up by themselves, still, I
wished to point out the analogy to the animals.

Still another objection might be raised against my
assumption, namely, that I have described the act of
coitus as not due to a feeling of positive pleasure, but as

caused by the desire to remove a feeling of displeasure. We have seen that accumulation of the semen and the tension and distress of sexual thoughts and feelings are the main causes impelling to ejaculation and contrectation. In the last discussion the point was continuously stressed, however, that what one seeks in the many trials and attempts, is to find such contact and position which will afford the greatest positive pleasure. But this contradiction is only apparent. I consider it very self-evident that in the last analysis the fullest sensation of pleasure will be sought after, this resting on an inherited egotistic tendency in man. It is true, that I consider the really impelling power the desire to remove the sensation of displeasure. But the removal and replacement of the feeling of displeasure by a strong positive pleasure and the heightening of sensuality directly proceed from this. The voluptuous sensations cannot, however, be regarded as the primary drives impelling to perform coitus.

There are still other reasons to believe that in man the entire motor complex leading to coitus is not as ingrained as in animals. Of course, man also possesses certain movements which are inherited. Darwin showed that many such movements are completely congenital. The case of Laura Bridgman is a convincing proof. Laura could not have learned the facial expressions by imitation because she was blind and deaf; still she laughed when she was overjoyed, clapped her hands when she was amused; when a letter from a beloved friend was read to her in her "gesture" language, the blood rose to her cheeks. On other occasions she was observed to stamp with her feet in an attack of rage. It will be admitted that though numerous impressions might have been communicated to her through the sense of touch, methodical guidance and imitation could not have caused her to perform such movements as laughing and stamping of the feet; rather, they are to be considered innate and inherited movements.

Laughing and stamping of the feet are comparatively simple movements, whereas the movements in coitus are complex, because two persons are involved in it. Aside from this, there is another fact which leads one to believe that in coitus we are not concerned merely with an inherited movement but also with movements which are the result of trial-and-error. These facts are supplied from a study of ethnology. In almost every species of animal coitus is performed in the same manner. In most mammals the male mount the female. Some mammals, *i. e.,* the aquatic animals (seals, whales, otters, etc.), perform it belly to belly. Birds, too, do it in a specific, almost never varying manner. In some species of birds, *e. g.,* the parrots, the male mounts the female, the two birds holding fast with their beaks. In every species, coitus is performed in the same manner and position. In man, the position varies according to time and place. Ethnologists have compiled numerous reports regarding the various positions of coitus among different peoples. To cite only a few examples: In Australia, according to Miklucho-Macley, coitus is often performed a posteriori. There are many other positions of coitus, such as that in which the partners sit opposite each other. It is remarkable that in Classical Times coitus was performed a posteriori. This position was highly recommended by Lucretius. Ploss, the famous ethnologist, has written the comprehensive reports about this question of the positions during coitus, practiced by different peoples. He draws a distinction between positions customarily employed by the various races of the earth, and those other positions which are merely the result of a refined sensuality and the arts of love. The European peoples commonly perform coitus belly to belly, the woman lying on her back. The Bafio-Negroes perform it lying on their sides. Among the Szuahilis in Zanzibar the man is on his back and the woman on top. The Sudanese are said to perform it in a standing position, the woman bending forward, her hands on her knees and her buttocks protruding, while the man performs coitus a posteriori. The Eskimos do it in a similar manner, resembling coitus of quadrupeds. Nevertheless, in spite of all these variations, Ploss designated the normal position in coitus as that position in which the woman lies on her back and the man kneeling against her, belly to belly. He also supposes that the majority of primitive races perform the act in that manner. Definite deviations have thus been observed in different times and places. It is quite probable that these deviations are not due to inherited dispositions, but to imitation and guidance.

Up to now I have represented the union of the two sexes in coitus as being partially due to trial-and-error methods, the source lying in the attraction which the two individuals exert upon each other. But I have an important reservation to make here, a reservation which, though it cannot directly be proven, is very probably true. I believe that the attraction is not only between the two individuals, but also between the genitals of each sex. The act of introducing the penis into the vagina, in my opinion, is due to an inherited mode of reaction and not merely to the desire for the greatest amount of pleasure in such contact. It is the observation of pathological cases that mainly leads me to this opinion. We find, namely, that coitus as a means of gratification is generally sought after only by persons with a normal sex instinct. The entire mode of reaction is then uniform and normal. In cases of sexual perversions, however, there is no desire to perform coitus. If the desire to perform the act were merely the result of peripheral stimuli, coitus would always be sought after as a means of gratification, whether a perversion existed or not. To cite an example, the handkerchief-fetishist, has the desire to masturbate into the handkerchief of his beloved; the shoe-fetishest into her shoe, and the foot-fetishist on her feet. In short, the object which affords the greatest amount of pleasure is brought into contact with the genitals. It follows from this that the nature of the sexual sensation exerts an important impulse upon the strength of the impulse to perform coitus. It is difficult to conceive an inherited mode of reaction because we know that we have either been told how to perform it or have tried it out for ourselves. It is significant that in almost all cases of perversion coitus is not felt to be gratifying. The libido-stimulus is present only in the specific perverse act. It should be mentioned, however, that certain transitional cases may be found in which coitus is the sex act sought after in spite of the presence of sexual perversion. Occasionally some sort of perverse act is then sought after as a means of sexual excitement. Such, for example, is the maltreatment of the wife, the killing of an animal; but gratification is in the end found in coitus. Generally, however, this is not so. The intrinsic hereditary nature of the normal sex instinct extends beyond mere contact with the person of the opposite sex. Nothing is left to sheer accident or trial.

It is characteristic in this connection that in sexual perversion, as already mentioned, other means of sexual gratification are sought after. But when these sexual perversions are only of a periodic nature, coitus, and no other act, is desired during the normal period. This will be demonstrated in the following case of a periodic boot-fetishist.

CASE XXXII. Mr. A. V., 35 years of age; has been married for nine years. He is the father of four children, all well developed in body and mind. Several of his brothers and sisters are dead, a few having died in early childhood. His father had been suffering from asthma. Tuberculosis prevails in the family. Otherwise no hereditary traits can be discovered. It should be mentioned that A. V.'s grandfather was a shoemaker and his father had to help out in the shop up to the age of 20.

A. V. was very strong and lively as a child. His education was very strict; his step-mother treated him very harshly. Once, at the age of six, he received a pair of leather shoes, though usually he wore his brother's shoes after he had outgrown them. He recollects that these shoes gave him great pleasure, that he touched and sniffed at them with a strange joy. At the time he also experienced pleasure in being beaten or tortured by a friend who was several years his senior. But these sensations must have disappeared very soon afterwards, for he does not recall that he ever again had such inclinations.

When he was 12 he left the strict home of his parents to enter high school. At 13 he began to masturbate for reasons unknown to him, at first by pulling narrow rings, strings and similar objects over his penis, thus inducing an ejaculation. Later he used to masturbate with the aid of the bootstraps of a friend at the boarding house; but this was only a temporary expedient. A short time afterwards he went to live in another boarding house. It was then that his predilection for female footgear began to manifest itself. It was new cloth shoes into the stiff pull-straps of which he would insert his penis; then he induced ejaculation inside the shoes or alongside of them. But the shoes had to be trimmed in leather and had to have high heels. Cloth shoes without leather trimmings did not excite his libido. At the time A. V. used to buy shoes with these desired qualities. He wore them at night while taking strolls and afterwards masturbated into them when he came home. Sometimes he looked out of the window for hours in order to see whether women with such desirable shoes were passing by. Then, at the sight of them he masturbated into his own shoes. Sometimes he gave himself up to excessive masturbation, after heavy beer-drinking he indulged in with his friends. This may perhaps have increased his excitement. At the age of sixteen he went into military service. He had to give up drinking beer and then he began to fight against the passion which he himself recognized as harmful. For some time he was victorious But after a while he succumbed to it again. Inasmuch as he had very little occasion to look at ladies with beautiful shoes he often took walks in lonely places frequented by such ladies in order to masturbate at the sight of their shoes and especially of the high heels. He again dressed up in women's shoes, etc., etc. But this form of gratification occurred only very infrequently, beginning with his

17th year, so that he did not perceive any deleterious effect on his body. In the meantime A. V. had occasion to practice normal intercourse. Though he was potent sexually, he did not experience the same pleasure in it as he did in fetishistic masturbation.

Between yielding to his pathological inclination and the struggle against it he reached at the age of 22. Everyone regarded him as an ambitious young man and he was much liked in company. He liked very much to associate with mentally alert girls. As such times he refrained from any sexual activities. At the same time he also made the acquaintance of the woman who later became his wife and fell in love with her at first sight. She answered his love, and their engagement took place very shortly after. For a long time he was able to control his secret passion, though at their frequent meetings the shoes of his bride often excited his libido. He tried to get into possession of her high buttoned shoes in order to use them for the purpose of masturbating. His exclusive predilection for buttoned shoes with high heels began at that time. He also induced his bride to wear only buttoned shoes under the pretext that other styles did not suit her well.

At that time other makes of women's shoes hardly excited him. This situation was changed when he was away from his bride for some time. During the time he again spent several hours at windows, to spy at the women passing by and especially at their shoes. In times of severe excitement he bought some additional ladies' shoes. Several times he also tried to cure his passion by performing intercourse with prostitutes. Though he was quite potent he always felt disgusted afterwards. Later he abstained from it also for fear of infection. He then tried to pacify his sexual cravings in masturbation which really proved quite successful. He remarks that is was impossible for him to do any work when he failed to gratify his desires for some time, and that he could work again only after his libido was satisfied. In the latter case he was able to work continuously, while during the time he fought against his libido he disliked any kind of mental exertion. When he was gratified he showed such diligence that he was able to pass his examinations with distinction. During his year of military service he lived normally, but his fetishistic ideas persisted.

A. V. hoped to improve his condition through marriage, which he was sure would prove successful after having read about the influence of marriage on masturbation—he knew nothing about fetishism as such. He therefore married. He was fully potent the very first night, without any imagery of shoes. He thought that he was cured at last. But during his wife's pregnancy and confinement his fetishism again was strongly aroused. He again began to use his wife's shoes for the purpose of sexual gratification. At times he would again look out of the window to glance at the passing women. When a strong desire came upon him the sight of their shoes would be sufficient to cause ejaculation. A few years passed thus during which he was gratified equally by normal coitus and by fetishistic masturbation. He continued to fight against the latter and finally made up his mind to leave his domicile in the belief that his mind was sufficiently occupied to distract him from his strange passion. Another reason for moving to a larger city was that he hoped that the frequent sight of beautiful ladies' shoes would tend to dull his passion.

He intentionally took up a profession calculated to occupy his whole activity and energy. For a time everything went well. The increased activity and responsibility brought with it good results. But after a few weeks, when he was forced to separate from his wife— she went to a bathing resort for her health—the old impulse was reawakened in an intense degree. A. V. began to do what he had never before done—to look at the shoes of the ladies in the streets and to ejaculate at the sight of them by exerting pressure on his penis through his trousers. Normal coitus again set in when his wife returned and his fetishism somewhat receded. But soon it grew more and more severe. His wife had borne him four strong children. A physician whom she consulted regarding her growing weakness warned her that another pregnancy would prove fatal. He advised that they cease from sexual intercourse altogether. From then on A. V. performed coitus only very rarely and always only coitus interruptus. Soon, however, he tired of that method and at last very carefully confided to his wife about his predilection for shoes. After caressing his wife, he kissed one of her shoes, at the same time touching her other foot with his penis. But his wife's sense of shame soon made such situations impossible. In the belief that he would be able to cure himself in another manner he induced his wife to wear a style of shoe which did not excite him in the least: laced shoes with low heels. He made a long trip to the country; took extensive walks, rode bicycles and refrained from beer, wine and tobacco. For eight weeks he was completely free from an fetishistic thoughts. But then he began to suffer from hemorrhoidal troubles. He had been suffering from hemorrhoidal nodules since his 19th year and now a strong bleeding from the piles set in, which had occurred before. When the bleeding stopped he suddenly experienced a strong erection and libido again became extraordinarily severe. He had to drop the most urgent work in order to run into the street to get the much-desired gratification. Afterward his fetishistic attacks came upon him in regular intervals of about three to four weeks. Sometimes the inelegant shoes of his wife, too, would excite him; but the greatest pleasure he felt at the sight of shoes of the above named description. His aesthetic requirements for the shoes increased more and more and finally only the most elegant and expensive shoes could excite him. He spent many hours outdoors in order to look at such shoes. Their heels must not be too high nor worn away; the instep highly arched, the leather of the finest kid, and the shoes well-fitting. Shoes without these qualities at times excited him also; but his libido then never reached the point of ejaculation. Still, his ideal attitude toward his wife remained the same. His inclination towards her has always been of the same degree. Her signs of affection were wearisome to him only during his attacks. Sometimes she then complained that he did not love her as heretofore. In the intervals between attacks he is perfectly normal emotionally. He often then shows no inclination towards masturbation or fetishism. He feels even repugnance to these practices. During the "clear" intervals he cannot understand how it is possible for him to be carried away by his fetishistic inclinations. He can understand it the less inasmuch as he can control himself in every other respect. After a period of three weeks at most, a new attack sets in. The whole of A. V.'s mind is then dominated by fetishistic ideas. After yielding to it for a few days the attack subsides again and he becomes normal again in body and mind.

His eyes were opened to his condition a few months ago after he had read about fetishism in Krafft-Ebing's "Psychopathia Sexualis." Thereupon the fits ceased for about eight weeks (whether accidentally or not, he does not know). Later, however, a relapse occurred and since then the fits have repeated themselves in the wonted intervals, sometimes mild, at other times more severe. Recently there was a long interval lasting about eight months. He hopes therefore that he may be freed from his attacks.

It must further be mentioned that frequently, before the onset of puberty, he had masochistic ideas in the sense of being trodden upon by elegant ladies' shoes. Usually, however, he imagined himself kissing the shoes or holding them to his penis. If the woman in question was pleasant, of medium height, slender and of an elegant appearance; her mere sight would awaken voluptuous sensations. He had no masochistic inclinations in respect to the plain shoes of his wife. Prostitutes and women dressed in loud colors in spite of the fact that they wore elegant shoes, made no impression upon him.

A. V. is completely engrossed in his business and in his family affairs. He neglects duties towards his relatives only during his attacks. No other pathological inclinations may be ascertained.

In fetishism the usual thing is the contact of the genitals with the cherished object or bodily part. It is true that there are exceptions to this rule, as the following observation, which I adduce here as a parallel case, will establish. Here, too, we are concerned with a fetishism which made its appearance periodically, being now homosexual, now heterosexual As we shall see, patient's heterosexual intercourse consisted either in coitus or in unnatural forms of gratification, which, however, had nothing to do with his foot-fetishism. His homosexuality expressed itself in all sorts of masturbatory acts and other activities. Touching the objects to his organ, as in usually found in foot-fetishism, did not take place.

Case XXXIII. Mr. N. D., 31 years of age. Patient's parents are alive. His father is suffering from diabetes mellitus. He is 18 years older than his wife. The latter is a nervous, hysterical woman, easily excitable. Patient stresses the fact that his father is of a very taciturn nature, whereas he is unusually talkative, nay, even garrulous.

He inherited nothing of his father's strong and energetic character. He is of a remarkably unstable nature. He claims that his parents did not treat him with any loving care, though he was not punished often. He refers to his mother with extraordinary veneration; he calls her a genial and angelic being, possessing unusual musical talents. One of patient's brothers is his direct opposite, always diligent, energetic, purposive and talented. He is not said to show any sexual abnormailty. Several of his relatives are suffering from severe ailments. Some have even committed suicide for unknown reasons; a few other close relatives are weak-minded.

N. D. is not gifted mentally. School was a great burden to him. His mother's endeavors to help him through school were of no avail. The required material covered in school he never mastered. His chief mental traits are straying, irregularity, dependence, and lack of energy.

These qualities have remained the same up to the present.

Patient informs me as follows regarding his sexual life: "My father and mother have never really seen through me. The evil germ that was in me from early childhood has landed upon very fruitful soil; it has grown rankly upon it for the last 25 years. It is inconceivable to me that my parents and the house-physician who meant so well with me, knew nothing about my feeling, and have withheld from me information so valuable to my health, from a sexual point of view. Yet the trained eyes of a physician were not needed to observe my inclination to masturbate. From very early youth I was inclined sensually, a curse that winds through my entire life like a red thread, hindering me from accomplishing anything worth while."

At the age of six he met a pretty young girl during an outing in the country and liked her very much. He believes that he can trace back his predilection for feet to this early incident. At the time it was the feet of the servant-girls which he observed with admiration when they washed the floor. He remembers very little of his life between the age of six to twelve. Later he does remember a few incidents. One incident is especially vivid in his mind. A young girl was standing barefoot before the stove in his parents' home. N. D. used this occasion to squat down on the floor directly in front of the girl's legs, under the pretext that he wanted to look into the fire. He greatly longed to touch her feet or to kiss them. But this must have appeared repugnant to him, or at least he was too timid to give in to his desire, because of the presence of another person in the room. He further adds: "On account of my timidity—and I am inclined to believe that it was this cowardice which later became the starting point for all my troubles—I had to suffer much. Had I kissed the girl on that occasion, with all my heart, I would have grown to be a healthy and happy man.'' Further close questioning could not elicit the meaning of this statement. He also recalls at the time a young house painter whom he eagerly observed when the latter painted the floors. His interest was not turned to the man's work, but rather to his bare feet. At that time a girl suffering from nervous twitchings used to come into the house often. A story went about that if someone should bite the girl's large toe during one of her fits she would be cured from her ailment. N. D. remembers the great desire he had to do this. But this time he was just as timid as before. He is surprised himself at his timidity then, for later in life he used to approach men sexually without any fear or care, and even under the threat of punishment. His first ejaculation occurred at the age of thirteen. The incident is still vivid in his mind. Some examples in arithmetic were to be done in class and at the last moment before the teacher collected the copybooks N. D. wanted to correct an error; he became excited and had a seminal ejaculation. He remembers experiencing great pleasure on that occasion. He is not sure whether he began to masturbate right after this. At all events, from the age of 14 to 16 he gave himself up to the practice, with great passion. With the exception of a period of a year and a half, during which he had a ''serious affair'' with a young woman, he has continued masturbating until very recently.

From his 13th to his 15th year he had a burning zeal for the bare feet of women. Consequently, he always used to spy upon the servant-girls when they washed the floors. Such a spectacle always induced an erection. Afterwards he went to a selected spot to masturbate. He stole the girls' shoes and stockings, sniffed at them until ejaculation took place. He licked the insteps of the shoes, moistened one of the stockings and then sucked it dry. He then put on the stockings and shoes and ejaculated into them. For want of such objects he sometimes performed the same acts with his own stockings. Frictions against these articles of clothing afforded him the greatest pleasure. He liked to prolong the excitement as long as possible, to the point of ejaculation. When he felt that the moment of ejaculation arrived he always interrupted his activity and resumed it after a few minutes. At night he used to sneak into the servant-girls' rooms, steal their stockings and shoes, and masturbate. Then he replaced them near their beds. On afternoons when the girls were away doing laundry work and when no one else was in the house—he used to watch for such ideal moments—he would take off his own shoes and stockings, lie down into the bed of one of the girls and masturbate in the above-described manner.

A young servant-girl pleased him especially. During meal-time he sometimes permitted himself to look amorously at her and to tell her some pleasantries. Sometimes he stopped her when she cleared the tables. This often resulted in severe reproofs on the part of his mother, the father never interfering with him. His mother frequently admonished him about his behavior but the meaning of her reproaches was never clear to him. ''The thing I got from my mother's remarks was that my behavior would surely turn me into a lazy and dissolute person. I am filled with piety and love towards my parents but I cannot help looking back upon that time with great bitterness. I am convinced that right guidance and a few proper hints might have turned me into a happy and healthy being and not have forced me into the wrong path. While my friends slept with the buxom servant-girls every night, I imitated the girls' washing of the floors always thinking of their feet. I fetched brushes and rags from the kitchen and masturbated into them. I also did it while taking a warm bath.'' He masturbated so excessively that his penis began to hurt. He even inflicted wounds on it. But the resulting pain did not, as in the case of masochists, cause him any voluptuous sensation. When he became aware that semen was induced by friction of the penis he became worried. He then cleaned the bath-tub very carefully in order to be sure that the semen should have no ill consequences on his sister, in case she used the tub after him.

When he took a walk he always counted the people going barefoot, men, women and children alike; but not the number of persons, rather the number of toes. For example, when he came home he would say: "Today I saw 10, 50, 200 toes."

When he was 16 his liking for feet took on a different aspect. It was no more the toes of any description which gave him pleasure; the feet, had to be provided with finely shaped nails. He found no more pleasure in feet with corns, feet of old men, or old women, or the feet of very young children. When he counted the toes of the passers-by he omitted the latter altogether. His excitement at the sight of feet did not diminish. In the summer time, when it was raining, he found an especial delight in watching the people wade through the pools of water, their feet bare. One day, when he was about 16, while bathing with a friend he stole into the latter's locker, picked up his stockings and boots, and masturbated into them in the above-named manner. Another night he crept up to the bed of his sister, put his head' beneath the quilts and licked her toes with his tongue. He left her and retired to his own bed only when she began to roll over in her sleep.

About that time he remembers also an incident at school. A teacher who was very fond of him and whom he esteemed very highly, uttered once some vague remarks regarding the dangerous behavior of young people, but he was vague about his point. Only these words remain in his memory—"and in the end he perished miserably on the roadside." The teacher at the same time looked fixedly at two of his fellow-students and disregarded N. D. completely. He knows quite well that the two boys later were happily married, whereas he himself met with an unhappy fate. This obscurely worded exhortation of the teacher made no impression upon him. Yet even then he was aware of the noxiousness of his behavior. He was constantly looking for articles on masturbation in encyclopedias. He made up his mind to be done with it, but still continued to indulge in it. "Were it not for this impulse to masturbate my youth might have been a very happy one, for I was full of quips and pranks; but my character was weakened by this irresistible impulse." After masturbating a feeling of sadness and dreariness always came upon him. Yet he had not the will-power to pull himself together out of his evil passion. Thoughts of bare feet played the main role during the act, with all kinds of variations. He envied people who could walk about barefoot. When a

woman told him that in some parts of America   even
rich people let their children walk barefoot, a great
longing came upon him. It was pitch-dark and they
dared each other who could fetch a certain article from
the other end of the garden. No one would do it. N. D.,
who, as he states himself, was nervous and cowardly,
eagerly took up the idea. When he was a few steps
from the house he took off his shoes and stockings and
then, with great sexual excitement, he ran for the goal.

At the age of 12 or 13 or perhaps even earlier, after
his first visit to the theater, he began to develop a burning zeal for several beautiful actresses. Even at the
present time he preserves their images in his memory.
He took a corner of the quilt into his arms, as if it were
a doll and caressed it, imagining it one of those actresses.
Later, from the ages of 16 to 20 and even later perhaps,
while saying his prayers before retiring, he always
would mention the names of several beauties of the town,
whom he didn't even know personally. Two of these
women he had seen at church, during services; their
beautiful appearance turned his attention from the
prayerbook and the sermon. These non-fetishistic inclinations, however, were only very transitory episodes.
Strange to say, it was always blondes who attracted him.
He also had similar non-fetishistic inclination towards
men. He remembers meeting a well-known actor in a
mountain resort; he had often seen him in roles of a
hero. He looked up at this "beautiful man" with great
enthusiasm and passion.

He performed his first coitus at the age of 16. Together with a few friends he went to a brothel; but he
did not have any pleasure in the act. He does not recall
how he had performed the act, but he remembers quite

well the second time he had intercourse. That time, too, he went with a prostitute. During a period of two hours he performed the act six times, but it caused him great pain, and he found neither pleasure nor gratification in it. The woman was a common prostitute with misshapen feet, "which had nothing of the charm and delicacy of the servant-girls' feet." N. D. subsequently performed coitus irregularly. He retains no pleasurable memories in regards to these acts, performed from time to time. On the other hand, he always gave himself up to the practice of masturbation with great passion and with the thought of new means of indulging in it. Although he occasionally continued to go to prostitutes he never dared kiss their feet, even those that were attractive to him. His predilection for feet remained unchanged. When he was sixteen he went to live in a boarding house where his room was situated in such a way that the servant-girls had to pass through it when going into the kitchen. When he saw them running barefoot by his bed he was "terribly excited" and then always resorted to masturbation. At the time, just when he left school, he was for some time employed in a factory in order to learn his trade. During working hours he regarded with interest the workers who sometimes went about bare foot; when he was not observed he used to masturbate at the sight of their feet, and also in connection with memory pictures of the feet. Even in the house, in the presence of his parents he would do it, when he thought that he was not observed. He believes that formerly masturbation had a stronger hold upon him than now. But he never could get rid of it. This condition was even more aggravated by the unpractical mode of life. Life was very monotonous, loafing about impossible for he always had to stay at home. He had no real pleasure in drinking or similar pleasure. His timid attempts to approach the better kinds of girls were fruitless for he did not know how to begin with them. He still remembers a beautiful girl from a good family whom he met when he was 18. ''The girl possessed the finest hands I have ever seen; beneath her pretty shoes I imagined the most graceful feet:'' When his father discovered that he had bought an expensive gift for the girl on the occasion of a ball, he reproached him very severely. His parents did not permit any scenes in the house, and according to patient this attitude increased even more his disinclination towards normal intercourse with women.

When he was 19 he went to live in a large city. There he frequented the brothels, but he had no spiritual pleasure in the act. On the other hand, he began to kiss the prostitutes' feet—a thing he had never before done. At home he continued to masturbate. At the time he was pursued by the attentions of a man who had taken a great liking to him. In order to escape these attentions N. D. removed to another part of the city. He gradually took to unnatural means of gratification with prostitutes, inducing them to let him insert his penis into their mouth and to kiss their feet. This caused him great delight. Now and then he also tried to titillate the women's genitals with his tongue, but he soon began to loathe this act and finally desisted from it. A certain incident of that time he can still remember. He had made the acquaintance of a girl, who, though not beautiful, had a well-proportioned figure and ''feet more beautiful'' than he had ever before seen. He covered the girl's feet with passionate kisses. In his mind's eye he can still see the girl's face full of surprise at his strange ecstacy. He refused to kiss the girl's mouth, because to him this was just like kissing the genitals. In spite of his intercourse with prostitutes he also ran after women in the street; this caused him great sexual excitement without gratifying him. He often made out a programme for his procedure with the prostitutes, whereby their feet played the main role. He desired to clean their feet, to pare their nails, etc. His ill-feelings at the lack of sexual gratification caused him to lose all pleasure and interest in the house of close relatives with whom he stayed. Even severe sickness in the family did not move him because his love for them had diminished. This feeling caused him to reproach himself. But he thanked God that his relatives did not recognize his sad passion which had induced him to become so neglectful in his duties towards them. His inclination towards the feet of men and women grew stronger and stronger. He desired to kiss the feet of a servant-girl in his relatives' house. The girl was very decent and reserved, which excited N. D. even more. One day, when the girl fell asleep on the kitchen table, he kissed her feet in a spot laid bare by a torn stocking.

The next few years passed in this manner. Physically he was somewhat stronger then. He took up swimming, gymnastics, and made use of other means to strengthen his body. At the time he masturbated less. He remembers a boy of 12, a cadet, whom he used to admire for his pretty face. beautiful body and elegant feet causing him distinctly sexual sensations. He saw a servant-girl walk barefoot in the street and followed her to the third floor of some house; he only desisted from his pursuit when she cried out. He would walk into strange houses when he knew that the floors were being washed. Still as a whole, he was more at ease. Once, when he was on an extensive tour to the mountains, a guide who accompanied him, a man of about 40, asked him if he would permit him to sleep in the same bed. N. D. consented. He recalls that he touched the guide's penis as well as his thighs and bluttocks, but did not succeed in gratifying his desire for the man became angry and threatened to get out of the bed immediately if he did not lie quiet.

In spite of all these occurrences he was not in the least aware that he had homosexual inclinations. Once while on a trip he made the acquaintance of a Frenchman, a man of about forty, They talked about women and the stranger expressed the opinion that it was also pleasurable to practice intercourse with men. N. D. did not understand this reference and kept a reserved mien. Then he told the man that he considered such form of intercourse abhorrent. Another time, when the talk turned to the subject of a man convicted of committing indecent acts with boys, he himself was the most indignant in condemning it.

When he returned to Berlin he made the acquaintance of a girl, who impressed him as being a prostitute. He associated with her and performed coitus with her. The girl's honorable nature, which he later discovered was merely feigned, made a good impression upon him. After the act the girl refused to accept any money; she took it only after he insisted. A sexual relationship was formed between them, lasting for a year and a half. The girl exerted a charm upon him through her personality. He states that though she had a beautiful appearance she was coarse and hot-tempered, but her behavior did not prevent him from coming completely under her influence.

She knew how to charm him with a few words, so that he even forgot the dreary surroundings she lived in. It was not necessary even to kiss her feet for him to get excited. "I may say that those were very happy days—the happiest of my life. I used to visit the girl regularly, two or three times a week, and recently even more frequently. Sometimes when I didn't come to see her she would send a servant to ask for money. For though she at first seemed to accept my money only relunctantly, this very soon changed. After eight weeks she informed him that her menstruation had failed to make its appearance. Pregnancy took its normal course and she gave birth to a boy, who died after a few days, however. N. D. was convinced that the boy was his own child, but today he is not sure of it. In the association with this girl he learned much about the pangs of jealousy. Often he waited for hours when he did not find her home. He thought he might catch her in an act of infidelity, but he never succeeded. He felt somewhat relieved when the midwife told him that the child seemed to resemble him completely. After the birth of the child his relationship to her continued for a time. But his former liking for her disappeared. For fear of another pregnancy he performed only coitus interruptus. Even today he at times reproaches himself for not having been saddened enough at the death of the child. He used to free himself from these self-reproaches by the thought that death had saved the little creature from a miserable life and a sad future—a fate allotted to all illegitimate children. A short time after the birth of the child he desired to separate from his mistress. But she kept him for a few months longer by feigning suicide, claiming to have swallowed arsenic. Until the last three months of their relationship N. D. had been with no other woman. Nor does he remember all this time ever having masturbated or showing any special interest for feet. He himself states that this period of life was the happiest, in spite of the bitter experiences with his mistress. The pleasant moments of his life are from that time. After some time he separated from her but with the kindest of feelings for her; the girl herself left their common domicile. In spite of their differences the separation was painful to him.

Immediately after the separation the fetishistic inclinations returned. He had a pair of boots made which were delivered by the shoemaker's boy. The latter was about 13, wore low shoes without stockings; this caused N. D. to be aroused. He asked the boy in the most harmless fashion whether he would let him try on one of his shoes. The boy laughed shyly without consenting to it. N. D. used to visit the nearby "swimming-hole" to look at the feet of the bathing boys; afterwards he usually masturbated. Occasionally he also had normal intercourse with prostitutes.

On the recommendation of a young man, Mr. Z., he left his domicile and removed to another city where he believed he could earn a better living. Mr. Z invited him to his own house and it being a hot day, they took a cold bath together. On that occasion he saw the young man's bare feet and also his penis—this excited him very much. He lived far away from Z.'s house, so the latter asked him to stay over night. He said that though there was only one bed, they would get along all right. At the prospect of that night, his head was filled with the wildest thoughts. He was especially delighted in the thought of being able to kiss the other's feet. However, he came home dog-tired and very intoxicated by alcohol, so that his plans came to naught. Business cares, unpleasant social relationships and quarrels with relatives brought him a more and more desperate state of mind. He took to gambling. His sexual life became wilder and more dissolute. Now he would perform cunnilingus with prostitutes, now coitus, and again sexual intercourse with men. His frame of mind became quite hopeless. He had thoughts of suicide. He changed quarters every other day and at last began to travel from city to city. His friends who observed his strange behavior told him that he made the impression of a demented person. A friend who knew nothing of his sexual perversions advised him to marry a certain girl. N. D. had no liking for her, so that all plans were frustrated. Without any fixed occupation he knocked about in different places. He became afraid of the sight of people. He had no desire to approach decent girls. His only associations were with prostitutes. At the time he saw a handsome, girlish-looking working man who walked a few steps in front of him. He wore slippers. N. D. lost his head completely. He went up close to the fellow and dropping a gold coin and then picking it up, he asked the man how much it was worth. He knew how ridiculous he must have looked in the fellow's eyes; but his strange passion had deadened all other emotions in him. He told the fellow openly that he would give him the money if he would let him kiss his feet. At first the fellow refused to give in to his desires, but later he followed N. D. to the dark passage of some house. Here he had to take off his slippers. It was pitch-dark. N. D. could not see anything. At last the fellow let him kiss

his feet, take his toes into his mouth, etc. Not satisfied
with this N. D. embraced him passionately, took hold of
his penis and put it into his mouth. He had previously
asked him how old he was and was told that he was 17.
He is not quite sure whether he had asked this question
in order to make sure that he would not be criminally
liable for his act, or merely in order to ascertain whether
the fellow was sexually mature. Moreover the fellow
seemed to be well acquainted with homosexuals, for he
knew that money could be easily earned in that manner,
in certain parts of the city.

When he again met the fellow accidentally he induced
him to come to his own rooms on the promise that he
would give him a silver watch. He did this with great
precaution in order not to be surprised by his neighbors. When he was in the room alone with the fellow
he acted like one gone raving mad. He proceeded with
him in the same manner as at their first meeting in the
dark passage-way. But he soon discovered that in
the dark he had been led astray. This time neither the
fellow's penis nor his feet pleased him. Nevertheless,
he licked the fellow's penis. However, when he recalled
that in his first encounter he had swallowed a few drops
of his semen he was disgusted and finished the act very
rapidly. The fellow's behavior toward him took a sudden change. Not satisfied with the watch, he demanded
more money and N. D. had to give it to him. But the fellow had to assure him that he would tell no one of what
had taken place between them. If he should be asked
how he came into the possession of so much money he
was to say that some lady had given it to him. N. D.
was very much afraid. He became aware of the crimin-
ality of his act and was always in great fear of detec-

tion. He had no friends at all. His relatives did not care about his well-being, though his shy nature should have been noticed by them. He feared that his presence might contaminate the society of decent people. He left his domicile like a fugitive and went to live abroad. His flesh still creeps when he thinks of the first few evenings he spent there, alone, in his room; for he had no fixed income and no friends. At last he found employment. He thought he would go crazy. He feared that he might be blackmailed and persecuted for his former evil life. Out of despair he gave himself up to masturbation and to intercourse with prostitutes. But coitus with them did not afford him any pleasure. For several months he was free from his homosexual inclinations. He believes that this was due more to the fact that he rarely saw men with bare feet. He kept away from homosexual intercourse for more than 13 months. It seems unbelievable to him at present that his homosexuality should have lain dormant for so long. One day the following incident occurred. After having been with a prostitute he met an omnibus conductor who had a handsome, girlish face. He immediately had a strong liking for him. In the course of the next few days he frequently rode in the 'bus of this conductor. He would figure out exactly when the car would pass his house. He gave the man cigars and this made him more docile and friendly. But N. D. was at a loss how to propose to the man. Once, late at night he rode in the 'bus for a few miles to the end of the line. When they arrived there he invited him to a drink, at a bar. But he had no opportunity then to speak to him alone for several of the conductor's friends sat down to a common table. When they left, N. D. apparently separated very soon from the company; in reality he followed them at a distance, and as soon as he saw that each went his own way, he ran after the conductor. At last he stopped him in a deserted street. He told him that he was quite infatuated with him and asked him to let me kiss his feet. "Though the man was not angry with me, he was very much surprised at this strange proposal, and disinclined to satisfy my desires." But promise of money made him very pliable. The conductor then proposed to masturbate him; this idea was new to N. D. and the act gave him great pleasure. Afterwards he masturbated the conductor. For several days these acts were repeated. N. D. lost his shyness and began to feel much happier. Things went along in this manner for some time. Other individuals, too, began to excite him sexually. Now it was cadets, now waiters, whose feet he desired to kiss. He again resumed coitus with prostitutes. After a time N. D. went into the mountains where the following incident, proving the strength of his fetishistic inclination, occurred. On the road he met a mechanic's apprentice who asked him for money. N. D. proceeded on his way without being disturbed by the fellow. He was a long way off when the thought came to him to ask the fellow whether he would give in to his desires. He ran back and promised to tip him well if he would let him kiss his feet. The fellow gave in readily. They found a quiet spot in the woods where the fellow took off his shoes and stockings. For a long time N. D. gave himself up to passionate kisses of his feet. Not entirely satisfied with this, he held his penis, and then embraced his whole body. At the last moment, however, he became disgusted and he had a strong desire to make a quick end to the procedure. In this case, too, licking and kissing of the feet was sufficient to bring about erection and ejaculation. When he was about to part the fellow demanded more money, which N. D. refused. But when the fellow began to shout out loud he had to give in to the extortioner. At the end they became friendly again. The last words of parting which the fellow shouted after him on parting were: "You will never get rid of this passion!" Those words have pursued him to this very day.

When he returned to his home town he made the acquaintance of a 'bus driver. He was very strongly infatuated with him but did not dare come near him. Then he fell upon the curious idea of addressing a love note to him full of such endearments as he had never directed to a girl. This letter he at once handed to the man, with the request that he read it at home. In the letter he asked him to answer him under certain name, at the nearest post office, telling him whether he would give in to his desires. N. D. soon became fully aware of the danger he had placed himself in, for while calling at the post office for an answer he might be arrested. His passion was, however, so strong and uncontrollable, that all his fears were conquered and he went to call for an answer. This answer read as follows: "Not in the least insulted. Letter destroyed. Cannot, however, fulfill your desires at the present." N. D. hurried to the omnibus company where the driver was employed, full of joy and excitement. He met the driver, gave him some money there and then, and they agreed what evening to meet. They at last met. "The driver was a beautiful man." This time it was not the feet that excited, for he could tell from the shape of his boots that his feet were not well-shaped. It was rather the whole man which stimulated him: his beautiful hands, the finger nails and the handsome girlish face. They performed mutual masturbation. N. D. kissed his penis and he did this also in subsequent meetings with the man.

The following days he alternated normal coitus with homosexual intercourse; for some time the latter had no fetishistic character. Intercourse with men soon led him to attempt pederasty, but he was prevented from performing it on account of his physical condition. He went through all forms of sexual gratification. This was mainly due to the fact that he went about with male prostitutes. Through it he again came in contact with extortionists. Three men in open daylight attempted to exact money from him; they robbed him of all his cash. He was naturally worried by the fear of meeting these individuals again. Shortly afterward he had another fanciful attachment for a young, decent girl to whom he proposed; but she refused him. He could not give up his resolution to break with men. He again took to masturbation. At times he would do it in the open street while following people going barefoot. He also took "water cures" merely in order to watch the man persons in the institution who went about barefoot.

Let me recapitaulate what I have said regarding the impulse towards coitus. When coitus is not performed as a result of instruction, seduction or imitation, it is discovered through trial and error method. Coitus would probably take place without any instruction. The act would be brought about by the desire for the greatest amount of pleasure. It is just this intense orgasm in coitus that is hereditary. This is conditioned partly by the greatest peripheral stimulus. It seems probable, also, that the female genitals exert attraction on the man subconsciously. The cynical remark that what man loves in woman are her genitals, is thus actually justified.

In spite of occasional aberrations most normal men have the impulse not only to press their penis to some part of the woman's body, but rather, to introduce the penis into the vagina. And though it has not been fully proven that this impulse rests on an inherited capacity I believe we may assume that man has an inherited disposition for coitus. What seems to point especially to this conclusion is the fact that what is sought for in most cases of sexual perversions, e. g., in cases of fetishism, is a different form of gratification. For, if in the case of the fetishists it were merely a question of using the beloved object for purposes of excitement, it would suffice him to look at the object while masturbating. But the sexually excitable fetishist seeks for the object of pleasure in the same manner as the normal person seeks for the vagina. He takes possession of the beloved object as does a normal man who is in the act of introducing his penis into the vagina. Assuming that under normal conditions the criterion is the strongest possible stimulation of the penis as best attained in the introducing of it into the vagina so it is remarkable also, that the fetishist brings his penis in contact with the beloved object. I believe that the seeking of the greatest possible stimulus is the most important criterion. There is also an unconscious impulse to introduce the penis into the vagina.

I have intentionally refrained from going into further detail in this discussion. I have tried to show that detumescence and contrectation have developed phylogenetically, as well as the role of natural selection. With the significance of the latter the appearance of both instincts in one individual is self-evident. It has been pointed out that the impulse to perform coitus is caused by natural selection. All individuals in whom the two instincts were divided or who possessed only one of them, and lacking the impulse to perform coitus, could not produce any offsprings. For neither a person who merely masturbated and thus satisfied his organic impulse, nor one who felt a Platonic love for another; resulting in only embracing and kissing, have any children. Reproduction was possible only when the two instincts occurred together and resulted in coitus.

A few cases will show that even people showing no distinct perversions there may be a deficiency in the impulse for coitus. Though they show the aspect of heterosexuals they are not impelled to perform coitus but to vague and indefinite acts. It is a well-known fact also that some people seek gratification by means of flagellation. But such acts belong to the region of the perversions which I shall not discuss here.

Case XXXIV. Mr. T. B., 25 years of age. His father is dead. He is said to have been weak-minded in his last years. His mother is sick. In his youth he masturbated excessively. He has a distinct inclination towards women but not towards coitus. Nor has he any erection when he is with a woman. In order to excite him the woman must not be naked. Bare feet and the odor of perspiration especially repel him. When he comes in bodily contact with a woman congenial to him and presses her close to him he often does have an ejaculation. He is also very fond of kissing women, but as already mentioned, he lacks all impulse to perform coitus.

There are many other similar cases. There are also men who are capable of performing coitus only with women fully dressed. It cannot be denied that in such cases the individuals inherited reaction complexes have been weakened during life. It is not any more the woman in her natural state who exerts the stimulus, but the woman dressed.

In the following case, the impulse to perfom coitus is present at times, at other times it is feeble or not pronounced.

Case XXXV. Mr. B. T., 32 years old, merchant. His family has hereditary taints. He began to masturbate in his early childhood and continued until the age of fifteen. He performed coitus at the age of 16. Coitus to him is only a form of masturbation; for he is hardly ever impelled to perform it. He is completely heterosexual, but he has no desire to have normal intercourse, he shows only the tendency to occupy himself with women in a vague sensual manner. He is excited by certain parts of a woman's body, by her thighs, wide hips, without showing, however, any marked predilection for any specific part. He shows no direct inclination to touch the female. He is also very inconstant in his likes. For example, when he speaks to a woman who attracts him he will soon lose all interest for her when he perceives another woman, though the latter be less attractive. He did practice intercourse but because he lacked another interest. Recent attempts to perform coitus have failed on account of impotence, no erection took place, flow of semen without erection took place.

Let us sum up the discussion in this chapter. In all

higher animals sexual reproduction takes place by means of coitus, an act in which two sexually differentiated individuals come together. Impregnation of the egg-cell by sperm follows. Not only with mammals but also with insects and birds and even some species of fish, reproduce by means of copulation. When we consider that both detumescence and contrectation may be proven to exist in all higher animals, we must assume on the basis of heredity and comparative anatomy that contrectation in human beings is inherited and not acquired. We must assume also that contrectation has its foundation in the organism. We must reject the claim of Meynert and others that everything with the exception of the peripheral genitals has been acquired. Is it possible to believe that in man the act of coitus recurring for many thousands of generations was only a chance discovery, that the sex impulse is caused by accidental associations? Such a state of affairs seems impossible from any standpoint of teleology. For if their claim had some truth it would have to apply to animals. Here the question arises: is it possible that animals get instruction regarding their urge to mate and of performing the act from older animals? Butterflies just crawled out of the pupal stage, the tiniest of male insects find their females, the male fleas find their female with an ease that many a man will envy. The butterfly could not have been instructed because its parents have been dead long ago. At the moment the egg was deposited no individual of the species concerned itself about the fate of the egg. No sooner do the new individuals slip out of the pupa than they begin to produce. In spite of th fact that some fish have been hatched artificially when set free the male fish will find the female and copulate with it as though it had been hatched by its parents. For, otherwise, if the psychical process were not heterosexual, it would be difficult to conceive why detumescence should appear in connection with these psychical processes. Why is an excretion of the body eliminated as superfluous? But the fact that the semen is carried into the body of another individual can be uderstood only when we know that the other individual belongs to the opposite sex.

Of course, I do not maintain that everything in regards to the sex instinct of human beings is inherited. It is quite probable that the life of the instinct, including sex, like many other cultural phenomena, has been modified by civilization. We know that a few of the instinct of animals have been modified through domestication. Let me cite the case of the silk spinners which when domesticated will devour the base of the leaf on which it rests so that it falls down and thus is led into its own death. We know also that changes occur through the change from a normal environment in an individual's sex instinct. We cannot seriously accept that thousands and thousands of years of development should result in such change that heterosexuality lost its hereditary element. We see it in all the higher animals as well as in some of the lower ones. The assumption that the sex instinct of many is not inherited is far-fetched and exaggerated. Heterosexuality merely requires an inherited mode of reaction activated by stimuli originating in the opposite sex.

In summing up we find the following:
1. The physical and mental qualities of man are the

product of heredity and environment. Natural science
knows of no other factors. In regards to the sex instinct
and especially in regards to its direction only these two
factors are to be considered.

2.   There can be no doubt that detumescence is one
of the two components of the sex instinct; and that it
is inherited, just as the impulse to urinate is inherited.

3.   The sex instinct of the male is directed towards
woman, and vice versa. It is a disputed question whether
this direction of the sex instinct is inherited.

4.   Exact experiments to decide this question as far
as it concerns man cannot be undertaken. Neither cases
of wolf-chidren, nor those of somatic pseudo-hermaphrodites can be used to prove the point for they contain too
many sources of error for observation and to give us a
pure experimental data. In animals we do have exact
observations permitting us to draw clear conclusions
regarding this matter.

5.   However, it is not necessary to assume congenital
or inherited ideas in order to prove the direction of the
sex instinct is inherited.

6.   Just as instincts exist which are released by specific external stimuli based merely on a congenital or
inherited reactive capacity, so also is it sufficient to assume regarding the sex instinct, the existence of inherited reactive capacity aroused by the specific stimuli of
the opposite sex.

7.   Observations on normal men, as well as on blind
persons, and on others deprived of one of their sense
organs have proven that the specific stimuli of the opposite sex exert their influence on several sense organs.
For persons with normal sight, the visual sense is the
most important.

8. The impulse towards another individual may be awakened through one of the sense organs, *e.g.*, the eye, and again deadened by another sense organ, *e. g.*, the sense of smell.

9. Stimuli(*e. g.*, the features of another person) hitting one sense organ (the eye) may be made ineffectual when other stimuli (*e. g.*, a hairy body) hits the same organ not in harmony with the first stimulus.

10. It follows from this that in mature normal persons numerous sources of stimuli of the opposite sex are to be considered. Since these stimuli-sources, as we have seen, exert an influence only when there is present a reactive capacity for them, it follows also that the direction of the sex instinct is determined by a complex of reactive capacities.

11. Psychical qualities of the other sex belong also to the factors exciting these complexes of reactive capacities. Thus courage and energy in the male are sexually exciting to the women, while woman's shyness is sexually exciting to the male.

12. Though we must assume that most of the complexes of reactive capacities are inherited, still observation teaches us that events during the life of the individual may influence these complexes greatly and even change them greatly.

13. Though it is true that certain means of sexual excitements are the same for all races of men, *e. g.*, the female breast, yet for some races this does not hold true. Similarly there have been differences also in various periods of history. And just as there are certain reactions and peculiarities to a race, so also, are there peculiar reactive capacities in each individual.

14. Numerous persons exist with incomplete and im-

perfect complexes of reactive capacities. In some men this complex is not marked exclusively by a receptivity to specific stimuli emanating from woman. This fact explains why some men feel themselves attracted to women with masculine features; also why some men are attracted now to males, now to females. Furthermore, that some men will love only such males who possess definite feminine qualities. The reverse is true of the women who deviate from the normal.

15. The theory of Darwinism is the main argument for the inheritance of the direction of the sex instinct. Experience teaches us that qualities are transmitted to one sex. Thus the testicles, the other male sex organs and the beard are transmitted only to the male sex, while the ovaries, the female genitals and the breasts are inherited only by the female sex. The same is true of some psychical qualities, characteristic only of one sex. From the fact of unisexual heredity we must also assume the unisexual heredity of the direction of the sex instict, *e. g.,* males inherit the receptivity for the specific stimuli coming from the female and vice versa.

Natural selection too argues for the inheritance of the direction of the sex instinct. Inasmuch as we must regard the growth of the embryo in the mother organism as a means of protecting the offspring such embryos could no longer develop outside of the mother after a certain stage in the history of evolution had been reached. For such offspring had to perish in the struggle for existence. It was due to natural selection that only such offspring was produced whose parents possessed the impulse to perform the impregnation inside the mother organism and this impulse was transmitted to the offspring.

Sexual selection together with uni-sexual heredity effected the inheritance of the direction of the sex instinct. Only those male can participate in the competitive struggle for the female who possess an impulse towards the female. The same is true of the female.

16. It also follows from the teleological point of view that the inheritance of the direction of the sex instinct of mutual adaptation and of copulation and reproduction point to this conclusion.

17. Also, certain peculiarities of the sex instinct forces this conclusion. Among these factors belong the disappearance of the sex instinct after premature extirpation of the sex glands; the periodicity of the sex instinct in most animals, the disappearance of the sex instinct of many animals after impregnation, the almost simultaneous onset of contrectation and genital maturity. Also the fact that animals, with only rare exceptions, copulate only with other animals which will result in fruitful offspring.

18. Finally also the observation in animals, and in some men, proves that the impulse towards the opposite sex, and the impulse to perform coitus owes its origin to heredity.

FINIS

BIBLIOGRAPHY

BIBLIOGRAPHY OF ALBERT MOLL.

Works dealing with psychosexualis.

1

Die Kontrarie Sexual-ampfindung.

—Berlin, 1893

2

Les perversions de l'instinct genital.

—Paris, 1893

3

Homosexualität eines Weibes mit passivem Flagellantismus und Koprophagie.

> *—International Centralblat fur der Physiol. und Pathol. der Sex-Org., vol. iv, Leipzig, 1893.*

4

Problem in der Homo sexualität.

> *—Zeitschrift für Criminal-Anthropologie, vol. i, Berlin, 1897.*

5

Untersuchungen über der Libido sexualis.

—Berlin, 1897.

6

Wann durfen homosexuelle heirathen.

—Berlin, 1902.

7

Sexuelle Zwischenstufen.

—Zeitschrift fur ärtz Fortbild., vol. i, Jena, 1904.

8

Analyse des Geschlechts triebes.

—Medisch. Klinik, vol. i, Berlin, 1905

9

Sexuelle Perversionen Geisteskrankheit und Zeurech-nungsfahigkeit.

—Berlin, 1905.

English Translation, Newark, 1931.

10

Sexuelle Erziehung.

—Zeitschrift für Padagog. Psychol., vol. x, Berlin, 1908.

English Translation, London, 1912.

11

Beruhmte Homosexuelle.

—*Weisbaden, 1901.*

12

Das Sexualleben des Kindes.

—*Berlin, 1909.*

13

Die Behandlung sexueller Perversionen mit desonderer Berucksichtigung der Assoziationstherapie.

—*Zeitschrif für Psychother. und medic. Psychol.,
vol. iii, Stuttgarten, 1911.*

14

Handbuch der Sexualwissenschaft: mit besonderer Berücksichtigung der Kulturgeschichtlichen Beziehungen.

—*Leipzig, 1912.*

15

Physiologisches und Psychologisches uber Liebe und Freundschaft.

—*Zeitschrift für Psychoth. und medic. Psychol.,
vol. xii, Stuttgarten, 1912.*

16

Sexualität und Charakter.

—*Sex-Probleme, vol. x:1, Frankfurt, 1914.*

17

Behandlung der Homosexualität: biochemisch oder psychisch?

—Bonn, 1921.

18

Funktionelle Impotenz des Mannes; Eheanfechtung und Ehescheidung.

—Aerzt. Sachverst. Zeitung, vol xxix, Berlin, 1923.

19

Die sogenannte Anästhesie der Frau.

—Med. Klinic, vol. xix, Berlin, 1923.

20

Der "reaktionäre" Kongress fur Sexualforschung.

—Zeitschrift fur Sexualwiss, vol. xiii, Stuttgarten, 1927.